Accommodating the Pedestrian

Accommodating the Pedestrian

Adapting Towns and Neighborhoods
for Walking and Bicycling

Richard K. Untermann

Department of Landscape Architecture
University of Washington
Seattle, Washington

with assistance by Lynn Lewicki

VNR VAN NOSTRAND REINHOLD COMPANY
NEW YORK CINCINNATI TORONTO LONDON MELBOURNE

Library of Congress Catalog Card Number: 83-10516
ISBN: 0-442-28823-9

Manufactured in the United States of America

Published by Van Nostrand Reinhold Company Inc.
135 West 50th Street
New York, New York 10020

Van Nostrand Reinhold Company Limited
Molly Millars Lane
Wokingham, Berkshire RG11 2PY, England

Van Nostrand Reinhold
480 Latrobe Street
Melbourne, Victoria 3000, Australia

Macmillan of Canada
Division of Gage Publishing Limited
164 Commander Boulevard
Agincourt, Ontario M1S 3C7, Canada

15 14 13 12 11 10 9 8 7 6 5 4 3 2 1

Library of Congress Cataloging in Publication Data

Untermann, Richard K.
    Accommodating the pedestrian.

    Includes index.
    1. City planning—United States. 2. Pedestrian
facilities design—United States. 3. Pedestrian areas—
United States—Planning. 4. Cycling paths—United
States—Planning. I. Title.
HT167.U58 1984   711'.74'0973   83-10516
ISBN 0-442-28823-9

PREFACE

The public right-of-way's most important purpose is to ACCOMMODATE THE PEDESTRIAN yet, the pathway has become the vehicle way. The pedestrian has been pushed aside and made subservient to the movements of the vehicle. This book makes recommendations for improvement of the American street through the comparative analysis of American and European land use and cultural and political practices. The living patterns on each Continent are vastly different and so must be the solutions for addressing pedestrian problems. While Europeans have been successful in closing main streets to traffic, there seldom is sufficient human activity in American towns to justify this. Nevertheless, Americans have many opportunities to enhance pedestrian places.

Many of our pedestrian problems have emerged through slavish adherence to automobile performance standards. Our preoccupation with automobiles and their needs has blinded us to our many opportunities for other modes of travel. Cars have improved our lives and served us well but the price we have paid is excessive dependency. Where other safe, convenient access modes can be accommodated, cars may be used less. "Accommodating" means finding room for the pedestrian within the existing framework of our public streets.

This book identifies factors that affect the behavior and attitudes of people traveling on foot. It suggests a variety of remedies for communities, including downtown and suburban environments, by proposing solutions that are practical and possible at this stage of our country's development. Recognizing that isolated pedestrian pathways meet only part of our needs, the book does not advocate creation of vast, internal open spaces like those conceived in our superblock planning era of the 40's. Though long, internal open space walkways are desirable in some places, today's need is for safe pedestrian access along the streets and roadways that take up to and from our daily activities. Only when this occurs will we have true public access, and relief from the air, noise, safety, and energy problems that have plagued us.

ACKNOWLEDGMENT

Ideas develop over a long time. They are nutured by many personal experiences and professional encounters. I begin by acknowledging my childhood experiences of growing up on foot—aided by a heavy, old balloon tired bicycle. It was a memorable beginning. As a teenager, I exchanged this simple, pleasurable way of getting around for the power, excitement and convenience of a car. But then, a twist, and I acknowledge the University of California at Davis—a bicycle college for extending my childhood transportation mode. Sure enough, given relatively compact land uses, bicycling works. From that bicycling time, rediscovering my feet was easy and fun. I also acknowledge recent developments in shoes—firm arch supports, crepe soles and wide styles. Eventually, relationships between walking, other transportation modes and land use became apparent. If you could just give a little here, and take there, life on foot seemed possible. Twenty five years of walking and bicycling have reinforced the joy flowing from this primitive transportation form. Continued professional practice in "pedestrian cities" —San Francisco, Boston, Munich, Cape Town and Seattle have fostered my knowledge of how to improve the safety, convenience and pleasure of walking and bicycling.

I am grateful for a 1977 award by the Fulbright Commission to study land use characteristics of successful pedestrian environments in the Federal Republic of Germany.

I acknowledge Mayor Charles Royer for appointing me as Chair of the Seattle Design Commission which allowed further exploration of the politics of integrating pedestrian needs in community planning.

I appreciate the merchants and town fathers of a number of small communities in the Seattle area who engaged me to help plan their towns for conversion from auto dominated towns to ones achieving greater pedestrian balance.

I appreciate the American Society of Landscape Architects for publishing my earlier text on pedestrian circulation.

I would like to acknowledge one individual, Robert E. Small, an old friend and colleague at the University of Washington for his council on this text. We have both investigated non-motorized circulation for the past ten years, and exchanged many ideas, feelings and information.

Many other colleagues offered suggestions, reviewed chapters or indirectly supported my efforts. Among these, I am particularly indebted to Robert Buchanan, Gordon Burch, Lee Copeland, Josh Lehman, Dennis Ryan, Sally Schauman, and Jack Sidener.

Special thanks is due Lynn Lewicki, who patiently edited the text, and to Alberta Gordon of Van Nostrand Reinhold for guiding the manuscript through the production and publication process.

INTRODUCTION

During the past 40 years, rapid development has changed the face of the American city, town, and countryside. Following the Depression and World War II, inexpensive energy combined with newly developed technology to fuel rapid economic growth. Governmental transportation and land use policies accelerated this growth by encouraging extensive physical development as America sought to house and employ the large number of returning war veterans. Making all of this possible was the abundant and inexpensive fuel-oil which propelled vehicles, heated new homes, powered industry, and encouraged retail merchandising. There have been many gains: We have comfortable places to work, play and live in; easy access to almost any destination; increased diversity and choice of life styles, and expanded personal opportunities. But these benefits came with costs. Our air has been fouled by toxic auto emissions; sacred and distinctive landscapes have become monotonous and ugly places. We have reorganized America's landscape to fit the dimensions, speed, and patterns of motorized movement.

We have lost the ability to walk. We have forgotten what neighborhoods are about. We have relinquished the rewards of diverse, richly mixed communities. Yet, we cannot escape the ugliness at the roadways which lacerated our cities, towns and countrysides nor the frustration of seeing our children spend more time being driven to places than they do being out of doors. And now, to make matters worse, we are told that there may not be enough fuel to sustain the automobiles we have become dependent upon. Can we survive with less oil? Of course—millions of people throughout the world live comfortable and productive lives using far less energy than Americans do. These people walk and bicycle more, live closer together, and consume less.

WE ARE ALL PEDESTRIANS. This one fact escapes more of us as we remain excessively dependent on our automobiles. Even in the 1980's, a substantial portion of our population doesn't drive. These stranded Americans include children, the elderly, and those who cannot afford to or choose not to own a car. For many of us, being a pedestrian means only walking to and from our car. But beyond our forced "parking lot" trips, we spend plenty of time on our feet. We are becoming a society of runners, hikers, and strollers. More people are choosing to live where they can walk or run to work. With this trend comes the need for safe and pleasant pathways where we can walk or bike to work, to lunch, and to play.

WE HAVE MADE PROGRESS. Though we still revere our Mechanical Bride, bits and pieces of our towns and neighborhoods slowly are becoming pedestrianized. Narrowed streets, new sidewalks, safety diverters, benches, trees, and awnings make walking more pleasant. Increased den-sity and mixed land uses are becoming more common, so that many suburban communities now have more apartment dwellers than single-family residents. Bicycle improvements are beginning to weave their way through the landscape of Western cities, and mass transit service is growing in spite of American's preference for automobiles. Each step brings us closer to a pedestrian-accessible landscape. Yet, we still have a long way to go. Each ill-conceived road-widening project extends the wait until our communities become safe and enjoyable to walk in.

OUR ENTIRE COMMUNITY MUST BE ACCESSIBLE. Extensive community observation and citizen based planning leads the author to conclude that our entire landscape—city to country, suburb to hamlet—must be made safe and accessible to pedestrians. It must accommodate all transportation modes, but most importantly, pedestrians and bicyclists. Current "pedestrian" plans that develop small, isolated pedestrian precincts do not reduce our overall dependence on the automobile. Despite increased awareness of the advantages of walking and the value of energy conservation we are driving more than ever. We continue to create pedestrian problems, pollute air, generate noise, waste fuel, and dehumanize our cities. Vast amounts of land have yielded to automobile-oriented development at the same time that the cost of transportation, in real and personal terms, is increasing exponentially.

OUR DESIGN STANDARDS MUST CHANGE. America's roadways, constructed over the past 35 years, are deteriorating. New repair and maintenance programs must reflect new attitudes and needs. Emphasis on improved "maintenance" may result in further road widenings to comply with existing design standards. These standards often promote increasing traffic speed and volume to the detriment of pedestrian and bicyclists. Expanded widths and depths increase traffic speed, creating higher volume which make street crossings dangerous and the air more polluted. Depths refers to the slow change of adjacent land uses to accommodate the automobile. New buildings are spaced farther apart, set-backs are increased to accommodate parking in front, and traveling from one store or house to another without a care becomes unpleasant and unsafe. As a result people opt to drive, increasing traffic at precisely the most congested points.

WE MUST CONSUME LESS. Our excessive national energy consumption is directly related to automobile use. Vehicular transportation accounts for about 34 percent of our national fuel consumption. The automobile now uses half the oil consumed in the United States. One out of nine barrels of oil used worldwide is burned as gasoline on the American highways. America has postponed the energy crisis temporarily by improving the fuel efficiency of motorized transportation, but the fact remains that fossil fuel supplies are finite. Within the next 20 years, we will be forced to rely less on gasoline to power our private cars. Land use changes that reduce the need for driving, offer fuel reduction potentials. Although up to 40 percent of our auto transportation mileage is spent commuting, the distances traveled are, on the average, relatively short, and travel could be accommodated in places by other means. Family business trips account for the second most intensive fuel use and are, on the average, even shorter than commute trips. Relatively little fuel is used for major trips and vacations, so we needn't radically change this travel pattern. In most instances, we can stretch fuel efficiency simply by enhancing the opportunities to walk.

Since up to 60 percent of our air pollution is attributed to auto emission, expanded opportunities for walking also hold potential for significantly reducing air pollution.

LET'S RECLAIM OUR STREETS. Streets historically have played many roles in our communities, serving often as marketing and gathering places as well as traffic channels. For a street to function as a true public place, increased non-vehicle space is absolutely essential. Federal and state highway standards applied uniformly degrade pedestrian safety and community identity. In earlier days of light traffic and smaller populations, occasional traffic problems seemed a fair trade for easy access to nearby towns. However, centralized modern merchandising practices and improved private car transportation have increased enormously the number of driving trips. Popularity of living in rural communities has further increased traffic, and the once-popular two-lane highway has grown into four. With that has come strip development and the conversion of rural landscapes into amorphous, homogeneous service streets. THE TIME IS RIPE FOR CHANGE. As our urban communities mature, leisure time increases and the emphasis on cultural and community activities is strengthening. This is slowly having an effect on how residents perceive their towns and cities. There is a new appreciation of architecture —public spaces, historic buildings and the overall quality of the physical environment. People moving at 3 mph instead of 35 mph can see quite clearly the short comings of their physical environment.

I have great hopes. There is interest in new physical planning concepts, in altering our hierarchical approach to highway planning, in mixing land uses, and in seeking proper residential densities. We may be at the threshold of major changes in the way we run our communities. Each person who tunes in to the need to accommodate the pedestrian and the bicyclist enlarges the possibility of new life in our community. Travel on foot allows people to meet and greet one another, to look at and become part of their neighborhood. It allows improved transportation options and true accessibility to the life within our communities.

CONTENTS

Accommodating the Pedestrian

THE PEDESTRIAN AND THE BICYCLIST — THEIR NEEDS

We are pedestrians. Even though we have become increasingly dependent on automobiles for transportation in this country, we do walk—even more than we may realize. Daily activities both at and away from home involve walking. We walk to clean house, mow the lawn, shop for groceries, and to reach our offices. Even car trips involve walking, before reaching and after parking the car. The actual distances we walk to accomplish our daily activities may surprise us. It is not unusual for a person to walk two miles while shopping at a regional mall or to walk one-half mile between home, car, and work. Housewives may walk ten miles in a day to accomplish their chores, while a casual weekend walk in the woods may cover six miles.

Since we walk so much, we might expect that facilities for pedestrians would be commonplace and well designed. Not so. Pedestrian safety, comfort, and convenience have been seriously neglected in most places. In the last 40 years, since the automobile has become the dominant mode of transportation, planning has been primarily concerned with the automobile and motorists' comfort and convenience. Walking has become a secondary consideration in transportation and urban planning. As a result, pedestrians face such problems as delay, congestion, discomfort, poor or no accessibility, poor visibility, and accident danger. Bicyclists face similar problems that also result from a lack of planning and facilities.

Until the 1940s, the pedestrian had the right-of-way in most towns. Then they began to lose it to motor vehicles. Since then, few good pedestrian facilities have been constructed, while, as we all know, roadway construction has proliferated. Areas for safe and pleasurable walking have slowly diminished, with pedestrians relegated to narrower and narrower channels. The pedestrian crosswalk is an example of assignment of street rights to the automobile, with pedestrians strictly limited to use of the street at the defined crosswalk. This type of channeling defines responsibility in case of accident, providing more freedom of movement for the car and less for the pedestrian.

Pedestrians are now comfortable only on small, isolated islands among a sea of autos, that is, in private gardens, parks, college campuses, shopping centers, and newer apartment developments. But these places that offer safety and comfort for pedestrians are invariably separated from the street where the real activity occurs. Thus, improving and extending pedestrian safety and comfort along all our streets is essential for viable communities. Furthermore, new and improved pedestrian routes and shortcuts, bicycle routes, and better public transportation combined with concentrated and mixed land uses will benefit us all.

There are also subtle problems that have to be acknowledged before we can begin to think about making improvements. These problems diminish the quality of life in our communities, a price previously assumed as a reasonable trade for the advantages of the car, but which many people are now questioning. Our land-use patterns force us to drive to undertake even the simplest tasks. For instance, American parents spend perhaps one-quarter of their lives "chauffeuring" children to various activities. Youngsters, and elderly people as well, have restricted mobility due to a lack of adequate public transportation and pedestrian-oriented facilities. Then, too, suburban communities generate such a buildup of internal traffic that it has become necessary for shoppers to drive between stores, when in fact walking would be easier. While in urban communities, traffic peaks in the morning and afternoon, with lower volumes occurring during the day. In suburban communities, traffic volumes remain high from morning until evening.

People are beginning to value and use their free time more carefully. In the past, higher salaries were a principal concern of employees. But when a comfortable income is reached, increased free time becomes a prime employee concern. Recreation and quality of life issues are now more frequently discussed. Daily chores are being scrutinized and uncomfortable or tedious parts eliminated. This may signal a changing view of life's purposes with personal enjoyment of time becoming more important than productivity. People may feel that regaining control of their lives is rewarding. There is resentment for the time spent in traffic jams, and an understanding that time spent walking, running, or bicycling isn't wasted if the experience is pleasant. The pleasures of quieter, pre-auto times, with greater self-awareness, out-of-door activities, clean air, and personal freedoms are again being sought by many people. Gailbraith's comment that the test of our economic achievement is *not* how much we produce, but what we do to make our lives tolerable or pleasant, perhaps best sums up what this author feels is a changing attitude in this country.

Lately, the fun of recreational driving has been diminished by the crush of traffic and the high cost of gasoline. True, the car has opened new territory, creating the possibility of seeing more and more, but we must travel farther and farther until the destination becomes lost in the trip, and the hours getting there seem fruitless. Conditions become worse as more people discover and go to popular recreation places, so that many people are beginning to feel that leaving the car marks the beginning of their free time. Thus, some people are looking closer to home for recreational activities as evidenced by the increased interest in running, walking, racketball, tennis, swimming, bicycling, and other non-car-oriented activities.

To be sure, the car has played an important role in improving our lives. It has increased opportunities in housing, recreation, work, and education for those who can afford one or two cars. Thus, proposals to correct car-created problems should *not* eliminate these desirable advantages. The author believes it is essential to determine what purpose each mode of transportation (car, foot, bicycle, and public transportation) best serves, and to utilize the best qualities of each, adding new facilities where appropriate.

ABOUT PEDESTRIANS AND THEIR NEEDS

Why Do People Walk?

Walking can increase socialization, enhance health, contribute to recreation and relaxation, and allow independence. Social contact between people on foot or on bicycle is easy, while contact is almost impossible between people in cars. Most people enjoy walking, sitting, watching other people and talking as opportunities for relaxation and enjoyment of leisure time. People in Europe, where walking is facilitated, have always enjoyed these pleasures. Americans on European holidays most likely have spent time in outdoor cafes relaxing and watching other people. Part of the enjoyment is the ever-changing scene that people walking around help to create.

Cars isolate people and can even change their personalities. Drivers become impatient and may visibly lose control if a delay or congestion occurs. The increasing number of "normal" people involved in fights and scuffles stemming from minor auto accidents further points out this phenomenon of personality change. Some drivers display an undue sense of power, particularly the young or those not able to

Places to sit and rest are essential downtown, particularly for the elderly. Wood benches with backs are warm and comfortable to sit on; however, other level surfaces of differing height will be also used.

satisfy their egos in other ways. Good manners often disappear as drivers isolated in their cars aren't controlled by the usual social pressure. On the other hand, these characteristics are seldom associated with pedestrians.

Pedestrians help make a neighborhood more livable, safe, and comfortable to be in. People who walk regularly see and become aware of conditions, other people, patterns of users, and the neighborhood in general. They can often recognize outsiders and detect irregularities such as vandalism, burglary, and mugging. The presence of pedestrians on the street makes outsiders feel uncomfortable. At one time, pedestrians in this country policed their own neighborhoods. But while that protection is now the responsibility of the local police departments, the police are unable to be everywhere at the same time. The addition of pedestrians' watching, policing, and just being there, helps. Pedestrians can also watch out for older people by noticing their houses as they pass and perhaps noting minor differences suggesting sickness or an emergency. Pedestrians, too, can keep an eye on children as they play in the neighborhood.

Pedestrians aid in the development of a neighborhood's "sense of community," a common bond that ties a neighborhood together on broader issues of need, comfort, and survival. People living in a neighborhood with a sense of community are aware of the quality of the neighborhood, of traffic that moves too fast, of crime, and of poor maintenance. Sense of community occurs when people recognize and acknowledge their neighbors. In a time of need, it is easy come together and begin discussing pertinent issues. These kinds of meetings are often not possible in auto-oriented communities, since travel is accomplished within the car and there is little chance for people to get to know each other.

Walking has economic advantages besides the cost of saved fuel. For many, it may mean not having to buy and maintain a second car. For the poor, the opportunity to satisfy daily needs by walking or bicycling could mean that money saved could be spent for necessities. There may be other cost savings. Children who can walk or bicycle safely to school could reduce the high cost of busing. (Seattle, Washington, uses approximately 5,000 gallons of fuel each day to transport its 20,000 students on private buses.) Communities set up to accommodate walking may reduce the costs of commuting, delivery of goods and services, and police and fire protection. Pedestrian improvements have revitalized many small community shopping areas, creating new jobs in what formerly looked like financial and community disasters. Most pedestrianized districts report increases in private-sector building. For instance, Nicolete Mall in Minneapolis helped attract new buildings worth $400,000,000.

Many health advantages accrue to regular walkers, runners, or bicyclists. These rewards include physical activity that leads to better fitness, aesthetic pleasure activating the senses, and potential sociability. Regular and relaxed walking can lower high blood pressure, reduce fat concentration in the blood, and stimulate body circulation. Besides the low cost of walking, it creates no environmental pollution, unless the walker litters the landscape.

What Has Transportation Planning Done?

Improving the pedestrian domain is more than creating a landscaped downtown mall. Pedestrians need safe, comfortable, and accessible routes *covering the entire city.* In recent road-building efforts spurred by phenomenal increases in the number of cars, roads were constructed quickly without much planning and with little integration and less thought about the impact on nearby residents or pedestrians. American traffic planning has catered almost exclusively to the automobile, building roads instead of balancing public and private transportation with pedestrian and bicycle access, and ignoring land use and density. Even though transportation studies have often been preceded by a land-use analysis, it was evidently forgotten in efforts to solve such problems as bottlenecks, corridor efficiency, and increasing costs. Even transportation studies conducted on computers have not explored land-use patterns that might be best served by buses or pedestrians. For example, the 1966 Chicago Transportation Study, the "grandaddy" of them all, ignored pedestrian trips even though, of the 14,000,000 daily trips in Chicago, 4,000,000 or 28 percent were made on foot. Imagine how different Chicago would be today if 28 percent of all Chicago's road-building funds had been used to improve the pedestrian domain instead of roadways. The study ignored any figures on walking that occurred at the end of each car trip, further depressing the actual amount of walking considered. This study, like many others, considered too few alternatives, had limited goals and objectives, and ended by favoring the automobile and ignoring transit, pedestrian, and bicycle needs.

In the end, most transportation studies have used projections almost exclusively to justify automobile improvements, with only a residual amount applied to public transportation, bicycle, or pedestrian needs. Most studies have ignored the old adage that "a good transportation system minimizes unnecessary transportation." Thus, our transportation organizations have neglected to bring goods and services to where they were needed, opting instead to let users settle where land costs were lowest, and drive to get

Recreation routes should follow water courses and other amenities.

Parking on the sidewalk and planter strip should be prohibited and policed. The parking makes pedestrians feel unsafe, and tramples the soil so vegetation cannot grow. The open parking lot on the right, with a barbed wire chain-link fence increases pedestrian discomfort.

Safe, separate, and pleasant walkways should connect all bus stops to shopping or living areas.

the goods. On the other hand, if goods, services, and people are concentrated within a limited area, there is a choice with a minimum of travel.

As some concerned citizens have predicted, the problems of putting all our transportation eggs in one basket has come to a head. Some obvious problems of our overdependence on the automobile are known. Its high energy consumption is made more explicit by our growing awareness of limited and expensive energy supplies. And other problems attributable to the automobile are: the bothersome levels of motor vehicle noise and air pollution; the safety hazards to pedestrians, bicyclists, and drivers alike; the frustrating hours spent commuting and tied up in traffic jams; and the characterless landscapes of our parking-lot-dominated towns.

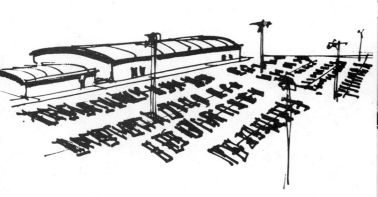

What Constitutes A Good Pedestrian Environment?

The preceding discussion suggests walking has been made difficult and unpleasant by our overdependence on the automobile and the resulting land uses that have developed. Correcting these conditions involves reducing travel distances; increasing land-use flexibility; eliminating pedestrian barriers and obstacles; leveling walking routes; assuring continuity of travel; providing protection from wind, rain, noise, cold, and pollution; eliminating conflict; and increasing character, randomness, visual diversity and amenity. Visual diversity and amenity ease boredom, obscure unpleasant aspects of a trip, and make a walk more enjoyable. Levelness of travel, elimination of stairs, protection against weather, and shortening of distance make a walk more pleasant physically. Separation of traffic horizontally, vertically, or by time reduces perceived fears about safety and eliminates conflict between pedestrians and cars.

Balancing our over-dependence on the automobile involves:

- reducing travel distances
- increasing land-use flexibility
- eliminating pedestrian barriers
- leveling walking routes
- assuring continuity of travel
- providing weather protection
- eliminating conflict
- increasing character

Pedestrian loading and drop-off zones reduce the need for parking. This handsome drop-off zone with trees, attractive lighting, benches, etc., lacks a ramp for wheelchair access. Note the two jaywalkers, an indication of the chances people take to reduce their walk length.

Impromptu sidewalk entertainment encourages recreation shopping.

Integration of transportation by cars, bicycles, and public transit is essential to produce good pedestrian environments. Since people can't walk long distances in reasonable time, they need the assistance of wheeled vehicles, in moderation. Thus, to best integrate modes of transportation, the following are needed.

• Auto access drop-offs and concentrated parking that comes within a reasonable distance of final destinations, with walkways leading from parking places to destination points. The auto should be made *inconvenient* for short trips, enhancing and making possible greater pedestrian travel.

• Integration of public transportation with access by pedestrians and bicyclists. The success of a bus system depends on whether people can get to and from it comfortably on foot or bicycle.

• Improved bicycle circulation is essential in all communities, especially with the trend toward commuting by bicycle. Bicycles can extend travel distances possible in a short time to the two-to-three-mile range if proper facilities and separation from the automobile are provided.

Who Benefits From Pedestrian Improvements?

Since we are all pedestrians, we are all affected by the quality and continuity of our community's pedestrian system, if one exists. Likewise, we all stand to benefit from efforts to improve or provide facilities to accommodate walking. Yet, each community has a slightly different group of residents who will most benefit by pedestrian improvements, and these people should be identified and considered when priorities are established.

Part of the current interest in improving pedestrian circulation can be traced to Americans' recognition of people with some handicap who move around as pedestrians. These people, symbolized by those in wheelchairs, include permanent and temporary handicaps such as blindness, deafness, and ambulatory disabilities. Temporary handicaps include broken limbs and recovery from surgery, pulled muscles, pregnancy, and other conditions. About ten percent of our population are impaired from free movement by some handicap. Thus, planning emphasis should be put on efforts to assure continuous accessibility and safety to handicapped persons. Elderly Americans should be given special attention in the planning process. To many, walking is their only form of mobility. While they are dependent upon walking they are also handicapped by the lack of appropriate and safe facilities and by present land uses as well.

Good drop-off zones with covered walkways connecting facilities increase pedestrian comfort. This arcade connects the drop-off zone with the theater and protects pedestrians from the rainy Vancouver weather.

Problem areas to be considered in planning pedestrian environments to accommodate the elderly are: lengthened physical reaction time; the nonstandardization of street signs; impairments in sight and hearing; the excessive width of streets and the inadequacies of street crossings and signals; and the aggressive behavior of drivers. Furthermore, urban designers usually plan for a typical pedestrian rather than an older pedestrian. This causes some problems for elderly pedestrians in the following areas: location of community facilities; lack of pedestrian hardware such as handrails, benches, lighting, and ramps at curbs; speed of pedestrian control signals at lighted intersection; and provisions for personal protection.

What Areas Are Already Pedestrianized?

Shopping centers are prime examples of places where people walk. Once shoppers park their cars and enter a shopping center, all activities are reached on foot. A center's success combines easy car access with a compact, planned pedestrian precinct free from cars. The pedestrian space is clean, bright, landscaped with fountains, benches, plants and varied paving, and is surrounded by a diversity of shops. Stores and shops have been carefully planned with major department stores at each end drawing shoppers past the smaller specialty stores located between them. Food, places to people watch and rest, and entertainment are available, as is a range of comparative shopping.

Mid-block crosswalks allow pedestrians to cross without going to the corner, define parking, and provide a place for seating and trees. Note the shortcutting near the end when all was safe.

Familiar pedestrian places include Venice, Italy; Fez, Morocco; the pedestrian core of Munich, Germany; market towns; and downtown Boston around the Quincy Market. (6 photos)

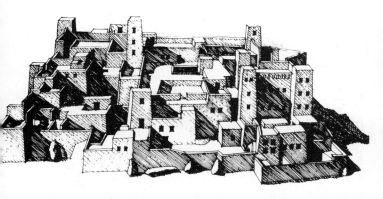

Some downtowns have auto-free pedestrian streets. People who use these streets almost uniformly express satisfaction if there is a variety of stores and if parking is relatively easy. Such downtowns may be preferred by many to new shopping centers because they are less homogeneous.

Most college and university campuses have a central core free of traffic, with buildings compactly arranged so students can easily walk. These campuses are usually parklike, and present a strong image of what car-free living can be like. Their organization may be an appropriate model for communities: main circulation on the periphery, short cul-de-sac penetrations for trucks servicing the campus, parking on the periphery in small lots, and bus service through the campus (see sketch).

Most parks exclude the automobile except on the periphery, providing a quiet, safe and pedestrian-scaled refuge for entertainment and relaxation. For instance, driving in the central part of Yosemite National Park has been prohibited. Instead, the park service has substituted a bus system paid for through admission fees. This system has markedly increased the park's capacity and user experience.

Recreation and entertainment parks such as Disneyland in California and Disney World in Florida are total pedestrian environments. Disney World, for instance, is patterned after an American "main street," where all activities are carried out on food.

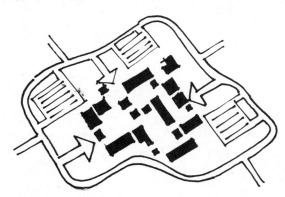

New towns like Columbia, Maryland, Radburn, New Jersey, and Reston, Virginia were organized for easy pedestrian and bicycle circulation. Walkways and bicycle ways separated from traffic weave through each community, connecting neighborhoods with schools, shopping, bus stops, and places of work and play. Each pathway is landscaped and designed for pedestrian or bicycle protection and comfort. Residents of these communities are generally pleased. While Reston has had some financial difficulties, it has generally been successful. Its problems can be attributed to the short-term interests of American housing developers, not to shortcomings in the design.

Some Americans have had the experience of walking in Europe, visiting cities that have auto-free downtowns. These downtowns are usually served by rapid transit, with all types of shopping, eating, entertainment, and cultural facilities within walking distance. Tourists often find the time spent in these downtown precincts to be the highlight of their vacations. Many a sensitive traveler has surely thought: "Why can't we do something like this in America?"

Many small European towns have developed tourist attractions for city dwellers. Some have developed a farmer's market, attractive places to eat out-of-doors, a street and park system closed to traffic and pleasant for walking. (3 photos)

Many large apartment developments have separated cars from recreational and pedestrian activities. These developments are organized so that all housing units and activities are focused on an auto-free, parklike interior. Cars are parked on the periphery so that housing and recreation are reached by walking.

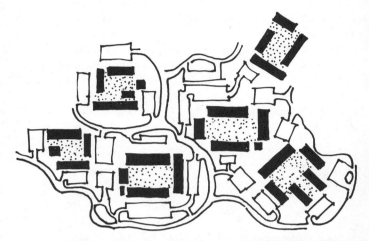

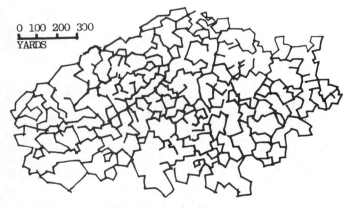

0 100 200 300 YARDS

Fes, Morocco—A fine-grained city

Many suburban apartment developments have internalized pedestrians by surrounding them with roads and units. This leaves an incomplete pedestrian route since most systems don't interconnect, and many don't even traverse their own development. However, connecting these internal spaces over a longer distance could turn them into an active, neighborhood-oriented space. (It may not be immediately popular with the residents.) (4 photos)

Planners internalized pedestrians to counter the loss of street space, separating walkers from drivers. The "super block," with its ring of auto traffic encircling buildings that encircle a separate pedestrian system, allows pedestrians to avoid noisy, polluted, unsafe, and unpleasant streets. While cars have access to all shopping, work, and recreation services, the interior pedestrian spaces serve only short distances and lead to few necessary activities.

Beneficiaries of Pedestrian Improvements

Residents of urban and suburban neighborhoods would benefit from improved pedestrian comfort and safety. Improvements could mitigate the impact of heavy and fast-moving traffic, traffic noise, drive-in businesses, unlandscaped roads, and large parking lots. Many neighborhoods are divided by arterials that have been widened over the years often without public meetings and without residential approval to allow more and faster traffic. There are ways to alter roadways to reduce the adverse impact of cars.

Improved pedestrian facilities would benefit motorists as well by eliminating or lessening conflicts. Where there are no sidewalks and people must walk in the street, they interfere with the flow of traffic. Where crosswalks are poorly defined, pedestrians may cross randomly, further interfering with and slowing traffic.

Downtowns would benefit from pedestrian improvements. Older downtowns, historically the center of activity for metropolitan communities, were originally structured to serve pedestrians. The concentrated, mixed-used physical layout of such downtowns fostered walking. Sidewalks connected stores, trees lined streets, residences were nearby, stores were narrowfronted, and parking lots didn't overwhelm the landscape. Even during the car's early days, downtown was still a place for walking. Window displays attracted attention, drive-in businesses didn't obstruct foot traffic, and the scale of the streetscape was geared to the pedestrian. But the automobile has changed that in many cities. With increasing parking lots, downtowns lost their essential pedestrian character. Buildings were actually torn down to create more parking space. Some stores eventually moved to suburban shopping centers, while others chose to locate on strips. Eventually the retail prominence of downtown disappeared. Empty shops were converted to housing, storage, manufacturing, offices, or even left vacant. Each conversion reinforced the downtown's decline, until there was little reason for pedestrians to be there. Through traffic on main streets increased and sidewalks were narrowed. Drive-ins replaced some marginal stores, and downtown began to take on the character of a strip development. Although many downtowns have been revitalized in the last ten years, many more could benefit from improvements that would encourage pedestrians to once again enjoy walking there.

Cars should be prohibited (and policed) from parking on the sidewalk. Some drivers fear that with increased speed passing motorists will scratch their cars. Lowering the speed limit and policing may allow motorists to park legally and safely in the street.

This handsome, older downtown has been converted to serve the automobile traffic with large overhead signs, narrow sidewalks, excessive street width, lack of pedestrian amenity and crosswalk definition, absence of defined parking lanes, etc. The wide roadway generates noise, allows cars to move quickly, and is uncomfortable for pedestrians.

Drive-in businesses such as banks, restaurants, cleaners, etc., should be prohibited on main streets. If they are needed, access should be off an alley or side street with fewer pedestrians. The drive-in creates a hazard as cars enter and exit, interrupts street continuity, and is visually degrading to the pedestrian domain. The driveway sloping to meet the street may cause unwary pedestrians to lose their footing.

When pedestrian density increases, the narrow sidewalk is *not* satisfactory. Note there is no room for window shopping, and several people are walking outside the trees next to busy traffic. Widening this sidewalk from 9 to 12 feet would provide comfort and window shopping access.

BICYCLISTS AND THEIR NEEDS

Bicycle riding in many American towns and cities, like walking, is neither enjoyable nor safe because of the dominance of the automobile. For bicycling safety and comfort, a certain degree of separation between automobiles and bicycles is necessary. This can be done in an existing roadway or on a separate path. Thus, bicycle-oriented improvements reflecting good planning and providing appropriate facilities can attract riders. With rising energy costs and dwindling supplies, efforts need to be made to attract riders to use bicycles for daily activities. Traffic planners estimate that over 50 percent of daily trips are less than three miles in length, an appropriate bicycling distance for most people. Many trips by children and adults could be made solely by bicycle or by bicycle and public transit. The appeal and convenience of daily bicycling, though, depends on sensitive planning for bicycle routes that provide safety, comfort, and visual attractions, and that go where people want to go.

With light pedestrian traffic, a nine-foot-wide sidewalk is adequate. It allows room for sidewalk sales, street lights, and pedestrian amenities while users can move out of each other's way.

PLANNING FOR IMPROVEMENTS

Planning for nonmotorized circulation employs approaches that are different from those used in planning for cars. Traffic planners using strategies developed for the motor vehicle to plan pedestrian and bicycle facilities are bound to fail. Differences between motorists and pedestrians and bicyclists that can influence planning are discussed below.

1. Cars *equalize* drivers. Regardless of age, health, or physical capability, all drivers are equal. When they step on the gas they are capable of traveling at similar speeds over similar distances with similar opportunities for comfort, entertainment, and protection. This equalization has led to widespread car usage and, in turn, to congestion and delay. To counter congestion, traffic planners try to "unequalize" drivers by forcing some onto larger, specialized streets such as freeways and arterials. These drivers must travel farther, or slightly out of their way, but may get there faster, saving smaller, local streets for drivers who must carry out specific activities and will therefore drive slower.

Pedestrians and bicyclists are not equal in the same sense. If, and how much, they walk or cycle depends on their age, health, and physical condition. Not all cyclists are able to cover similar distances at similar speeds, and the same is true for pedestrians. Nor are conditions of exposure to weather, protection, and safety the same. Thus, a principal planning objective to improve walking and bicycling is to help *equalize* the way, making everything and every place accessible to all. Establishing a safe boulevard or special walk doesn't necessarily do this unless people need to travel where that walk goes. Thus, the recommended approach is for development of *fine-grained networks* that allow working people to commute safely and efficiently, and that allow recreationists to travel safely, leisurely, and pleasantly. Pedestrian and bicycle routes should be planned for maximum use, protection, safety, variety, and amenity.

Planning, too, should aim to make all daily activities as easy to accomplish on foot and bicycle as in the car. In some places within the networks of pedestrian and bicycle routes, the car may be excluded; in others, accepted but planned around. Land uses may have to be changed to encourage and accommodate walking and cycling. Old and new sidewalks may be integrated, intersections upgraded, and shortcuts provided to increase flexibility of travel. Parking may have to be reorganized so people can walk to several destinations without moving their cars. These are just a few of the possible changes that could be made to better accommodate pedestrians and bicyclists and that could be related to their specific needs.

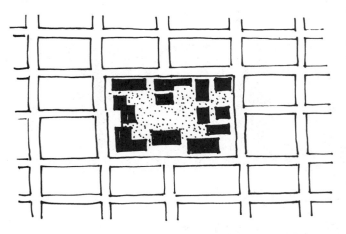

An adequate number of bicycle racks near an entry may prevent vandalism or theft, and brings the riders close so they don't need to ride throughout the shopping area. As bicycle use increases, bicycles should be parked centrally so shopping trips can be carried out on foot. Note the lady bundled against the cold and damp pulling her grocery cart. Bad weather isn't a deterrent, as long as distances are reasonable.

Angle-parked cars reduce the street character and attractiveness for walking. The rest of the sidewalk has pedestrian scale, with a variety of building materials, narrow-fronted shops, display windows, awnings, signs designed to be read by the pedestrian, plants, an occasional tree, and paving diversity.

An idealized mixed-used development with shops on the ground floor and living above. The shops are narrow-fronted with window shopping and awnings. The units overhead are set back slightly, include decks at several levels, provide views of the street, and are residential in character. Access and parking is off the alley and street trees assure a green view from the living unit.

Is there a place for grand boulevards? Certainly, but they won't serve everyday walking needs. Boulevards serve recreations, urban design, and open-space purposes, bringing the country into the city. They serve pedestrians whose daily trips happen to cross it and may be perfect as part of a bicycle route. However, boulevards shouldn't be proposed to serve the transportation needs of most walkers, since they rarely go where walkers need to go.

2. Pedestrians and bicyclists are unlike motorists in their movement patterns. Pedestrians and bicyclists are more maneuverable but less mobile than motorists in their vehicles. Motorists generally use their cars to move from one place to another, while bicyclists and pedestrians usually travel for the experience as much as the destination.

Since the car has become a temporary "environment," roads generally serve only to link different points. Inside cars, there is comfort, climate control, and entertainment. The road environment through which the car passes is not as important as the speed, efficiency, and continuity of the trip. Consequently, our roadways are just part of a dull but efficient vehicular movement system, connected to destination points with many parking places.

Pedestrians and bicyclists, on the other hand, can't move easily over long distances and are therefore directly involved with the environment surrounding them. They have no climate control or personalized entertainment and are at the mercy of the sidewalk or open-space planner to provide their comfort. Pedestrians and bicyclists need not be channeled into efficiency lanes or move at a continuous pace, but instead should be able to meander, rest, warm up in the sun, stop, visit, or seek protection from the rain. Walking environments must be much more varied than road environments. For drivers, the road is a medium, while for pedestrians and bicyclists, the route is an experience.

A shuttle bus, modeled after San Francisco's cable cars extends tourists' walking distance. This shuttle loops between two business districts so shoppers can reach both. Note the textured paving blocks.

The car is so much a part of our lives that we almost don't notice it anymore. Typical of many places, cars come unnecessarily close here and because of noise, requirement for space, danger, pollution, and garish color, reduce the livability of the area.

3. There has been a change in the speed factor for which planners design. We now live in environments designed primarily to serve the speed requirements of those who drive. There has been a subtle shift over the last 40 years from a design scale based on the speed of foot travel to a new design scale based on the speed of travel by car. Thirty miles per hour has replaced three miles per hour as the new speed architects and engineers use to evaluate how their buildings will be seen. New buildings are wide-fronted, smooth and shallow, so passing motorists driving at 30 mph or faster can see and identify each one. Previously, buildings were narrow-fronted, deep, and intricate so pedestrians could walk past many without becoming bored.

Architects have responded to the automobile by simplifying buildings and environments. Narrow shops became longer without decoration or windows, and with larger and simpler signs for road visibility. Window displays and trees disappeared. Our restructured streets, simplified in favor of the car's speed of travel, proved a disservice to those traveling at foot speed.

There is some justification for simplifying auto-oriented environments and making pedestrian spaces more complex. The human eye visually encompasses about three objects every second. Fewer than three per second can induce boredom, while more are likely to create confusion. A driver traveling at 25 mph passes a 30-foot-wide shop in slightly less than one second, distinguishing two or three objects. On the other hand, a pedestrian traveling at 3 mph can distinguish and comprehend 21 different objects in the same 30 feet. The average bicyclist travels about 10 mph and can perceive about six objects in the same distance. Thus, motorists benefit from *decreased* complexity of visual messages, while pedestrians and bicyclists benefit from *increased* message complexity.

Pedestrian Scale. Pedestrians walking at two to three miles per hour are aware of every passing detail and require continuously varying details to relieve boredom. It is important that each object be approximately the size of the human body, be close at hand, be constructed of small pieces, and be diverse. Display cases changed regularly, concrete paving blocks interspersed with brick and cobble cross-lines, pedestrian billboards and combination benches with low-level light are attractive elements in the pedestrianscape.

17

4. There has been a change in the use of streets. Before people in this country became dependent on the automobile, streets gave cities and towns their form and provided, as well, a place for people to move and carry on business. Then most movement was on foot, and so the street was scaled for pedestrians. With the advent of the automobile, greater pressure was put on the street, and both walking and commercial activities were compromised. The specialized nature of the car, which requires clear linear channels for movement and large spaces for storage, forced commerce to spread out and pedestrian spaces to become increasingly smaller. The street was literally abandoned to the car everywhere except in a few downtowns.

Is this the new suburban pedestrian streetscape? Have we replaced the street with narrow, interior-access corridors? Is it viable for stimulating and enhancing a sense of community? Is it a place where you can meet your neighbor and talk? Is it a place where your children can play?

A normal relationship of houses and apartments on a public street with sidewalk, street trees and lights, planter strips, drop-off and parking areas. The street is connected to the houses by a front porch with several steps for privacy. Each unit overviews the street and residents can observe street conditions and help protect neighborhood quality.

5. While local and state governments have devised ways to pay for construction of roadways and related facilities, ways to pay for development of pedestrian and bicycle-related improvements are still ill-defined. The need to construct, police, and maintain different pedestrian and bicycle environments on the street and away from the street, compounds the problem.

6. Most people seem to enjoy the experience of driving more than that of walking. There is evidence to prove that most people will drive rather than walk, even if it takes more time. Why is this? Is it because people just don't like to walk, or is it because they've become conditioned not to walk? This author feels the latter is the case, primarily because our cities and towns are not designed to make walking safe, comfortable, or pleasant.

Potential improvements to accommodate pedestrians and bicyclists can be classified in to two broad categories that can provide frames of reference for planning and implementation.

Utilitarian Improvements. People with a set mission, destination, or task are concerned about utilitarian improvements. Making the route continuous, direct, free of obstacles, and safe are paramount objectives. People benefiting most from utilitarian improvements are commuters and those who walk or cycle daily.

A new pedestrian underpass in Stevenage, England, on the main street. With careful attention to grading, the underpass works effectively, even in close quarters, and is used regularly by walkers and bicyclists.

Aesthetic Improvements. Many people walk or bicycle for recreation: to make social contacts, shop, pass time, exercise, and relax. Their experience is enhanced if the place is pleasant, relatively quiet, landscaped, well maintained, and well lit, and provided with some street furniture. Downtowns, shopping centers, urban parks, neighborhood business districts and malls are examples of places in need of aesthetic improvements.

This old town well recycled as a fountain with ledges for seating and trees is an interesting streetscape element that passers-by can't resist stopping to look at.

Many planners, believing that both types of improvements can be achieved, propose that all routes be safe, clean, attractive, and landscaped, free of impediments and traffic delays, well lighted, policed, and maintained. Sometimes they can be, but the reality is that often only one type of improvement can be made without financially burdening a project. Thus, it is important for planners to have a well-defined notion of the principal objective of a project—that which must be done, as well as the secondary objective—that which might be done.

IMPLEMENTING IMPROVEMENTS

Plans for improvements can be successfully implemented only if they fit the community and the timing is right. Moreover, public enthusiasm and support, as well as sympathetic and informed decision makers, are essential for a project to proceed from the idea stage to the point where funds are earmarked for construction. Since ways to fund improvements for pedestrians and bicyclists are without much precedent, devising ways to obtain money will require some creativity. For instance, one way to correct pedestrian problems caused by the automobile would be for improvements to be paid in large part with tax revenues from gasoline and auto licenses. Since the need for most pedestrian improvements can be traced to excessive intrusion of the automobile, auto users should share the burden of putting our environment back in order.

Our next wave of public road work should include a commitment to quality for pedestrians and bicyclists. Costs for recapturing pedestrian and bicycle space can be reduced if roadway space is used and improvements are incorporated with the next road-building efforts, which in most suburban communities and urban communities will be within the next 15 years.

Moreover, communities should develop design standards to insure that facilities for pedestrians and bicyclists are routinely incorporated. These would include a safe sidewalk area, bicycle lanes, defined parking areas, expanded intersections, bus stops with covered waiting areas, benches, and landscaping.

THIS TEXT'S APPROACH

The approach put forward in this text advocates an eclectic, go-slow method of correcting obvious pedestrian- and bicycle-related problems—first where possible, and then where necessary. The author does not believe that communities need to commit themselves initially to massive changes, but rather that they should start slowly and implement improvements over a period of time. The text outlines a process to correct pedestrian and bicycle barriers and problems in our cities and towns, and suggests methods to reduce nonessential auto traffic. The book also discusses how pedestrians and bicyclists can coexist with cars. The focus is on access rather than on traffic and transportation, and the emphasis is on using whatever method seems appropriate for each situation.

The text identifies changes that are appropriate to different communities, adapting to their size, scale, regional position, and character. Large and small towns obviously require different types of pedestrian solutions. The concluding discussion is about longer-term changes in land use, density, and public transportation.

This approach is, in a sense, the reverse of what one might expect in that it proposes immediate improvements which might later have to be changed or redone. How-to suggestions are proposed before the question of "why" is investigated. This is primarily because most "why" questions have not yet been answered, either politically or economically. The how-to approach, on the other hand, works better in the short term to accommodate existing

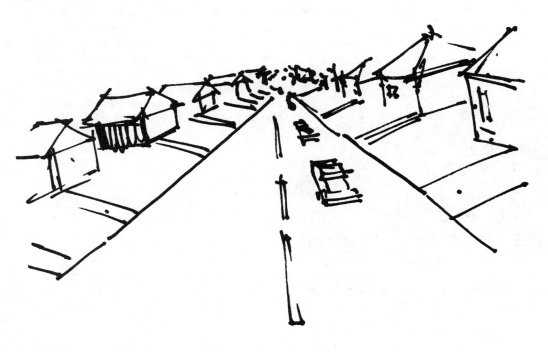

pedestrian traffic and to solve an immediate problem. When we have additional pedestrians, political pressure for comprehensive planning and new specialized facilities will surely surface.

Providing facilities to encourage walking and bicycling won't keep people from driving their cars. Then, too, the road-building process is not yet over, with many suburban communities still projecting a 25-50 percent increase in traffic during the next ten years. Yet, some people are beginning to realize that dependence on the automobile has compromised many valued qualities of their lives. These people are looking at their towns in a social, rather than a purely physical way. They are thinking of how they want to live, and how their community can foster this lifestyle. They are becoming concerned with the relationships of human beings, and in developing settings that nurture these relationships. They believe there should be interesting things for people to do in their spare time, and stimulating places to be and to see. And, there should also be relief from the many inconveniences that have been eroding our daily living patterns. A community that makes walking convenient, may be addressing some of these problems.

CHARACTERISTICS OF WALKING

Walking is done every day, everywhere. People walk at home, at work, at play. People tend to walk where it is easier, faster or cheaper than to drive. In high-density districts, people tend to walk instead of ride where car travel is hindered by congestion and lack of parking. They also tend to walk in older medium-density neighborhoods where there are sidewalks, destinations and continuous changes of view. Walkers are attracted to mixed-use urban districts where there is activity involving people—people watching, socializing, being seen, and just being around other people. Most week-end walkers hike where there are natural attractions such as trees, grass, rough terrain, farms and water, and few other people. Thus, walking for recrea-

tion is usually done in low-density or rural areas near water, where the natural surroundings are invigorating and quiet and where the view changes continually. People are less willing to walk in single-use, industrial areas, single family suburbs, etc., where destinations are distant and the unfolding view is monotonous.

WALKING VERSUS DRIVING

The availability of a *faster* or *easier* alternative to walking is usually an overriding factor in choosing between walking and riding. We have spent billions of dollars improving our road system to make driving easier, often at the expense of the pedestrians, buses, and bikes. Americans have become so conditioned to using the car for every trip, that most of us have forgotten that some trips are easier, and perhaps more fun on foot or on bike.

The reasons for selecting auto travel over bike, bus or foot are common sense, but often carry the key to changing mode of transport. Some include:

- Car ownership is a prime factor, with two-car families making more trips than one-car families.
- Family size, with larger families making more trips than smaller ones.
- Permanent families in single family developments are usually better integrated into the community and generate more trips than transients (but not that many more).
- Higher income leads to increased trip making.
- The 15-20 year old age group produces more trips than older people.
- Travel is a function of human activities, and is usually to:
  1) work or school,
  2) during work or school,
  3) for social, sport or recreation,
  4) to shop and serve other people (Mom's taxi service).
- Travel time is an important means of probability of trip making, with people willing to go farther to work than to shop and still farther for recreation, which may include shopping or dining.
- Roads foster trip making. People will go where roads let them go.
- Between 80-90% of all journeys begin and end at the home. Residential patterns are key to improving pedestrian activity even though some are difficult to serve except by automobile.
- Commercial and industrial land-uses are second most frequent trip generators, followed by shopping, educational and recreational activities.

WALKING DISTANCES.

Factors Affecting Walking Distance.

Four interrelated factors affect the distance Americans are willing to walk. They are: *time, convenience, availability of auto transport and a land use pattern* that is not conducive to walking. They are all correctable and elaborated as follows:

Time

The free time a person has—witness our willingness to walk 15 miles on a week-end hike but *need* to drive one-quarter mile for a work day lunch. Recreation journeys serve no income generating purpose and the exercise, fresh air and pleasant experience can't be measured in dollars. People shopping for entertainment might walk for two hours, and can easily travel two to three miles, even though they might not be aware of it. Yet, lunch-going executives automatically head for the car, when the walk may not be sufficiently longer. Americans lump commute time with income producing time, and if the commute is long, think of it as lost wages. Walking, bus-riding and biking are perceived to take additional time. Traffic planners value commute time at approximately 25 percent of one's salary. This fabricated "loss" wage has been used to develop a positive road-building cost/benefit ratio, and is patently absurd. No one is paid to commute, and most people seem willing to set aside a reasonable amount of commuting time in exchange for pleasant living conditions.

Convenience

Our dependence on auto travel has reduced the quality of many pedestrian areas, and lengthened the walking distance necessary to accomplish daily activities. The shift has also reduced bus transportation, making it difficult to live without a car. Some people have ambulatory disabilities, and can't walk long distances. Shoppers carrying packages or tending children are more aware of time and distance and may not be willing to walk more than 1,000 feet. Older people tire easily and may not be able to walk long distances. Bad weather—rain, snow, cold or hot climates discourage walking. Most of these conditions can be improved by design with rain protection, wind screens, and buildings and streets oriented to allow sun penetration to walk and rest areas.

Our efforts to construct an outstanding road network has been a factor in lowering the quality of the pedestrian system. When drivers don't need to walk long distances, the need to develop good walkways disappears. The cost of walking is low, consisting of the time involved minus any inconvenience. In many places, the inconvenience of battling a car-oriented world is a greater problem than the lost time. Perceived costs (or disbenefits) go up when the walk is unsafe or unpleasant.

Availability of Automobiles

Americans have grown dependent on the car. It is convenient, somewhat inexpensive, fast, flexible and allows us to accomplish much during each day. We use it extensively because we have developed a fine road system, easy parking and a spread out, single-use land pattern that makes alternatives to driving difficult, impossible or unattractive. Getting to work, play, shopping or school in low-density communities is easy by car and difficult on foot. On the other hand,

European communities place a high cost on driving, offset by better public transportation, compact, mixed-use community organizations that encourage Europeans to walk and bike longer distances than Americans.

Land-Use Pattern

Our single-use land pattern and superior road system has made it difficult for suburban families to carry out activities on foot within a reasonable time limit. In spite of the single-use land pattern, auto trips in urban areas are shorter than most people imagine and there are denser, mixed-use places where foot travel is (or can be) faster than motorized travel.

20-25% of personal trips are under one mile in length, 20% are 1-2 miles and only 12-15% are 2-3 miles. Thus, over half of all urban trips are *under* three miles in length. Solving the time problem will require combining travel modes—utilizing motorized travel to cover longer distances and foot travel for short distances in districts once reached by car, bicycle or bus.

DISTANCES PEOPLE WILL WALK.

The old rules of when, why and how far people walk are slowly being broken. New rules, based on the availability and quality of pedestrian facilities can extend the distance people walk. *Just as better roads extended the distance people would drive, separation from cars, improved transit, weather protection, shortcuts, attractive shop windows, planting, street furniture, visual stimulation and other improvements extend the distance that people are willing to walk.* Rich and poor can benefit from improved conditions. Rising affluence increases free time, which could be spent walking, running or bicycling. Increased interest in maintaining good health to offset sedentary jobs has increased our willingness to walk longer distances. People who can't afford to drive, may be able to get around with improved pedestrian conditions. The distance people are willing to walk to accomplish every day tasks is lengthening, and should continue to increase as long as gasoline costs increase and alternative transportation options are developed.

Americans are thought to be lazy when it comes to walking, but the facts don't bear this out. Given a recreation setting, Americans can walk as far as members of any other culture in the world. Our number of joggers exceed any country in the world. Why is it then that Americans seem unwilling to walk to accomplish purposeful activities? A person walking or running for recreation could run or bike to work, but most don't. Part of the trouble is that we do *not* have good walking facilities. Though we construct paths for walking in the forests, we organize our communities for driving, and this makes walking difficult.

Walking is the most convenient means of transportation for short distances up to 500 yards, but as distance increases, the car or bus or bike becomes more attractive. The present desire to walk in American cities can be depicted as a steep tapered curve, with most people (70%) willing to walk 500 feet, fewer (40%) willing to walk 1,000 feet, and tapering off very quickly until only 10% are willing to walk half a mile.

The secret of pedestrian improvement is to reduce the walk length with shortcuts, to intensify activity, and to improve intermediate distance substitutes—bus, bicycle and taxi. Shortening the walk length to *500 feet* (say a new pedestrian bridge, that reduces walking distance from 900 feet to 400 feet) benefits more people than shortening a 2,000-foot distance to 1200 feet.

People who live in cities are willing to walk longer distances than suburbanities, because the driving alternative is more time consuming and expensive. *The average walking distance increase as development becomes denser.* Auto users who drive near a busy destination face the alternative of a longer walk or paying more for parking and possibly becoming involved in heavy traffic. Conversely, people living in older, small towns are often willing to walk longer distances, perhaps because they are used to it, or perhaps because the walk is comfortable.

The Bureau of Public Roads lists 800 feet as an average American commuter walking distance from car to work. New York City transit riders walk farther with the average being about 4.5 minutes or 1300 feet. Walking trips from private automobiles and taxicabs are shorter than those made from public transportation as drivers, accustomed to private car comfort, won't walk far. A ten minute or 2,300 foot walk seems to be the maximum distance American people are willing to walk today, but as transportation costs increase and traffic worsens, people may walk further. In Holland, the average walking distance from home to a large department store is about 3,000 feet or 12 minutes. In Germany, suburban shoppers walk at least 2,400 feet to reach a convenient shopping center, and then may walk farther while shopping.

Most traffic and transportation surveys underestimate the amount of walking people do. For instance, the Nationwide Personal Transportation Study conducted by the U.S. Bureau of Census in 1977 instructed respondents to count as trips "all walking or bicycling where the destination and origin are *not* the same address". This definition excludes much walking for pleasure, e.g., the walk around the neighborhood (a person isn't walking to any destination except, eventually, back home). It also excludes most jogging, and such activities as playing in the road. Yet, people are exposed to the risk of accident regardless of whether a trip has a purpose.

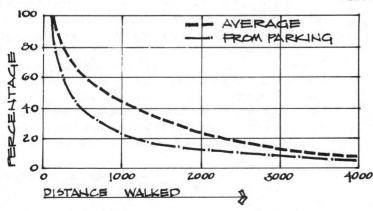

CAPITOL IMPROVEMENT SUMMARY
- Wind/rain shelter
- Resting places
- Visual diversity
- Curb cut ramps
- Night lighting
- Protection from traffic
- Maintenance

THE WALKING EXPERIENCE

Improving safety, convenience and pleasure enhances and encourages walking. *Safety* improvements are aimed primarily at reducing conflict with cars. *Functional* improvements extend the walker's physical limitations, while *pleasureable* changes in environment are sensory and extend our psychological limits.

Safety

Most reasons for pedestrian accidents are obvious and so difficult to solve that they are accepted as a necessary by-product of efficient auto movement. However, with over 350,000 U.S. pedestrians struck by vehicles each year, resulting in more than 10,000 deaths plus thousands of permanent injuries, the problems must be addressed and political pressure exerted to establish new pedestrian safety priorities. Elements to consider in improving pedestrian safety are: road design; traffic intensity and speed; the continually changing pedestrian environment; the physical and mental state of both pedestrians and drivers; weather conditions; and time of day. *Conflict with the car accounts for most pedestrian safety problems.* In urban communities, between 30-35 percent of all vehicle-related deaths involve pedestrians. Most urban community car/pedestrian conflicts occur at intersections of arterial roads. In suburban communities, most serious car/pedestrian conflicts occur along roads with no sidewalks, and at intersections. Residential streets have the smallest percentage of pedestrian accidents.

Elderly and handicapped people have a particularly difficult time crossing streets. Signals often allow insufficient time for slow walkers to cross the street, causing some elderly to run the remaining distance. Turning vehicles are particularly frightening to a slow walker who is in a crosswalk, and many people simply turn back out of fright. Some become so fearful that they refuse to walk places, even if walking is their only means of transport. These might seem like isolated examples but just observe how elderly and handicapped people cross busy streets, and then speculate on why so few try. Until these people are able to perceive that our towns and neighborhoods are safe places to walk, their anxiety may prevent them from carrying out their daily activities on foot.

A large number of serious pedestrian accidents do not involve the motor vehicle, and are not reported. They are falls on level surfaces, and falls while walking on stairs. They are the result of tripping, stumbling, falling into or over obstacles in the way, falling because of poorly designed or maintained parts of the pedestrian area.

Fear of muggers and other street criminals is a concern to many potential walkers. The elderly, women and children, who may feel more vulnerable than others, share this concern. The shift to predominant automobile use has created three conditions that contribute to increased fear of muggings and petty crimes. It has:

- Reduced the numbers of pedestrians by shifting them to the car. Larger numbers of people walking make streets safer (though there can be other problems if crowds become too large);
- Disbursed retail activity and services so that most people don't or can't walk to carry out daily activities;
- Created environmental problems such as noise and pollution that cause residents to turn their attention away from the street. The previous large number of "eyes" on the street helped make it safer for pedestrians.

A concerted effort is needed to change and improve these three conditions.

Convenience

Pedestrian convenience depends on the directness, continuity and availability of the walk. Removing obstacles and installing sidewalks where none exist is the first step. Providing aids to street crossing and reducing numbers of stairs helps. Shortcuts, a fine-grain network of routes focusing on desirable destinations such as schools, shopping, play and work, reduce walk distance. Extending traffic signal "WALK" time to ½ second per foot of roadway width assures adequate time and freer movement. Within a downtown area, providing shopping carts, lockers or check-in points to store packages and a low cost delivery system allows extensive foot shopping without the burden of packages.

Walking can be enhanced by removal of walkways of such barriers as parked cars, construction equipment, newspaper racks, utility poles, fire hydrants, street signs, and ruts and holes caused by poor maintenance. Certainly, pedestrians can change direction and go around obstacles, but not without a sense of disruption. No study accurately measures this stress, yet parallel analogies show that our patience can be limited. Think of the number of times car drivers become furious at slow drivers in their way, or how long it takes after the light turns green for an impatient driver to honk. Admittedly, part of the driver's frustration is the helplessness of being trapped in a car with no way to self-correct a problem, whereas pedestrians can change direction and walk around a barrier. But what if a pedestrian

CONVENIENCE EQUALS WALK

— Directness
— Continuity
— Availability

is in a hurry, seeks relaxation, or if the barriers are frequent and difficult to move around? Then the pedestrian may decide the walk is too disjointed and drive instead. Though there is little concrete evidence, one suspects that a walk with few barriers contributes to psychological well-being and walking pleasure. Barrier elimination also speeds up traffic flow and increases the walk's capacity.

Reducing the amount of internal auto travel in cities improves pedestrian circulation. Improved bus and taxi service can extend foot travel distance. A mini-bus interconnecting several shopping areas eases long distance walking problems. Shopping by phone and consolidating each trip to maximize a person's activity should be encouraged.

Pleasure

Walking pleasure is enhanced by providing *protection, coherence, security and interest.* Separating the walk from major roads by a curb and six feet of planting reduces worry over impending car dangers. Protection from bad weather—rain, sun or wind with a series of semi-connected awnings, overhangs, arcades or bus stops extends the walk potential. Window dressing to better expose merchandise and outdoor display adds visual appeal and stimulation. At night when fear of crime keeps many urban people from walking, well-lighted and active streets provide a feeling of security. Thus, busy lit streets are more appealing for nighttime walking than secondary, dark internal walkways which may be more pleasant by day.

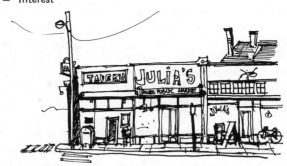

3 MPH Pedestrian Design Speed

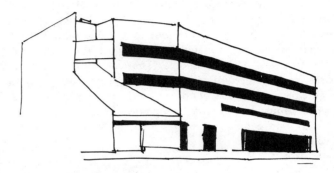

40 MPH Auto Design Speed

Cars have invaded all aspects of daily life, and aren't even willing to keep off the sidewalk area. Here the parked car hoods narrow the sidewalk in addition to creating danger to pedestrians as they park.

Pedestrian furniture—benches, planters, fountains, sculptures, detailed paving, etc., enhances the visual experience and reduces the apparent walk length. The change in travel speed from a 40 m.p.h. auto trip to a 3 m.p.h. walk requires a change in the way we design the landscape. At 3 m.p.h.,

people are aware of every detail, and become bored if the walk isn't continually changing and interesting. Narrow roads, continuous facades, signs, vegetation and foliage, overhead wiring all add to the interest of pedestrian spaces.

Visual stimulus is important to reinforce the progress being made by pedestrians. However, our recent design efforts have concentrated on developing streetscapes that are safe and comfortable when viewed from the automobile. At faster speeds, visual stimulus needs to be subdued. This is accomplished by smoothing out the route, elongating and simplifying buildings and landscape and adapting a regular and competitive pattern so drivers aren't disturbed by variety or unexpected features. This same design vocabulary has crept into the pedestrian world. Geometric and repetitive patterns that reoccur may set up a rhythm causing the pedestrian to consciously count each step. If there is little break in the repetitive pattern, the walk may seem longer and progress may seem slow.

In New York City, blocks are longer in the north-south direction than in the east-west direction. Walkers delight at their speed when walking in the east-west direction, while complaining of the lack of progress in the north-south direction. Though the north-south blocks are generally more crowded, travel speed is roughly the same while the variety in the smaller space of the short block makes the trip feel that much shorter.

In many places, adequate space for pedestrian flow is not as important as the festiveness of the experience. Because people like to talk, to mix, to watch, these activities enhance the total experience, even though they may actually impede flow. Shopping districts may benefit by encouraging through pedestrian traffic, that is, traffic with a destination other than the shopping district itself, such as people going to another work station, to the bus, to home, etc.

Like driving, the large part of walking involves waiting. People wait for buses, to be picked up by a spouse, to rest, or pause in the sun because it is pleasant. People wait to watch other people—the greatest spectator sport. Waiting can be made more comfortable with weather protection, seating, leaning rails, and space to talk. Waiting is more comfortable if it is slightly out of the line of traffic. A bench in nooks and crannies increases privacy and affords a better view of other people. The amenity of a plant or tree, good sun orientation or special paving makes waiting more pleasant. Intersections are good locations for benches, since people can be met from two directions at a given bench, and people waiting for a bus or to cross the street can use them.

Movable chairs in Munich, Germany allow users to determine their own arrangements. Note the irregular tree grouping.

Architects often determine bench locations based on geometric and plan form considerations, with benches located in the shade, out of the view area, or usable by only one or two people when perhaps three or four may want to talk together. Such seating is often not used, or else is used by street people or those who have no other place to relax, excluding use by others.

Where foot traffic is busy enough, food and beverage services should be encouraged. Though some merchants believe that allowing private vendors in the streets and parks should be discouraged, the benefits food concessions can provide should be examined. For instance, food concessions are very popular in European communities where people use their streets and parks for recreational entertainment partly because they can purchase and enjoy a cup of coffee, a beer or a light snack. The German beer gardens and street cafes with simple, outdoor furniture and sheds to dispense hand food are enjoyed by thousands on every sunny (and many dull) days. Services can range from simple portable shelters set up by different vendors, to more elaborate concession buildings with storage for fold-up tables, to complete streetside restaurants. Laws in our cities and towns should allow enough flexibility for such food concessions to operate.

Planters, curbs, rails, and other raised surfaces can be used for seating. Any height between 12 and 24 inches will work with 16 inches being best. A width of at least 6 inches, and up to 24 inches works fine. Sun exposure should be considered for late morning to late afternoon. Some permanent benches should be arranged so groups of people can use them while talking together. (See plan) Whereas permanently placed benches are generally used in this country, consideration should be given to the possibility of using movable furniture. Movable chairs make ideal seating because each user can determine the direction he or she wants to face, and move it to gain privacy, sun or a better view. Munich, Germany has movable, durable metal chairs in most public spaces for use by all.

Allowing sidewalk vendors to sell food, drink and other small merchandise benefits the shoppers. Shoppers can eat an inexpensive meal as they carry out their tasks, and this trailer stand is towed away each evening by the vendor. It adds an air of festivity with a brightly-colored umbrella.

WHAT ENHANCES WALKING?
- Mixed uses
- Activity/people
- Window shopping
- Restaurants
- Unfolding views/diversity
- Nearby destinations
- Compact land uses
- Public transportation
- Short cuts
- Sidewalks

WALKING SPEED

Average pedestrians without baggage can walk about three miles per hour or 260 feet per minute, slightly more for men and less for women; 470 feet per minute is considered running. A mile can be walked in about 20 minutes. Walking at 260 feet per minute is what people can do, not necessarily what they actually do. People who walk more slowly tend to cause others to slow down. The bunching of pedestrians because of obstructions such as traffic signals, intersections, slow walkers, window shoppers, prams, constricts flows.

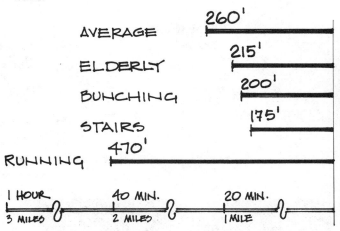

Diagram of average travel speed. Pedestrian congestion, bunching or platooning can reduce walking speed by up to 25 percent.

How much does bunching reduce flow? Quite a bit, as much as 25 percent reduction in walking speed. This type of slowdown, combined with the annoyance with a person's not being able to go where he wants as quickly as he wants, is a serious planning consideration. What can be done? The intersection sidewalk area can be enlarged providing more space for waiting. Shortening the pedestrian waiting time at signals allows a smoother flow, although this may be a disadvantage to motorists and may not be acceptable in many places. Sidewalks with shops could be widened to allow sufficient room for through walkers and window shoppers.

Pedestrian density affects pedestrian speed. As density increases, speed decreases. Each person requires a clear area in front to accommodate his/her stride, so that as space diminishes, so does speed. American pedestrians prefer to avoid body contact, so pedestrians seem less concerned with side closeness than with front and rear closeness. Pedestrians can become their own barriers. People don't like to walk behind or alongside unknown people, and tend to walk to the side and slightly ahead or behind an unknown person. This spatial relationship can force people to slow or speed up depending on what another person does, thus creating a barrier to other pedestrians. Many things slow down the average walker—age, sex, health, condition of the walker, slower people in the way, burden of carrying packages, daydreaming, etc. Older people slow down somewhat, to an average 215 feet per minute for a healthy 75 year-old. While walking on a crowded sidewalk slows one down, walking in winter cold is done at a livelier pace.

Crossing intersections is usually slower than normal walking. This slower pace is caused be negotiating the curb and the extra alertness necessary in crossing. However, when traffic is heavy, people are apt to cross very fast.

Speed of travel, when crossing an intersection, is reduced by bunching of pedestrians that have waited for their time to cross. It's further reduced by baggage-carrying walkers who force others to detour or travel slower, by elderly people who travel slower, and by the jostle that's necessary as oncoming pedestrians decide who's going to move to the right or to the left. Traffic signals should be set so the number of pedestrians who line up to cross are minimal.

Stairs reduce walking speed to about 1/3 the speed of level conditions and constrict traffic flows. Stairs should be avoided where large volumes of foot traffic must be accommodated.

Ramps impede foot traffic *less* than stairs, as more people are able to use them without difficulty. Ramps of less than eight percent (most wheelchair codes require a maximum eight percent slope) don't reduce the average walking speed, while stairs may slow healthy walkers down to about 100 feet per minute. A 20 percent grade reduces travel speed by up to 25 percent.

Mph	Mile/minute	Feet/sec.	feet/min.	yd./min.
60	1	88	5280	1760
30	1/2	44	2640	880
15	1/4	22	1320	440
10	1/6	14.6	880	293
6	1/10	8.8	528	176
3	1/20	4.4	264	88

Several factors affect walking speed: reaction to one's surroundings, purpose of trip and traffic interference. Let's stop a moment and think about the characteristics and design implications of:

- Walking to catch a bus
- Walking while window shopping
- Walking home from work
- Walking with a lover
- Walking to school (children)
- Strolling on a Sunday afternoon.

PEDESTRIAN DESIGN CRITERIA.

General road design criteria appropriate for pedestrian travel includes;

- *Safety.* Ease of movement with protection from automobiles,
- *Convenience*—most direct (shortest) route, free from delays, from one destination to another.
- *Comfort*—pedestrians must be at ease in all areas, just as car drivers should be at ease on arterials, local roads or highways,
- *Attractiveness*—should be just as important for the freeway as within the pedestrian precinct.

No hard-and-fast organizing rules will fit every case. The task is to develop approaches or rationalizations that solve the problems encountered.

PEDESTRIAN ACCIDENTS.

Causes of Accidents

1. Pedestrian and auto conflicts *in the intersection* cause most accidents. The greatest number occur as pedestrians cross and vehicles turn in the same direction, usually both on the green light. This suggests the need for more stringent auto-turning restrictions at busy intersections. Left-turning autos account for more pedestrian accidents than right turning ones. The reasons are unclear, but the contributing factors are the complexity of concentrating on oncoming traffic as well as blind spots that may obscure pedestrians in certain instances. Restricting left turns at busy intersections or changing auto design to improve driver visibility may help. Pedestrian signals for crossing in all directions at once also reduces conflict, because all cars remain stopped while pedestrians cross.

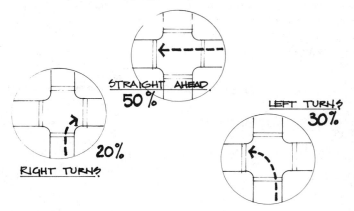

Intersection crossing Conflicts.

Busy intersections can be made safe with elaborate refuge and channelization. This four-way intersection combines automobiles, pedestrians and bicycles with a refuge between traffic lanes for pedestrians to wait before crossing. Constricted automobile circulation reduces their speed of travel. The crosswalk is marked with wide zebra stripes, and the signals are pedestrian-scaled on short poles rather than the traditional, large, cable-suspended traffic lights oriented to the driver.

2. Rainfall increases pedestrians' risk threefold during daylight and up to ninefold at night.

3. A high percentage of pedestrian accidents (about 70 percent) happen at night due to poor visibility. Darkness multiplies the pedestrian casualty rate by a factor of three, while it increases the chance for a fatal accident by a factor of six. Lack of contrast between pedestrians and background decreases their visibility. Vehicle lights often don't work well enough to light pedestrians in time to prevent an accident. This is particularly true at higher speeds or during wet weather.

4. Pedestrian casualty rates are highest in the five to fourteen, and the sixty-five year and older age groups. Children are likely to be pedestrian accident victims because of their small size, their unpredictable nature and their lack of understanding of the automobile and road safety. Children's small sizes may hinder them from seeing over cars and from being seen by drivers. Their unpredictable nature, coupled with their involvement in play may cause them to dart into the street without care or concern. Lack of familiarity with driving and the mechanics of traffic prevent children from perceiving the dangers. Furthermore, children learn bad street-crossing habits from adults. Older people as pedestrians have more accidents because of their deteriorating physical capacity including: reduced depth perception, side vision and hearing, as well as slowed reaction and slowness due to physical handicaps. Seven out of ten elderly pedestrian accidents occur in the intersection crosswalk, often with the pedestrian walking with a green light. Alcohol has been a factor contributing to accidents involving older people.

Narrow walks with little protection from adjacent cars are often perceived as unsafe by pedestrians, particularly those who are young or old.

5. Adult pedestrian accidents increase with winter months, primarily due to longer nights and inclement weather. Male pedestrians are more accident-prone, perhaps because they take more risks while crossing streets.

6. Accident risk increases as the road becomes wider, since the time of exposure to vehicles is increased.

7. Risks at intersections increase in winter, when markings are dull or worn. In attempts to dissuade crossing, some cities do not paint crosswalk lines at dangerous intersections. The effect is often not a discouragement to crossing but rather an encouragement for pedestrians to cross anyway. The street maintenance budgetary problems have forced tough decisions on what work is done and what work is not, and often pedestrian maintenance needs are postponed.

8. Accidents occur at school crossings without signal or attendance if there are inadequate gaps in traffic flow to permit children to cross safely. Many schools are located on busy streets where there is risk of accidents particularly as children queue up and peer pressure induces risk taking. Forty-foot-wide streets, for instance with more than 275 vehicles per hour do not allow a sufficient gap between cars for pedestrians to cross safely. All school crossings should have a "set time" speed limit that is set during school hours, of fifteen miles per hour and adequate policing to insure that limit is met.

9. Drivers backing into crosswalks when parking increase the chance for pedestrian accidents. This should be made physically impossible with a sidewalk extension Safe-Cross (see Page 37).

For more detailed information, the Department of Transportation has developed Highway Safety Standard No. 14 *"Pedestrian Safety"* and the National Highway Safety Bureau published the *"Pedestrian Safety Standard"*.

COMMON CAUSES OF ACCIDENTS

— Intersections
— Bad weather
— Darkness
— Age (particularly young and elderly)
— Taking chances
— Wide roads
— Careless drivers

REDUCING THE CHANCE FOR PEDESTRIAN ACCIDENTS.

Pedestrian safety is influenced by road design, lighting, pavement color, crosswalk marking, sidewalk design, separation between pedestrian and traffic, and the attitudes of both driver and pedestrian. Speed of travel, density of travel and local environmental conditions further complicate the picture. Long term, there is a need to promote pedestrian-conscious driving, making drivers aware of the human perceptual and judgmental limitations that exist. Conversely, there is a need to educate elderly and young people who may not drive and who may not be aware of the automobile's capabilities or limitations.

The following are some examples of steps that could be taken to prevent pedestrian accidents:

- The risk of crossing at a traffic light is less than at an uncontrolled crossing or between intersections. In addition, the scramble system, with pedestrians crossing in all directions at once, reduces pedestrian accidents, though it causes greater vehicle and/or pedestrian delay since cars do not move while pedestrians do (and vice-versa.) Also, eliminating delay of the pedestrian WALK light (used to allow right-turning cars to turn first) improves pedestrian safety.

- Three-way intersections are safer to cross than four-way intersections because there are fewer possible conflicts. Increasing light levels at intersections is known to improve safety, though the amount is unclear. In addition, testing all lighting prior to installation and encouraging pedestrians to wear reflective clothing can help make night walking safer.

- Sidewalks along the roadway decrease pedestrian accidents by as much as 35 percent. A row of parked cars or a planter strip between the roadway and the sidewalk can enhance pedestrian comfort and safety.

- House entrances facing away from the street on a semi-public open space separate pedestrians from auto traffic and reduce the chance for accidents.

- Improving night visibility through street lighting and lower speed to make the pedestrian more visible, reduces accidents. Pedestrians can make themselves more visible by wearing light colors or reflective material.

- Playgrounds and other spaces can reduce street play, and thereby reduce pedestrian accidents. Yet, since children are naturally attracted to the street, it will take a fine playground to attract them. Furthermore, special effort should be made to insure that streets leading to and from play areas are safe.

- Converting two-way streets to one-way makes road crossing safer, since pedestrians must look and worry about only *one* traffic direction. One-way street crossings can reduce accidents by 20 percent, unless traffic speed is allowed to increase.

- Eliminating bus or trolley stops in the middle of the road can reduce accidents by a substantial amount.

- Reducing auto speed limits reduces the chance for pedestrian accidents. It is suggested that the speed limit be *below 20 m.p.h.* in pedestrian areas and that stop signs or signals be installed to give pedestrians a chance to cross. At speeds greater than 25 m.p.h., drivers cannot easily stop to let pedestrians cross the street. Drivers who don't see pedestrians from a distance often will drive through a crosswalk assuming that pedestrians will wait. Since pedestrians cannot depend on drivers to stop at crosswalks, they often wait, reinforcing the drivers' perceptions of their right to continue.

- Prohibiting U-turns on heavily-traveled pedestrian streets reduces accidents.

- The use of school traffic patrols reduces accidents.

- Sidewalk rails and widened sidewalks should be used at schools that border busy streets to prevent children from accidentally running into the street, and drop-off cars should be directed to designated areas. Parking spaces should be eliminated where rails are installed.

- A six-inch high curb prevents cars from being driven onto the sidewalk while being parked, and protects pedestrians from being hit or scared.

- The use of light-colored pavement such as concrete can help make pedestrians more visible by increasing the contrast between people and the surface.

- Eliminating free right turns in heavily congested areas can enhance safety.

- Encouraging more pedestrians can slow down traffic as drivers sense the dangers and automatically slow down. It is difficult for drivers to watch pedestrians and anticipate their actions, thereby the need to drive slower.

What do pedestrian accidents cost? The National Traffic Safety Administration estimates the cost of each pedestrian fatality at $200,700 and the cost of each non-fatal injury at $7,300 (1971 dollars). Combining these with the pedestrian accident probability (figured to be $0.\text{X} \times 10^{-6}$), the resulting average pedestrian safety cost for urban crossing is approximately 0.01 or $1.00 per hundred crossings.

TO ENHANCE PEDESTRIAN SAFETY:

Create cul-de-sacs to reduce driving speed.

Create separate pedestrian ways.

Add garage doors.

Create buffers with planting strips and parked cars.

Encourage concentrations of pedestrians.

Separate parking lots from sidewalks and restrict drive-in curb cuts.

Add planting strips or a row of parked cars to buffer pedestrians from traffic.

Add curbs to separate vehicles from pedestrians.

33

STREET CROSSINGS.

Three types of crossings serve pedestrian traffic:

- Uncontrolled crossings such as crosswalks with painted lines, pedestrian refuges, raised crosswalks, safe crosses.
- Controlled crossings, that is, signals or traffic patrol
- Grade separations, that is underpassed or overpassed.

Establishing what type of crossing to use depends on the density of pedestrians and vehicles, and on the safety or experience sought by pedestrians. Traffic planners assume a "reasonable" pedestrian delay is necessary, forcing the pedestrian to wait in favor of increased auto efficiency. It is easier, they say, to stack 20 pedestrians waiting to cross the street than to stack 20 cars waiting for pedestrians. Signalized crossings are installed only when pedestrian crossings excessively delay automobiles, or when crossing the street is impossible because of high auto speed or volumes, or when a road has a dangerous configuration.

The most favorable crossing for both pedestrians and vehicles is an *unsignaled crosswalk.* Signals delay both pedestrians and vehicles beyond the time normally required to cross the street, by as much as 30 seconds.

However, unless pedestrians have an assigned right to cross, busy streets will remain a barrier. The most important aid to street crossing is assigning pedestrians the right to cross when they signal on comming traffic. The signal should clarify the crossing intent, by either pointing to the crosswalk, or by placing a foot forward as if to start crossing the street. All traffic would be *required* to stop when such a signal was extended. Traffic signals may be used advantageously when the volume of pedestrians is extensive and restricts auto flow.

Most street crossing occurs at the intersection, which unfortunately is also the location of the most traffic and the greatest potential for conflict. Intersection crossing can be made safer by being designed for the pedestrian with some of the following:

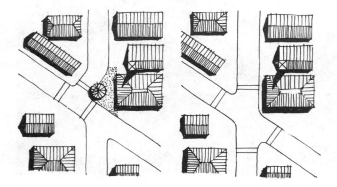

UNCONTROLLED CROSSINGS

Painted crossings on roadways reduces pedestrian accident risks about 50 percent. Markings, which are highly visible to motorists and pedestrians consist of wide white lines, parallel or diagonal or solidly painted areas.

Crosswalks. Many elderly people have difficulty perceiving perpendicularity, and the painted crosswalk helps keep them from wandering away from the general direction of the other side of the street.

Raised Crosswalk. Pedestrian crossings can be upgraded by raising the crosswalk to be flush with the sidewalk. This requires installing ramps for the automobile so it can drive over the crosswalk. The device serves two purposes: It warns that the pedestrian crossing is important, and forces drivers to slow down through the intersection. The absence of a curb to warn the pedestrian of the street is a problem. Paving the crosswalk with a different material such as brick, exposed concrete, or cobbles makes it more visible. Maintaining the curb line helps indicate the difference between sidewalk area and street. Wheelchair ramps are not necessary, since the curb ramps suffice. The raised crosswalk can also be used at the entrance to "pedestrian streets", that is loop roads or cul-de-sacs, which require slow vehicle travel.

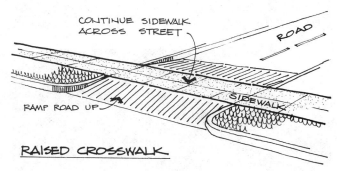

RAISED CROSSWALK

Safe Cross. Expanding the intersection sidewalk into the adjacent parking lane allows pedestrians a better view of traffic, reduces the street crossing width, and slows traffic due to the restricted street width. (See sketch).

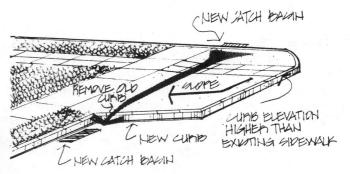

SAFE CROSS. Expanding the sidewalk at intersections and mid-block locations into the unused parking lane, allows more room for pedestrian waiting and allows quicker pedestrian line up for a fast start.

Drainage Options. Streets crowned for drainage may require a reverse slope on the Safe Cross, draining water back towards the old curb line. Run-off can then be removed through a Trench Drain, or swale towards a catch basin at the low side.

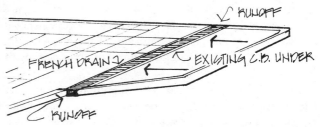

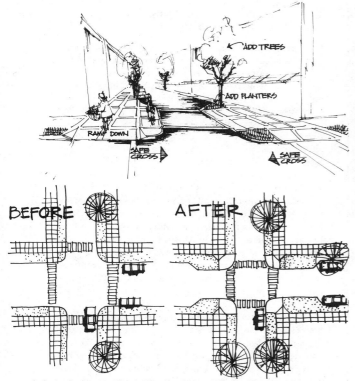

A Safe Cross may be fully paved, or partially planted with grass and trees. The curb radius must be enlarged by an amount equal to the Safe Cross width to accommodate turning trucks. It should be angled on the other end to return to the curb. Safe Crosses can be 4-7' wide, and 20-25' long.

Diagonal streets that intersect a grid pattern can be reoriented to the grid, creating a large pedestrian island as is shown here. This space has room for congregating, waiting, bus stop, or neighborhood image and identity.

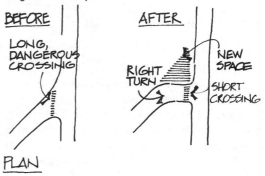

Pedestrian Refuges. Crossing wide streets increases accidents. A pedestrian refuge, a raised island in the middle of a wide (30 feet or wider) or busy street where pedestrians can wait until the traffic is clear, substantially improves pedestrian safety. The refuge allows slow walkers to concentrate on one lane of traffic at a time. Waiting time is reduced since pedestrians don't have to cope with both traffic directions. Pedestrians can accept the traffic gap as short as three seconds with a refuge instead of the normal five second gap. The accident risk is reduced by up to 50 percent with the addition of a refuge. The wider the street, the more advantageous a refuge becomes. If traffic signals are button-activated, it is essential to have a button installed on the refuge, as well as on both sides of the street so that people are not trapped on the refuge for long periods of time.

Pedestrian refuges should be a minimum of four feet wide, curbed to protect the pedestrian, and ramped for wheelchair and bicycle crossing. Refuges not wide enough to accommodate ramps should be flush with the road surface in the long axis and protected by curbs on either side. (See sketch). The refuge should be extended to encompass the entire crosswalk area. This may conflict with left-turning traffic, since the nose of the refuge must extend to the beginning of the cross street.

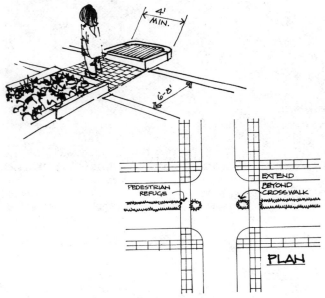

Refuges are best used in awkward intersections to channelize vehicles and to reduce the area of conflict between cars and pedestrians. Traffic engineers recommend against installing refuges where there are less than two traffic lanes per direction, but that is based on vehicular concerns which should be weighed against potential pedestrian gains.

Diagonal diverters, connecting opposite intersection corners, allow pedestrians a separate and safe lane to cross on. The diverter restricts and discourages auto traffic, making crossings even safer. Diverters are ideal for the blocks surrounding a school or park. (See sketch)

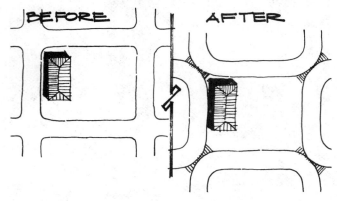

WHY STUDY EUROPEAN TRENDS IN PEDESTRIANIZATION?

Most central European countries are more advanced than America in converting their towns and cities for pedestrian use. We can obviously learn from them. However, European use of land, public transportation and town planning goals are quite different than American approaches. European towns are older, more compact, with higher densities, mixed land-uses and extensive public transportation. American cities, on the contrary, have separate land uses and lower density, with spread-out patterns planned to be serviced by the automobile.

Direct duplication would not be possible. But, even if the lessons cannot be applied directly in America, one should know what European communities are doing, how they are living and what they have experimented with. For instance, it's important to know that the automobile is restricted in speed to under 20 miles per hour in many places, and that European drivers have agreed to it. Likewise, it's important to know that in many neighborhoods using the Woonerf, speeds are restricted to 8 miles per hour, and the maximum speed for emergency vehicles is 15 miles per hour.

It's also important to know that many European towns have closed their main streets, converting them from automobile to pedestrian use. They have restricted traffic flows and restricted parking, and have people put up with it, merchants have survived and the quality of the environment has improved. While we might not replicate these patterns, knowing that other people have done them, have had successes, and that residents put up with inconveniences.

The following potential counter measures can reduce problems encountered by pedestrians at busy intersections:

- Improving law enforcement
- Improving driver and pedestrian education
- Clarifying pedestrian and driver actions with traffic control devices
- Improving pedestrian signal messages, colors, and displays
- Improving signal timing
- Improving crosswalk applications
- Shielding vehicle and pedestrian signals
- Improving visibility through lighting, etc.
- Providing far-side bus stops
- Increasing driver and pedestrian sight distances.

(*Urban Intersection Improvements for Pedestrian Safety* DOT-FH-11-8533, December 1977)

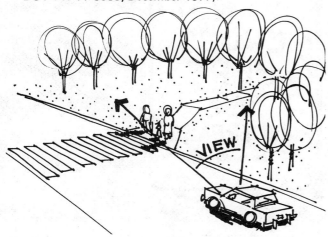

Open views of pedestrians at busy street crossings.

CONTROLLED CROSSINGS

A signalized crossing becomes advantageous to vehicular traffic when pedestrian flows reach about 700 per hour. At this pedestrian density, a signal will delay both pedestrian and vehicles, but vehicles will be delayed a shorter time than with intermittent pedestrian crossings. Intersections requiring signals are usually problem crossings with heavy, fast moving traffic or unusual configurations, and are difficult to make completely safe.

Most pedestrian crossings are designed to favor the automobile, forcing walkers to wait for a chance to cross. This is true even of self-activated pedestrian crossing signals. Once the button is pushed, a time-delay mechanism is set into motion which eventually stops auto traffic. Pedestrians usually prefer no more than a 20-second delay. Any longer delay increases frustration and may prompt some pedestrians to cross against the red light.

GRADE SEPARATION

Grade separation allows one mode to pass over another, a pedestrian under the automobile with an underpass or over an automobile with a bridge. Though grade separations increase pedestrian safety, convincing people to use them is difficult. There is usually time loss and extra physical effort, so people seeking the shortest route may chance a more dangerous ongrade crossing. Barriers can be installed to reduce ongrade crossing, but their installation would suggest an error in judgment in the design of the road and over/underpass.

Overpass. Extensive pedestrian bridge development may cause pedestrians to abandon the street below, and lower that street's quality. The street may become more hazardous and unpleasant to those forced to walk there and the increased auto orientation may pervade the street beyond where the bridges end. Pedestrians are effective agents in requiring that streets be pleasant, and should *not* be removed from this advocacy position.

To be sure, there are isolated urban developments with extensive second level pedestrian plazas, Golden Gateway in San Francisco, the Barbican in London and Nicollette Mall in Minneapolis, as examples. New large-scale developments can often include grade-separated pedestrian crossings at cost lower than on-grade crossing when calculated over the project's life. There are two reasons for lower long-term costs. First, new construction is less expensive than remodeling. Second, long-term cost/benefits to drivers and pedestrians may outweigh the initial construction cost if the time saved by drivers not having to wait for crossing pedestrians, or the cost of installing signals at a later date, or intangible benefits to pedestrians of not being harassed at a busy intersection are included.

ENERGY EXPENDITURES

It takes approximately *six* times the amount of human energy to use an underpass as to walk directly across the street on-grade. It takes approximately *nine* times the amount of human energy to walk up and over an overpass as it does to cross the same street on-grade. Crossing overhead requires more energy as the overpass has more headroom requirements than an underpass, therefore, there are more steps to climb up and down.

If a bridge can't be sited so users reach it without climbing stairs, it should probably not be constructed. Bridges connecting two major buildings, where users climb as part of the normal route (as a ramp leading past shops) or where natural elevations allow users to reach it without climbing stairs, may offer pedestrian advantages. (See sketch)

To date, no inexpensive pedestrian overpass has been devised. An overpass requires two feet of structure and should have a 15-foot truck clearance. To use the overpass, pedestrians must walk up and down 35 steps or travel two ramps, each about 210 feet long (eight percent grade, plus level rest areas). If possible, it is best to select a swale or low point for cars, build ramps and let pedestrians flow naturally over the top. (See sketch).

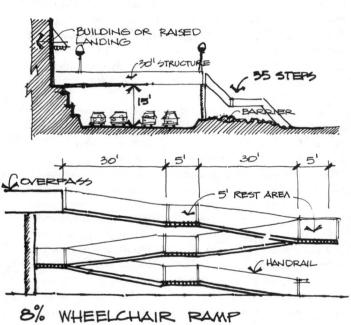

8% WHEELCHAIR RAMP

Skybridges decrease needed pedestrian activity at the street level and should be avoided unless the street is unsafe.

Underpass. Most pedestrian underpasses are expensive failures. The young find crossing the street faster (and perhaps more challenging), while the elderly are unable to walk easily up and down the stairs. Perceived dangers often keep people from using pedestrian underpasses which are usually too long, too narrow, poorly lit and maintained, infrequently policed, and have poor site lines. They have a reputation (often true) of attracting petty criminals and vandals. To extend underpass usage, they should be well lit, wide and visible from nearby active areas and policed regularly. Any invisible areas should be TV-monitored to increase the perceived safety and reduce the actual danger. Underpasses should be avoided unless:

1. The street they pass under is so busy that crossing is absolutely impossible. Even with these conditions, barriers on both sides may be necessary to physically prevent people from crossing. Underpasses should be at least 12 feet wide, well lit, preferably with daylight visible throughout, no longer than the road width without parking, and cleaned regularly. Following construction of many stair-accessed underpasses, Munich, Germany has decided not to build more unless they include ramps for wheelchairs and bicyclists. But, ramps consume considerable room, at least 145 lineal feet for a ten-foot deep underpass (eight feet of tunnel height plus two feet of structure). Some layouts are shown.

2. Access to an underpass can be graciously ramped into the tunnel so it doesn't feel like a detour. New, planned communities are able to allocate sufficient land, while built-up communities usually can't find the necessary space.

For most crossings, an eight-foot high underpass with two feet of overhead structure is necessary. At ten feet of depth, about 20 steps or a 145-foot long ramp for wheelchair access is necessary at each end. The road may be raised slightly to reduce ramp and stair length. Trench drains are necessary at the end of each ramp to collect runoff.

Grade entrances to underpasses at a maximum of 8%. Provide level rest areas at each 30" of elevation change. Ideally, a **handrail** would be included to aid unsteady walkers.

A Word of Caution: It is easy to become enamored with pedestrian/auto separation, and to assume many crossings must have complete separation. In principle, this might seem ideal, but cost, existing site configurations and the relative ease of crossing many streets usually prohibit it. Grade separation is space consuming and more difficult and slower for pedestrians than on-grade street crossings. Separation should be considered for special sites, including:

1) those that force children to cross a busy street to reach a school;
2) those that force many people to cross a busy street to reach commercial, transportation or recreational centers;
3) major extensions of the community open-space system;
4) areas where there are large volumes of automobile traffic and large numbers of pedestrians.

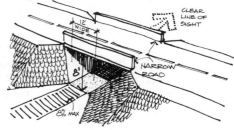

Free Crossings. Free crossing in residential areas, pedestrian-oriented business districts and small scale downtown areas would allow legal pedestrian crossings between intersections. This would relieve congestion at intersections and would allow a stronger pedestrian orientation to the street. Drivers, and pedestrians as well, would have to be on guard to avoid accidents.

Underpasses should be wide, with a gentle slope (preferably under 5%), and with a clear view to the other side. They may be the reason for creating a below-grade pedestrian plaza where city noises are muffled.

3. The underpass can be combined with shopping or other public facilities that make the walk-through pleasant. These underpasses need to be large and connected with transit or major parking to guarantee sufficient users. They are expensive to construct, must be carefully studied to assure that businesses will have enough customers to be viable. A large number of users can also allow for installation of escalators and an elevator for access by handicapped and elderly persons. This type underpass should extend as far as possible, should have exits leading to every adjacent street and should connect to the basements of nearby stores to encourage cross-usage.

Underpasses don't work everywhere. This complex system of underpasses that connect suburban neighborhoods to a small shopping district weaves its way beneath a maze of rotaries, over and underpasses. Though it is continuous and safe, it's circuitous, detached from the surroundings and uncomfortable. It isn't extensively used because potential users find it easier to drive to shops. Catering left to free automobile movement with the increased density and mixed use would short-cut the commute between home, work, shopping or a bus.

STAIRS AND RAMPS.

Pedestrians can climb a hill by (1) a ramp or inclined plain; (2) a series of steps; or (3) any combination of steps and ramps. Each mode has advantages and disadvantages.

Ramps under eight percent grade are easy for most people to negotiate. They can be used by persons in wheelchairs, as well as by emergency or service vehicles if constructed wide enough. Ramps under 8% do not slow walking speed, and are excellent for serving large crowds. However, ramps require a long length to traverse a small vertical height. In wet or cold weather, they can become slippery.

Steps are efficient for those able to negotiate them. They require minimum horizontal distance to negotiate a maximum vertical height, and are adjustable to width and site conditions. The principal disadvantages are that: they cannot be negotiated by those in wheelchairs or by wheeled vehicles, and they pose the danger of people falling in crowded situations. Steps can be informal or formal, long or short, narrow or wide. They can be made of concrete, wood, bricks, headered gravel—the combinations are almost unlimited. The steepness, width and detail of a stairway depends on where it is to be located, who will use it and how often, and what is the budget for construction and maintenance. Common sense prevails: steps for *public use* should be safe, secure, adequately lit, with handrails, and designed to minimize personal danger. On the other hand, steps can be steeper, narrower, and of variable tread and riser dimensions limited only by the capabilities of the users. Stairs slow people down by up to 30 percent. If flow is critical, wider stairways, wider entrance landing or a ramp can help keep flow even. Public stairs should have a parallel access route for wheelchair and handicapped use.

Combining stairs and ramps offers a choice to each user. Both solutions are functionally correct as wheelchairs have direct and clear route visibility and do not have to detour to reach level changes. The lower photo shows a 30-inch level change which is the maximum allowable under many codes without a ramp rest stop. A 30-inch maximum height difference is an important rule for designers to remember.

Wide, disappearing steps are difficult for many people to use. The limited number of handrails plus variation of tread height where it meets the sidewalk may cause them to fall. Additionally, the wide stairway makes its height seem even higher, and might discourage users.

Let's look at a proper stairway and leave the variation up to each designer.

- Public stairways must be a uniform grade with a constant tread to rise or relation over the stairway length, and have an alternative ramped route for handicapped use.
- Steps must be obvious to prevent accidental stumbling. They must have no fewer than three treads to avoid the hazard of one step which might not be seen.
- Rise or height must not exceed 6.5 inches.
- The top tread should be flush with the continuing pavement, but should match their stair treads in finish and in material. A change in material and finish on stairs provides a visual warning to pedestrians.
- Forty-two inches is recommended as a minimum stairway width to allow passing in the opposite direction.
- Steps must have a slip-proof leading tread edge and slope one percent forward to assure drainage. The leading edge should be level in the horizontal plain to avoid throwing users off balance. For long slopes, a level rest platform should be installed at a maximum distance of every 20 treads. This platform should be long enough for a person to walk three paces, approximately 6 feet.
- Projecting nosings or open risers on stairways are undesirable since toes can catch on them. (They are particularly hazardous for people in leg braces).
- A railing should be included on at least one side and project 18 inches beyond the top and bottom stair.
- In snow country, wide stairs should have a rail offset four feet from one side so the remaining wider portion can be roped off if the entire stair cannot be cleared of snow and ice.

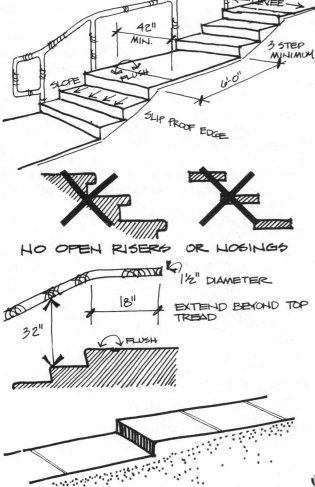

NO OPEN RISERS OR NOSINGS

Proper public stairways should avoid one-step "trippers".

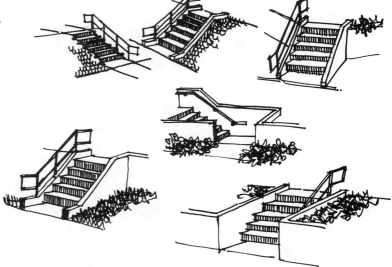

Tread to Riser Ratio. Step tread to riser ratio determines the number of steps and the horizontal distance (in plan view) required to climb a grade. Though there is little professional agreement on what is a proper tread/riser relationship, outdoor steps are not as steep as interior stairways to minimize hazards of rain, ice, and variable light. One formula combines two riser heights with one-tread depth for a total of 26 inches. This rule has evolved from the length of an average person's stride and is easy to use. One comfortable riser height is 5½ inches with a 15-inch tread, which uses a standard 2 x 6 for concrete form work.

For ease of calculations during preliminary grading, a 6-inch rise and 12-inch tread is convenient to allocate horizontal space for a given vertical distance. Once the rough grading is calculated, the exact stair tread to riser relationships can be calculated and final adjustments made. While a six-twelve ratio is handy for design use, it shouldn't end up as the final ratio. All factors considered, I favor a 6-inch riser to 14-inch tread which climbs steeply while affording a comfortably wide tread.

Stair Width. Twenty inches is enough but the very minimum for one person, provided the route is seldom used. Thirty inches is a comfortable width for lightly-traveled stairs. Forty-two inches allows people to pass comfortably, and an extra 24 inches is needed for every additional lane of travel. Different stair layouts include: (see sketch)

- On grade—with or without cheek walls;
- Pull in—requires cheek walls and favors pedestrians entering from below;
- Push-out—favors pedestrians entering from above;
- Diagonal—for those who can't make up their minds;
- Indirect—discourages use by those not initiated;
- Double direction—separated and organized routes.

Slopes that are too steep for a ramp, yet not steep enough for a set of stairs, are perfect conditions for a step ramp. A step ramp consists of a relatively long incline with steps introduced uniformly into the walking pattern. Steps should be shallower than normal, about five inches, and the distance between steps uniform and short enough so that the walker depends on the next step and doesn't accidentally trip. Six feet between steps works for most users. Paving material can vary from concrete to packed earth, but the riser should be secure, square and durable. A change in texture, color or material between steps and pathways warns of the step and delineates walk from step. The top step, however, should be the same texture and materials as the entire stairway. A light, reflective texture is preferred to further delineate the steps during nighttime and bad weather. (See sketch).

Stairway Lighting: A stairway with regular use should have shadow lighting to indicate its beginning, end and the edge of each tread. Shadow lighting requires a minimum of light and indicates by a shadow relief the edge of each tread. The simplest method is an overhead light, placed uphill to one side of the stairs shining down. The uphill position for light provides a more accurate definition of each stair tread than a downhill position. Stair lighting should be one foot candle power at the ground.

Indirect light fixtures mounted on walls alongside stairs and lighting three or four steps are intriguing to designers. They have construction and maintenance cost drawbacks, and are vandal-prone. One often sees more nonfunctioning than functioning flush mounted lights.

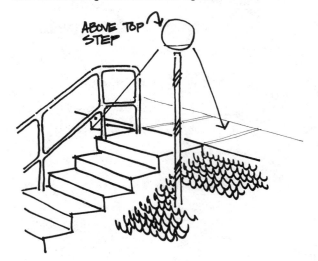

ABOVE TOP STEP

RIGHT AND WRONG. This stair, constructed prior to Barrier Free Access code adoptions, is correct in all ways except for lack of a ramped alternative and handrails. The steps include 3 treads, avoiding the 1 step "tripper", as a landing long enough for several strides, and then more steps. It is lit from above, and carefully integrated into the surrounding landscape.

Escalators: Moving sidewalks and escalators can aid walkers and improve flow, but only at considerable cost. Their use is limited to control environments where large numbers of people need to exit or enter quickly, as at subway stops or at exits from public events. They are used not so much to speed up traffic as to smooth the flow of traffic by allowing the less mobile to maintain normal walking speed. They also encourage people to walk where they might not: down an underpass or up to a second floor. Escalators are also helpful in department stores, airports and other places where packages or baggage must be carried long distances. In most places, justifying their cost will be difficult. Outdoor escalators are subjected to exaggerated wear, and need frequent maintenance and repair, increasing their operating costs. A canopy covering the escalator improves usefulness and decreases maintenance costs.

Escalators and moving sidewalks travel less than the speed of normal walking, so increased speed is only possible if users walk while riding. Escalators travel at 90 to 120 feet per minute as compared to 150 feet per minute for normal stair climbing. Moving sidewalks travel up to 120 feet per minute, compared to an average walking speed of 260 feet per minute. One principal disadvantage of escalators is that they don't serve those in wheelchairs or with severe ambulatory problems, making the addition of an elevator necessary for complete accessibility.

Escalators cost approximately $80,000 to install (new 1980 construction costs) for a one direction one-floor system. This figure is average, and does not include structural changes. However, initial construction costs are only part of the overall costs, as escalators require continuous, specialized maintenance, and monitoring to protect against vandalism and misuse.

BARRIER-FREE DESIGN.

Removal of barriers for those with handicaps that limit movement is now a widely accepted practice in street design. About *10 percent* of the population is impaired from free movement by some sort of handicap, such as sight and hearing loss or limited movement. People with moving impairments often are aided by canes, crutches, walkers or wheelchairs. They are usually further aided by automobiles which require special, convenient parking places. All new construction on streets and sidewalks should be designed for continuous accessibility for handicapped users. This means grades not exceeding 8 percent (one foot rise in 12-foot length) with ramps bypassing all curbs and stairs. Handrails should be provided and the continuity and accessibility of the total environment should be tested.

Wheelchair use has increased dramatically over the last few years as new ramps and accessible routes are developed. New facilities always attract users, and this is certain to continue as we upgrade existing routes.

Though the first generation of curb cuts and ramps, constructed in the 1970's, was a quantum leap for wheelchair users, these facilities tended to be out of the main traffic stream, forcing users to detour unnecessarily, or to search for *their route.* The next generation of curb cuts and ramps should be integrated in the mainstream of pedestrian traffic, allowing all users the obvious choice of ramp or step. Ideally, designers would think of the ramps as the principal route and then stairs and curbs as the bypass routes.

Handicapped Access. A major thrust in improving handicapped access has to date focused on making buildings assessible. Accessible neighborhoods, business districts, or entire towns do not yet exist. The pedestrian domain has developed around the needs of young, healthy adults, the so-called "average" person with normal perceptual, mental and physical abilities. Though this represents the broad cross-section of our population, it excludes those with lesser abilities such as the elderly, children, handicapped, etc.

Walkways and Ramps. In public places, a walkway should be no more narrow than 48 inches, allowing a person in a wheelchair to pass another person. Narrower walks are acceptable in private areas where traffic is light, and the pedestrian can step out of the wheelchair's way. Gates or doors must have a minimum clear opening of 2 feet, 8 inches (or 32 inches). *Note:* This is a clear opening, not just the door size. Wheelchairs require about a six-foot radius for turning. Widening of narrow walks to allow turn around space is important.

Ramps must be a minimum of 36 inches wide excluding side slopes, and should have continuous hand rails. Ramps are defined here as walks that slope more than 5 percent, but no more than 8 percent. (One-foot slope in every 12.5 feet of length). Ramps should have a 5-foot-long landing for rest in every 30 inches of vertical rise. Landings, of course increase the space needed for ramps; for instance, a 100-foot ramp covering 8 feet of vertical height would require three 5-foot level areas for a total of 115 horizontal feet. Landings at top and bottom require additional room. (See sketch). Landings and rest areas can be enhanced by the use of planting, benches, lights, etc. and are useful for all walkers.

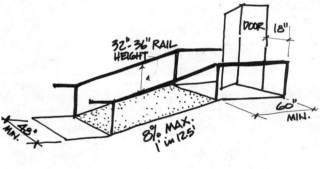

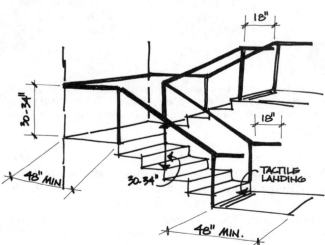

Diagrammatic access requirements to provide handicapped access for a typical building

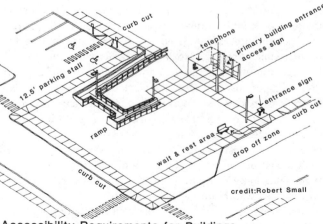

Accessibility Requirements for Buildings

Barrier-free Access. This elevated walkway connects a parking lot on the left with the post office entry. Since the parking lot and entry are both at the same elevation, level wheelchair access is possible. The entry has architectural integrity and is used by most customers to park in the lot.

Grade walks down by adding low retaining walls to reduce the grade of steep walks to under 8 percent. The ideal slope is under 5 percent.

This older ramp entry provides better wheelchair entry access than stairs, but the lack of handrail, steepness of the slope and lack of level rest space over the distance makes it too difficult for many users.

This ramp channels users unnecessarily. It appears as an afterthought and is poorly integrated into the adjacent planting beds. The left retaining wall could have been eliminated by grading the bank gently toward the ramp and then planting it. The effect would have been a smooth, inviting walk, not a channel.

An acceptable ramp, except for the ramp entry location. Note the stairs and ramp do not begin at the same place, necessitating a longer and indirect route for ramp users. The longer route may create a feeling of users as second-class citizens.

The surface of ramps should be slightly roughened without bumps or obstructions higher than 1/2 inch and stable enough to support the pressure of wheels and crutch tips. Asphalt and concrete are ideal surfaces, while gravel, lawn and dirt are less desirable. The designer should *avoid cross slopes over 2 percent on walkways.* Wheelchairs can handle up to a 2 percent cross slope (1/4-inch slope per one foot), but greater slopes unbalances the wheelchair so it is nearly impossible to maintain traction on two wheels.

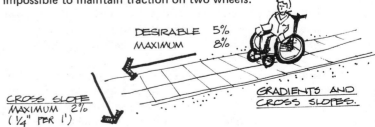

DESIRABLE 5%
MAXIMUM 8%

CROSS SLOPE
MAXIMUM 2%
(1/4" PER 1')

GRADIENTS AND CROSS SLOPES.

Measuring Ramp Steepness. A simple measuring device set at eight percent for site surveys can be made from a yardstick and inexpensive plastic line level. It can measure slope as well as door and aisle widths. Cut 2½ inches off the end of a yardstick, and glue it at right angles to the yardstick at the 30-inch mark. Use a block of wood to reinforce the joint. Trim an additional inch from the yardstick, leaving the overall size at 32 inches for measuring door openings. Fasten the line level over the angled piece with a rubber band. You might add a dot or the word yes on the left side of the level so the operator knows when the walk is *under* 8 percent. Simply set the yardstick on the ramp and see if the level bubble is in the center or on the left side, in which case the ramp slopes at or under 8 percent. If the bubble is to the right, the ramp slopes more than 8 percent. To determine how much more than 8 percent, raise the yardstick until the bubble is level, and measure the distance between the yardstick and the ramp. This difference can then be used to calculate the percentage. Use the 32-inch portion to check door and aisle widths for wheelchair access. (See sketch).

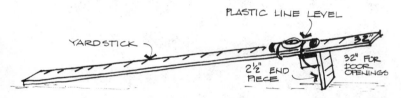

There are a number of small, mechanical lifts that can cover up to four feet of vertical distance in very little ground space compared with a ramp. For outdoor use, most people agree that a ramp is preferred, since it needs little maintenance, cannot be vandalized, is not affected by power outages and does not emphasize the difference between people with and without handicaps. Some conditions, however, may demand use of lifts, such as inadequate space for a ramp or immovable barriers (extensive concrete retaining wall, for instance).

Barrier-free code compliance does not necessarily solve the access problems of wheelchair-bound people. "Code" ramps may appear too long or too steep, thus discouraging people from using them. "Code ramps" that climb directly up to reach a pedestrian bridge may actually be too steep unless the wheelchair users are helped by another person. To succeed, the ramp must look and be accomplishable.

Handrails. Handrails are necessary for protection where hazards exist and on major routes that slope more than five percent (one foot rise in 20 lineal feet). It should be noted that the five percent plus slope handrail has been the subject of many arguments. If carried to extremes, it would imply rails on many sidewalks and places not traditionally protected. While this is not always reasonable, there are certain situations where rails are essential: sloping entrances to buildings, and main walks with concentrations of people. All new construction should have ramps and handrails to serve those with ambulatory problems. Handrails should be constructed 32 to 36 inches above a ramped or sloped walkway and should extend 12 inches beyond the end of the ramp. The handrail should be 1½ to 2 inches in diameter, and be separated from walls by at least 1½ inches.

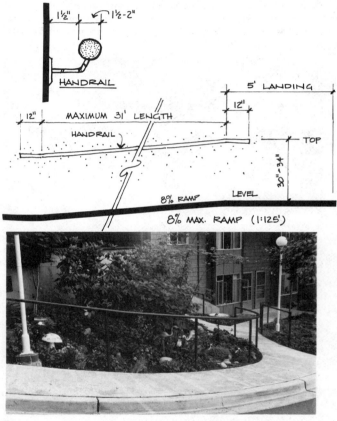

Add hand rails where the sidewalk is steep to aid people with ambulatory problems. This sidewalk, adjacent to a retirement home, allows residents to visit their neighbors with relative ease.

While handrails are essential in certain places, they are expensive and often visually disruptive to the landscape. There are ways to design without these disadvantages.

1. By limiting the need for handrails. Reducing the slope of ramps to less than five percent eliminates the need for rails. The ramp will either be longer or will need some portions that slope at eight percent, where handrails will be necessary. (See sketch).

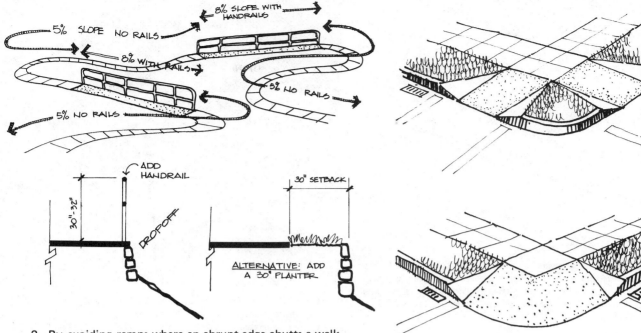

2. By avoiding ramps where an abrupt edge abutts a walk, this can be done by extending the level area with a small retaining wall and planting. (See sketch). Most codes allow a 30-inch-wide planting strip or retaining wall to replace handrails. Another option is to relocate the path 30 inches away from the edge and plant between path and edge.

Curb Cut Ramps. Curb cut ramps for wheelchairs and bicycles should be installed at all intersections. The ramp must be a minimum of 36 inches wide excluding side slopes, must not exceed eight percent in grade (one-foot slope in every 12.5 feet of length) and must be flush with the street and the sidewalk beyond (see sketch).

The primary design consideration is exactly where the ramp should be located. It is possible to construct two ramps, one for each street crossing, or one ramp to serve two directions. This second solution locates the ramp at the apex of the radius—halfway between and uniformly serving both directions. Other options are a ramp along the route of the heaviest pedestrian travel or a ramp onto the street with the fewest cars.

Depressing the entire curb offers ideal wheelchair access though automobile may, in turning the corner, cut it too close and endanger waiting pedestrians. The parked cars and stone bollards reduce that potential.

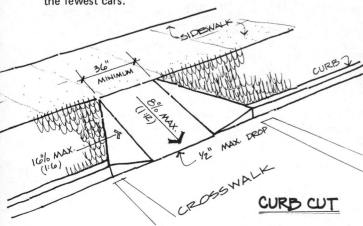

CURB CUT

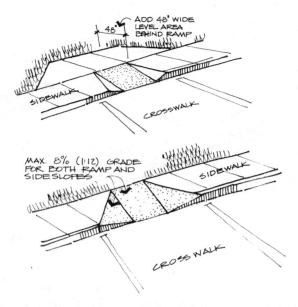

ADD 48" WIDE LEVEL AREA BEHIND RAMP

48"

SIDEWALK

CROSSWALK

MAX. 8% (1:12) GRADE FOR BOTH RAMP AND SIDE SLOPES

SIDEWALK

CROSSWALK

Another way to eliminate the curb is to fill the gutter until it is level, along the sidewalk to flow into the street. The principal disadvantage is the steep dropoff where the walk and gutter meet.

Curb cuts on narrow sidewalks can be made to operate by sloping the apron at less than eight percent. That avoids the need for backup space or landing at the top of the ramp. The side slopes become considerably longer than the typical, as long as six feet for a six-inch curb height.

It is worth noting that curb cut ramps can be hazardous to elderly and blind pedestrians who may not notice them and accidentally fall or move into the street. At crowded intersections when the curb can't be seen, people may trip on the side slope as they cross the street. Varying the ramp pavement detail, finish or color helps point out the depression and warns pedestrians of the dip. The ramp should have a uniformly sloping surface scored or heavily-brushed to reduce slippage, and flared to reach grade. Whatever pattern is adopted should be used uniformly through the city so both drivers and pedestrians become familiar with it.

Sidewalks flanked by a planter strip can be neatly depressed to reach street grade, with heavily-scored or exposed aggregate paving to warn the blind. (See sketch). Important pedestrian intersections can be constructed using a Safe Cross, and ramping a wider portion of the wait zone to meet street grade.

Curb cut ramps should extend directly from the sidewalk in the main line of travel. Some cities have offset the wheelchair ramps to just beyond the crosswalk (see photo) leaving the curb so that blind people with canes can identify the cross street, and so that waiting pedestrians are protected from cars. This location is inconvenient for users in that they have to leave the mainstream of travel at both sidewalks. Furthermore, it is potentially dangerous because it forces wheelchairs outside the crosswalk and out of motorists' line of sight. When light poles are located between the ramp and sidewalk, wheelchairs become even

Avoid locating wheelchair ramps in places where users are hidden from motorists' view by utility poles, mail boxes, hydrants, etc., or ramps that are out of line with the crosswalk.

less visible to turning motorists. A better solution is to extend ramps directly from the main part of the sidewalk as noted and provide textural change in sidewalk pavement before the ramp begins. This provides a cue for the blind and should be used consistently throughout the community.

Ideally, grates and utility covers should not be located in the route. But if they must be, they should have openings less than ½ inch across. The route should be graded to drain properly so as not to create puddles of water.

Cities and towns should begin reconstructing all existing sidewalks to ease movement by the handicapped and bicyclists as well. Standards should be developed to require that all new or repaired intersections include curb cut ramps. The remaining intersections could be remodeled on a priority basis within as short a time as possible. Appropriate places to start include: around public buildings, near downtown shopping, along major pedestrian routes, and near hospitals and elderly housing. Later, work could be done in less dense or active areas.

Parking for the disabled should be within 200 feet of buildings, unless the routes slope in which case parking should be closer. All accessible main entrances to buildings should display the International Symbol of Access (see sketch). Parking spaces should be 12½-feet wide, have signs for decal-only parking, and have curb-cuts and ramps as necessary to reach the sidewalk. Disabled people should *not* have to travel in the driveway to reach the sidewalk. The exact number of reserved stalls depends on use by disabled people. However, as a minimum, one space in every lot should be provided, plus one more for every additional 50 cars. Spaces for the handicapped should be located as near the public entry as possible. (i.e., in the most desirable parking location).

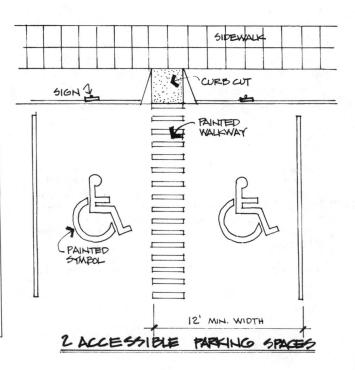

Blind people and wheelchair users have been on opposite sides of the fence in many recent barrier-free efforts. Blind people rely on cues such as curbs at intersections and narrowed lanes of travel for orientation, while people in wheelchairs require unobstructed clear ways. One principal concern is ramp location. The blind believe that curbs are necessary to warn them of cross streets, while wheelchair users prefer that curb cuts and ramps extend directly from the sidewalk. A reasonable answer seems to be a roughened pavement strip at the top of the ramp to warn blind people. The strip could be exposed aggregate concrete, concrete cast with ribs, cast terra-cotta, or cast metal. To warn blind people of cross streets, the roughened strip should be used whenever curb cuts are installed.

Parking and Drop-Off Areas. Successful barrier-free design depends on access both by pedestrians and motor vehicles. Provision of drop-off zones, bus stops and reserved parking spaces close to most destination points is essential. Wheelchair users should be able to travel from their car to building entrances without crossing roadways. Since wheelchairs are relatively low in profile, and users often can't see or be seen by drivers, access routes should lead directly between the vehicles and safe sidewalks without passing through the street. Allow two feet-eight inches between curb bumper strips in parking lots to assure through movement.

Drop-off areas for handicapped use need to be wider than the traditional drop-off zone, so that a wheelchair user can unload on the inside of the zone away from traffic. The unloading space should be a minimum of four feet wide and be adjacent to an accessible route of travel. A 12-foot wide drop-off zone allows the space. If the drop zone is less than 12 feet wide, a four-foot path should be added to the sidewalk area. Each drop-off area should be illuminated with an intensity of at least one foot candle power at the ground.

Creating equal access between ramps and stairs by locating them together is important. Typically walkers will choose the ramp if it is not out of the way.

Consumer Review. Citizens of a community sharing experiences and working together for a barrier-free community can have an impact on the planning process and can help produce better results. They can help set priorities, analyze building codes to see how they might help or hinder a project and insure that funds are allocated constructively.

American National Standards Institute (ANSI) standards for barrier-free access have been approved recently by the Federal Government. Although Federal projects must meet these standards, enforcement is limited. However, many states already have codes that are more stringent than the ANSI standards, and these apply to state and local projects.

DATA FOR PLANNING

Although most cities have collected extensive vehicular data to use in projecting future travel demands, few have good information on pedestrian flows, areas of congestion, purposes of trips by pedestrians, or variations occurring in daily use. Determining demand for pedestrian facilities by projecting past trends is impossible until cities begin to record this type of information.

Until a sufficient data base is developed, planners and designers may make their own pedestrian observations and counts in critical areas that are nearing capacity or where congestion levels should be impacted by any growth. Checks should be made of all proposed developments that may generate pedestrian traffic (shopping and department stores, office buildings, schools and employment centers). Pre-construction data should be gathered of the number of pedestrians currently using the surrounding routes in order to project the new development's impact on sidewalks and transit access. Information should include accidents, congestion and numbers of users.

PEDESTRIAN ENVIRONMENT SUMMARY

Street_____

	USE AND USE CHARACTERISTICS		
	Ped. Volumn	Ped. Activity	Land Use
BLOCK 1			
BLOCK 2			

	PHYSICAL FEATURES				
	Sidewalk Width	Street Width	Street Grade	Surface Texture	On Street Parking
BLOCK 1					
BLOCK 2					

	BARRIERS, CONSTRAINTS			
	Traffic Volumn	Pedestrian Accident	Paraphenalia	Curb Cuts
BLOCK 1				
BLOCK 2				

	SIDEWALK AMENITIES			OBSERVATIONS
	Weather Protection	Handicap Assist	Street Furniture	
BLOCK 1				
BLOCK 2				

The pedestrian realm is seldom planned, and usually happens as a by-product of some other activity. For instance, sidewalks are constructed when a road is developed, and circulation through parks occurs when the park is developed. These walkways occur as part of the normal design operation, but thought of catering strictly to the pedestrian in a traffic-planning manner is almost nonexistent.

Both weekday and weekend observations and counts should be made. Weekend counts are important in planning for shopping and tourist areas while weekday counts serve commercial needs. The following observations, made during periods of at least five minutes, could determine the number of pedestrians involved in the following activities:

- Traveling in different directions along a given street.
- Creating points of congestion.
- Crossing intersections and walking between intersections.
- Walking during commuting and lunch hours.
- J-walking.
- Stepping off curbs to avoid congestion. (Note, if possible, any shoving or anxiety of pedestrians.)

Aerial photographs are an excellent way to document conditions. Five-second, time-lapse photos are the best, since they can depict flows and blockages. If aerial photos are not available, the planner can take his own by holding a camera above his head and shooting down at the walk ahead. This technique is particularly useful at intersections where crowded conditions typically occur.

Observations should be made by places frequented by young and old people. Grade schools should be checked for *before and after school* congestion points where peer pressure may force some students into traffic. Checks should be made near areas where elderly people live to see if they can safely cross streets that lead to parks, shopping, and other services. It is also important to examine the length of nearby WALK SIGNALS to ensure there are sufficient times for slower pedestrians to cross the street. Allow one second per 3½ feet of street width.

Observations, too, should be made of the ways people use the sidewalk. Look for locations where people stop to talk or wait, and observe the problems that may cause. One person stopping causes others to shift directions and in turn to interfere with still others. Note general displacement of people along the sidewalk width, with emphasis on areas where the most and the fewest people walk. Check the numbers of people who walk in the strip adjacent to the curb containing parking meters, trees, light poles, etc. Observe where people entering and leaving shops or window shopping cause others to walk in that strip. It is typical for the central 60 percent of the sidewalk to serve 80 percent of the pedestrians.

WALKWAY CAPACITY

Walkway capacity is a measure of the number of pedestrians able to move past a point in a given amount of time, that is people per minute or people per hour. In theory, it is possible to calculate the exact walkway width necessary to accommodate an anticipated number of pedestrians. Solving for a known capacity is relatively easy, while predicting the number of pedestrians who will use the walkway is difficult. Many variables complicate the task of predicting: weather, staggered work hours, changes in transportation habits and land-use and the ease with which pedestrians move. Sometimes, even carefully planned, attractive and spacious pedestrian walks have generated much more traffic than a planner calculated. This has, in fact, happened in European communities planned for pedestrians. Nevertheless, predictions of potential users are essential to keep the calculations within the "ball park". Many of the theoretical and empirical approaches developed to determine highway traffic capacity can be used in discussing pedestrian walk capacity. It is possible to talk in terms of spacing, headway, volume, speed, density, interrupted and uninterrupted flows, etc. It is also possible to apply analagous speed, density, level of service, spacing and volume relationships used in traffic engineering for pedestrian planning, to develop theoretical uninterrupted flows capacity, and to apply a range of adjustment factors for different conditions. These approaches are helpful as long as the differences between pedestrians and motorists are kept in mind:

- Pedestrians do not travel in defineable lanes.
- Pedestrians moving in one direction generally are not separated from those moving in the opposite direction.
- Pedestrians are usually less predictable than motorists because their purposes are more varied (for instance, beyond just reaching a destination, pedestrians may want to shop, browse, meet someone, connect with transit, enjoy leisure time, or recreate or a combination of all these activities).
- Pedestrians are less concerned than motorists about rules of the road and are more likely to get in each other's way.

Walk capacity also depends on the user's purpose and anticipated experience. Pedestrians traveling with purpose to a set destination may be less concerned with crowding than those walking for recreation or pleasure.

Walk capacity must adjust for bunching characteristics caused by intersections, store entries and exits, bus stops and other obstacles. Each congested area affects adjacent walks by creating a crowded condition there too. To acknowledge the effect of congestion, we might figure that a walk has only 60-70 percent of its normal capacity. A capacity should be based on the *effective width* of a sidewalk, composed of the sidewalk width minus 18 inches for crowded curb conditions and 18 inches for the walk space adjacent to buildings. (See sketch)

PEDESTRIAN SPACE REQUIREMENTS

Since most sidewalks in *residential districts* have excess capacity, they need not be evaluated for capacity. Traffic volumes are so low and interruptions and so infrequent, that congestion seldom occurs. Corrective measures beyond provision of sidewalk generally cannot be justified. Thus, the rest of the chapter will dwell on considerations about walkways in commercial and recreational areas and areas of mixed uses. The following factors affect the capacity of sidewalks:

- *Interruptions.* Busy intersections that force pedestrians to wait for traffic before crossing causes pedestrian bunching, which slows walking speed after crossing has begun. Slow walking speed also reduces the experience, since higher density increases walkers' tension level. Other interruption factors that reduce capacity include: drive-in businesses, entrances to busy stores and offices, stairs, uneven pavement, bus waiting areas, news stands and other physical obstructions that may cause pedestrian density to increase, capacity to decrease and user comfort to lessen.

Sidewalks adjacent to busy streets are uncomfortable and often perceived as unsafe by pedestrians. Most of these sidewalks are not used. To increase use, add a planter strip with trees or a row of parked cars. NOTE: The planter strip and trees separating the sidewalk from the inside parking area in this photo.

Busy intersections, and intersections with traffic signals force pedestrians to wait to cross even when there is no traffic. This causes bunching, and slows down walk speed. Adjust signal timing to favor pedestrians by extending the walk time and reducing wait time. The addition of a Safe Cross with a bench provides more room for bunching pedestrians.

Prohibiting pedestrian access and through circulation interrupts flow and increases walking distances. Remove all barriers and prohibitions.

People waiting for buses, talking in groups and moving against or across traffic, form their own barriers and slow the walk speed of others.

Large planters and trash receptacles constrict pedestrians and interrupt traffic flow. A tree planted directly in the ground reduces flow less than planters and will grow faster and larger.

Sidewalk merchandising placed outside the traffic flow does not interrupt movement, and adds to the trip's pleasure by providing additional visual stimulus.

- *Sidewalk Width.* Wider sidewalk widths allow room for pedestrians to move in order to avoid obstacles and other people. How much room people need to comfortably walk in two directions is not easy to determine. Pedestrians' flow is generally random, but a pattern does develop as conditions become crowded. People tend to keep to the right, forming channels approximately 30 inches wide in each direction. Since people walk to the left or the right of persons in front of them, 30 inches allows for this offset. For planning purposes, this author recommends a three-foot width per pedestrian "lane" to calculate walk capacity. This width allows for the offset space of pedestrians and more correctly approximate the amount of space needed to accommodate more than one pedestrian. (See sketch)

- *Spacing.* In general, the greater the space between pedestrians, the lower the sidewalk's capacity. As spacing decreases, the sidewalk's capacity increases until the sidewalk becomes too crowded for movement. For those who walk for recreation or to enjoy the scenery, large spaces between people and low walk capacity enhance the experience of walking.

- *Volume.* As traffic volume increases, speed and spacing decreases.

- *Level of Service.* It is possible to use a *level of service* concept similar to that used in transportation planning to describe user comforts of walks, from free flowing to stop conditions. Fruin describes a level of service based on square feet of space per pedestrian which is based on the density of people. The author recommends a sliding scale, varying in measure for urban, neighborhood, small town and suburban conditions. Since walk capacity is increased at the expense of user comfort, the measure of comfort should depend on each community's perception of density satisfactory to its residents; for instance, pedestrians in an urban community, are psychologically prepared for more crowding and inconvenience as trade-offs for the convenience of many services close at hand. Residents of lower density communities may perceive their community as less busy and measure the amount of acceptable crowding on a lower scale.

- *User Expectations.* What users expect to get from a walk relates to walk capacity. For walks that serve people involved in recreation or pleasure, a low capacity is appropriate. As their purpose becomes more functional, a higher walk capacity is more appropriate.

- *Walking Distance.* Since increased capacity decreases walk speed, people who walk long distances are negatively affected by higher capacity. Reducing walking speed by 40 percent, by increasing the capacity, can elongate a 1,000 yard walk from 12 minutes to 19 minutes.

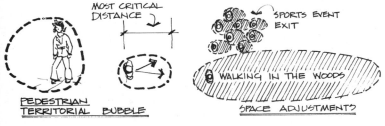

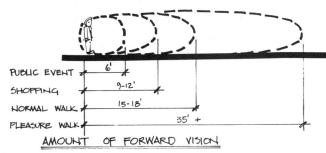

Pedestrian Planning and Design; Fruin, John J., Metropolitan Assoc. of Urban Designers and Environmental Planners, Inc.; N.Y., 1971.

Two measures are important in planning for pedestrians: the *comfort level* of the walk and the *capacity* of the walk system. The first helps indicate how likely people are to use the facility while the latter helps determine if it is possible to handle the number of people who will use it. Some characteristics of each include:

- *Comfort.* Comfort is related to crowded conditions, with reduced maneuverability and the pressures of uncertainty caused by a crowd. Comfort is affected by safety, and people's perception of their ability to move with ease. Comfort is related to conflicts with the automobile, as well as to the conditions of the surrounding environment. Loud or continuous noise, lack of rain protection, separation of cars from walkers, etc., all affect comfort.

- *Crowding and Space Needs.* Walk capacity is directly related to crowding, and the volume a planner feels is acceptable. It is related to the distance between pedestrians. As capacity increases, crowding increases and the flexibility of each walker to stop, turn, slow down, adjust to conditions and pass slower walkers is reduced. Walkway capacity depends on the amount of conflict a designer feels is acceptable for pedestrian comfort, which is related to the space separating walkers. The distance between people actually moves with each pedestrian as with the "territory bubble" described by Hall, Sumner and others. The concept of the terriotry bubble is that everyone has his own invisible territorial space in which he feels comfortable. That space is egg-shaped with the majority of the space in front of a person, the next largest space behind, and the least amount of space on either side. This territorial bubble varies with the situation and can become very small when people exit from a theater, football game or public event, and very large when people stroll casually in a forest. As might be suspected, fast walking requires more forward space for visual cueing and adjustment, and so any crowding reduces walk speed. (See sketch)

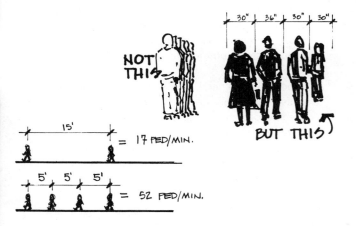

The most critical planning dimension is *forward space,* since it determines speed of journey, the quality of the walking experience, and the number of pedestrians able to pass a point in a given period of time. A forward space of 15 feet per person allows clear view of the ground ahead for comfortable adjustment to meet changing conditions, and serves a capacity of 1,000 pedestrians per hour per channel.

Walking is different on sidewalks or paths than on plazas. On sidewalks, the width is a crucial dimension, since passing is possible (comfortable) only when there is enough width to pass easily. On plazas, the crucial spatial dimension is square footage; the more square footage available for adjustment of path, the faster a walker can travel. As square footage is reduced, it becomes more difficult for a walker to choose a path and he has to reduce speed. Fruin notes that less than 10 square feet per person can force a pedestrian to stop and that less than 5 square feet is unacceptable.

Widening of Sidewalk. Widening the pedestrian zone at intersections may be the most effective way to increase the sidewalk's safety and comfort as well as its capacity. Extending the sidewalk into the unused parking space at the intersection decreases the amount of street to be crossed and provides more space for people to stand, and defines space for parking. This expanded sidewalk is called a Safe Cross. While safe crosses in this country have traditionally not been used on busy streets, they have been used in European cities on all types of streets with much success.

Raising the crosswalk to sidewalk level with ramps slows cars down and improves pedestrian safety.

Replacing one lane of traffic and parking with a widened sidewalk area in the heart of this New England town creates community image and a comfortable walking place with no fear of auto intrusion. The mixed use combination of apartments over shops provides a supply of in-town shoppers. Note the wide wheelchair ramps and simplified details. With this community, low pedestrian volume, the number of bollards, trees, lighting posts, flag poles, etc., makes it look busy and feel comfortable even when empty. Were it a busier corner, most of these elements would not be necessary or attractive.

IMPROVING WALKWAY CAPACITY

To improve a sidewalk's capacity, impediments to flow must be removed or lessened. Impediments include narrow sidewalks, unnecessary sign posts, parking meters, electric poles, news stands, and the bunching of pedestrians at traffic lights.

— Parents   — Commuters
— Elderly   — Shoppers
— Children   — Motorists
— Neighborhoods — Downtown

Locate bus shelters and waiting areas out of the main "through" walkway.

Slowing Down the Automobile. Douglas Schneider, Director of the District of Columbia's Department of Transportation believed that cities belonged to people and not to the automobile, instituted a number of programs that made driving in Washington, D.C. difficult including:

- Prohibiting and enforcing the no-right-turn on red law that provided extra protection and comfort for pedestrians crossing the street.
- Mounted a vigorous attack against illegal parking by creating his own ticket-writing force when the Police Department refused to cooperate.
- Returned a number of one-way streets to two-way traffic because they had become one-way rush-hour freeways and he believed that streets really belonged to the neighborhoods.
- Reserved the curb lanes of major thoroughfares for buses, attempting to make public transportation more convenient than cars.
- Battled vigorously for low fares on the bus system, arguing that low fares would be needed so transit could compete with the automobile he described as over-privileged, over-subsidized, and over-pampered.
- Used almost $2,000,000,000,000 (two billion) in Federal money for a new subway system, even though that money could have been used to build freeways and other road projects in D.C.
- Believed that it was immoral for somebody to drive a car downtown.
- Installed the transit director and staff in the most prestigious offices, while relocating the traffic engineers to an underground bunker near the expressway.
- Believed that the urban freeway was the ultimate symbol of irrational transportation planning. He noted that the urban freeway makes little sense as it takes up space in an already crowded area, removes land from the tax base, is ugly, destroys the city aesthetically, creates pollution, cuts off urban dwellers from city services, while it fails to accomplish its objective of relieving traffic. Instead it generates more cars. Though it may move the congestion around a little bit, it doesn't solve the problem.

The usable pedestrian area is *less* than the actual sidewalk width. Downtown sidewalks include the strip near the street used for street furniture as hydrants, parking meters, mail boxes, telephone and light poles, street trees, traffic signals and signs. The inside edge of the sidewalk abutting buildings or walls restricts pedestrian flow. Window shopping pedestrians restrict other pedestrians. How people use sidewalk space is related to how it is visualized. Most people's lateral viewing cone is approximately 10 degrees, equal to about a 5 foot distance perpendicular to the line of travel. (See sketch). Pedestrians can accurately perceive objects within this 10 degree or 5 foot range, so they avoid walls and other objects by 3 to 5 feet. The exact distance depends on the number of pedestrians and decreases with crowding. When forced to walk close to a wall, pedestrians slow down to improve their visibility.

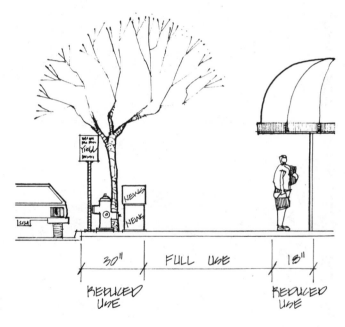

New fences, retaining walls and buildings should ideally be set back from the sidewalk by 3 to 5 feet to compensate for this lost traveling space. The ground between the walk and building can be paved (using a paving material different from the sidewalk) or planted with ground cover. In addition, the outer channels of the sidewalk used for street furniture can be compared to road shoulders, necessary but not regularly used and should not be counted in sidewalk width. The useful width of a sidewalk for calculating pedestrian capacity equals the total sidewalk width minus two 18 to 30-inch strips for street furniture and abutting buildings or walls.

It's not always necessary to channelize and separate pedestrians from vehicular traffic on sidewalks. In this case, the walk and driving surfaces are continuous with no curbs, gutters or changing elevation, allowing pedestrians to meander through the whole area. Drivers are alerted as they enter the Pedestrian Precinct, and controlled in places by these handsome stone bollards. The bollards also protect trees planted in parking spaces.

Boulevards. This boulevard is pedestrian-scaled with unit paving, closely-planted trees, benches, billboards and showcases. However, the distance seems endless and one can become tired while walking along it. Note how the poplars reinforce the horizontality of the space, and enclose and protect the pedestrians from heavy-moving traffic.

Removal of Street Clutter

- Unnecessary sign posts, parking meters, electric poles, news stands, etc., should be eliminated or grouped to free intersection space.
- Parking meters may be numbered and grouped one to a block, with each driver walking to deposit his coin.
- Some signs may be eliminated by painting their message on the street or curb.
- Electric utilities may be placed underground, thus eliminating poles.
- On news stand servicing both morning and evening papers may be installed flush on a building wall, preferably along the side streets of intersections.
- Placing light poles, news stands, parking meters, sign posts, etc., to the rear of the sidewalk in the zone usually occupied by window shoppers may help. Since this zone is often blocked by slow walkers, it frees up space nearer the street, and allows a flow shift in that direction.

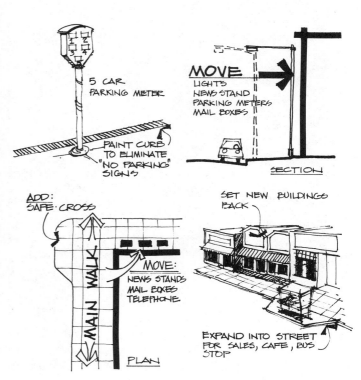

Though some of these approaches are expensive to accomplish, they do not require the acquisition of more costly rights of way or reduction of traffic lanes.

Staggering of Work Hours. Companies with large numbers of employees should cooperate to stagger employee arrival, lunch, and departure times to improve both auto and pedestrian traffic. A 15-minute stagger is adequate for pedestrian traffic, although it may not help auto congestion.

SHORTCUTS

The grid pattern on which most American cities are based is inefficient for pedestrians since long walks are needed to cover short distances. A network of short cuts through buildings, along improved alleys, between buildings, diagonally through blocks can ease the pedestrian's burden and decrease sidewalk congestion. Short cuts that reduce the walk length in the *low distance range* are the most likely to be successful. Most people will not walk long distances, generally not more than 1,000 feet. Therefore, a new alley that reduces the distance between stores from 900 to 400 feet would be better than a short cut that eliminates 1,000 feet from a 2,000 foot walk between two stores.

Short-cuts are essential. Paving of interior spaces and eliminating fences opens up new shopping opportunities and short-cuts. Passages don't have to be this wide—five or six feet work in places. Some could be landscaped and paved with brick or cobbles for access.

Pedestrian Protection. Pedestrian discomforts result from nearness of vehicles (particularly fast moving trucks) as well as climatic conditions, poor visual surroundings, or fear of a hidden attacker. Some solutions for protection from the automobile include:

- A lane of parked cars buffering pedestrians from traffic. If one row of parking is eliminated for sidewalk widening, the other will be safer if the parking lane is left to provide that buffer.
- Assymetric Sidewalk. When widening a sidewalk, the additional space can be added half to each side of the walkway or the entire width can be added to one side. While splitting the width might seem equitable, it costs more since there are two curbs to replace and it may not add enough width to make a good pedestrian space. Placing the entire "captured width" on one side of the street simplifies construction, and may add sufficient width to enhance the sidewalk. Deciding which side to widen is affected by the types of activities located on each side: ownership patterns, sun orientation, existing pedestrian patterns, origin/destinations, and traffic flows. Generally, it is best to locate the wider side with the most retail shops or the best sun orientation, probably the side receiving afternoon sun and temperate climates or afternoon shade in hot or humid climates.

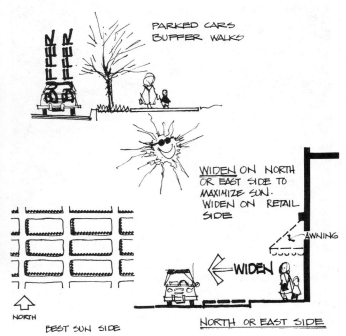

Though sidewalks separated from the street by a planter strip are more comfortable, this narrow walkway adjacent to the roadway works fairly well. The small scale and low speed of travel plus parking protects pedestrians and the right, steep terrain limits the space. Additionally, it is easier for drivers to get out of a car.

This speed bump raised six inches over a distance of eight feet forces passing cars to travel at a slow speed.

Add handrails where the sidewalk is steep to aid people with ambulatory problems. This sidewalk, adjacent to a retirement home, allows residents to visit their neighbors.

Gaining More Space. To determine if on-street parking is being fully utilized, the planner can count the number of users, verify where they go and how long they remain there. This information can be compared with pedestrian use to see if parking justifies the amount of space allocated to it. For instance, an eight-foot-wide parking lane on a 65-foot-wide street occupies about 12 percent of the space, yet it may account for only one or two percent of the shoppers compared with the numbers of pedestrians using the street. This disproportionate use could justify converting the parking lane to walking space.

PEDESTRIAN COMFORT

Paving patterns are important to pedestrians as 2/3 of our visual cone is toward the ground. Tree grates allow air and water to reach trees while providing safe walk surfaces. This pattern of random, rather than linear, tree-planting suggests movement possibilities in many directions.

Concession stands and restaurants should be allowed on sidewalks and streets where they are wide enough. The land can be leased to the food vendor and is a visual amenity and a place to rest and relax.

Trees grouped in asymmetric patterns often enhances the pedestrian route. The trees block views of the distant paths, creating variety and entry for the upcoming vista and reduce the rhythmic boredom of uniformly-spaced trees. They allow discussion of why they weren't planted in a row and are hiding places for kids playing tag.

ADAPTING COMMUNITIES FOR BICYCLES

BICYCLING TODAY.

Bicyclists are somewhat like pedestrians: they are slow moving compared with the automobile, are able to adjust to various conditions, are limited in travel distance, and are bothered by the automobile. They, like pedestrians, need to travel *everywhere* with ease, comfort and safety. On the other hand, there are subtle differences. Bicyclists are able to travel longer distances, move faster, cannot maneuver as quickly, can be almost as bothersome to pedestrians as automobiles are to bikers and generally operate in the roadway. Though biking is easier and more efficient than walking, bicyclists are exposed to bad weather and must use their own energy to get places. In spite of their differences, bicyclists and pedestrians alike share some of the same problems such as competition for space in the road right-of-way, lack of planning for their needs and lack of organization to represent their interests.

Even though light weight, ten-speed bicycles have made riding relatively easy, so that bicycling in urban areas takes about the same amount of time as driving the same distance, bicycle riding in most U.S. towns and cities is not as enjoyable as it might be and is often downright dangerous. Since over the last 20 years, America has been converted to serve the automobile, each street widening and each new parking lot has compromised walking and bicycling. The few bicycle paths hastily constructed since the early 1970's, hardly compensate for this loss; they were constructed as cheaply as possible by road engineers, who generally were not bike riders themselves and thus were reluctant to compromise the car's right-of-way.

Bicyclists were not well-organized, offering little advice to bikeway planners. Even among experienced bicyclists, there was some contradiction. Recreation and competitive riders sometimes spoke against in-town routes, fearing their construction would eliminate funds for county trails. Concurrently, a few commuters argued that special routes would only slow them down. The kind of bicycle way constructed would undoubtedly reduce their speed, but that was no excuse for not encouraging the construction of good bikeways. Thus, bicyclists were not able to get together to represent their mutual interests.

In a country where energy costs are soaring and energy prospects for the future are grim, coordination of efforts by bicyclists, local governments and planners is needed to make bicycling a safe alternative to driving. With appropriate facilities, bicyclists could be attracted to bicycle use for daily activities. Children should be able to ride bicycles safely to school and to other daily activities, reducing expensive busing and dependence on mother's taxi service. Housewives should be able to bicycle to shop or to work in their community to save cost. People should be able to cycle to work from suburbs or within the city. Retired people could enjoy leisurely bicycle rides to shop, visit, or relax. Park and ride bus stations and buses should be adapted so that workers can commute partway on bike and the rest of the way on the bus.

BICYCLE PLANNING FOR BICYCLE USE

Bicycle planning is commonly thought of as planning a bikeway system of paths, lanes, and routes all interconnected and spaced close enough to satisfy the travel needs of bicyclists. In fact, such systems would be prohibitively expensive. Scaled down systems currently implemented do not provide for the vast majority of bicycle travel. Existing roads, together with bikeways must serve as the system to provide for bicyclists' travel needs. Planning for bicycles must therefore be conducted in conjunction with planning for other transportation modes.

For bicycling comfort, some degree of separation between cars and bicycles is needed. For example, European bicycle routes, separated from traffic by extra width or raised above the street and associated with the sidewalk, and connecting daily destinations, are fun to ride and are used every day by people of all ages for shopping, commuting and play. Good planning and appropriate facilities attract riders.

That, however, has not been true in the United States where bicycle planning has been divided by two schools of thought on the best way to provide attractive and safe facilities. Many planners realize that our existing roads lead to places where bicyclists want or need to travel, making them ideal for bicycle travel, while others feel that our car-oriented roads are unsafe and unpleasant for bicyclists. The lines harden with the road advocates saying the best approach is to make the existing roads safe by restriping, signs, and other selective improvements. These people advocate primarily for commute bicycling, suggesting that non-commuters use only the safe side streets and that no additional protection is needed. Others advocating the best possible experience for bicyclists say that we must construct safe and handsome bikeways uncompromised by street traffic. They suggest separate lanes for bicyclists.

A well-developed bikeway with extra width, lawn areas, tree planting and lights about 100 feet on center.

NEW EMERGING BICYCLE COMMUTERS.

The bicycle commuters of the past consisted mostly of young, energetic, hearty bicyclists whose personality, character, nature and willingness to take chances allowed them to commute in our harsh urban environments. This author believes, based on European experiences and on the large number of potential bicyclists unwilling to brave these dangers, that the real need is to plan for accommodating more *timid* bicycle commuters.

Timid bicycle commuters are willing to ride during reasonably good weather, but won't go out when it gets real cold or rainy. These commuters would likely travel at slower speeds, taking an extra 10 or 15 minutes getting to work, and are less likely to travel on dangerous routes even though hearty bicyclists note that they are faster. These timid bicyclists are most important to cater to, as they offer a real potential for reducing automobile use. Encouraging them will require *safe* and *safe-appearing routes,* with separation in places, and all leading to sought destinations.

The European bike commuter is perhaps characterized by the Dutch bicycle rider. These people usually ride heavy, old-fashioned bicycles at relatively slow speeds on totally safe bike routes. There is a tendency *not* to ride bicycles fast, *not* to ride on high speed automobile roads, and to use the bicycle as a comfortable, pleasureable form of transportation, rather than one that requires a "grin and bear it" attitude.

TWO APPROACHES—INTEGRATION VS SEGREGATION

These two schools of thought have formed the basis for two different planning approaches that are currently used. The first approach advocates the development of a system of safe bikeways separated from the roadway to encourage new and

BICYCLE INTEGRATION

— Advocates road use
— Commuter-oriented
— Make all roads safe
— Restripe
— Add signs
— Vehicle code change
— Selective improvements (curb cuts, shortcuts, etc.)

BICYCLE SEGREGATION

— Advocates separate routes
— Abandoned streets
— Old railroad routes
— Utility and transmission lines
— Two-way to one-way traffic
— Traffic engineer/systems approach (hierarchy)
— Favors inexperienced or moderately experienced bicyclists.

to service accomplished riders, while the second approach suggests improving the existing road system to safely and pleasantly accommodate bicyclists. The first is an extension of traffic engineering approaches to vehicular planning. It systematizes the bicycle, and places it within the vehicular hierarchy, while not the actual space of freeways, arterials and local roads. Where there is order, these bikeways are problem-free. Bicycle riding on long, well-developed bikeways is truly a pleasure, particularly for recreational bicyclists.

Bikeway use by experienced riders is often less rewarding here, since they have to worry about the eratic move of slower, less experienced riders and of non-bicycling users of the bikeway who follow no rules. Separate routes are expensive, consume much planning time, require large construction and maintenance budgets, and are often the subject of much controversy in neighborhoods through which they pass. However, opposition seems to be greater before construction than after completion, when members of those neighborhoods can enjoy and appreciate the bikeway as an asset to their community.

The second approach was introduced by skilled bicyclists who ride daily in the street and advocate for few separate bikeways. They believe streets lead more directly to most destinations than do bikeways and that bicyclists should be able to use all streets just as comfortably and safely as do cars and pedestrians. They fear that separate bikeways may control and limit the bike, as well as that after separate bikeways are constructed, laws will be passed making it illegal to ride in the street. These advocates prefer minor improvements to the entire road system, eliminating chuckholes, paving the shoulders, opening shortcuts, installing curb cuts, as well as improved maintenance to keep glass and dirt from the road's edge. Pro street bicyclists also prefer reduced auto speeds, enforced traffic rules, and motorists who better understand and heed the special operating requirements of bicyclists. These bicyclists want more than token funding; they want changes in vehicle codes to make bicycling safer with greater uniformity for all road users.

Unfortunately for advocates of using the existing roadway, these improvements aren't politically visible. Consequently, politicians are more likely to choose a new and expensive bikeway separated from the roadway. Bicyclists really need the best of both approaches, with the most immediate effort being spent to make existing road systems accessible, pleasant and safe for bicyclists. Safe, continuous

and adequately separated bikeways are needed to accommodate families, children, new riders, the cautious, the elderly, and all recreationists. For commuters, adventurers and athletes, a streetscape improved for bicyclists is essential.

What does this mean in real terms? It means that:

1. all streets should be available to bicycles,
2. some completely separate, long-distance routes should be constructed,
3. a mini hierarchy of safe and convenient intra-neighborhood routes shared by both cars and bicycles should be developed,
4. repairs should be made to improve comfort and safety where needed, and
5. middle range road improvements such as removing or modifying parking or eliminating a lane of traffic should be done to allow more space for bicycle travel.

Bicycle improvements cost money, but then servicing cars costs far more considering the space, noise, safety implications as well as direct expenses. Thus every bike that replaces a car reduces that expense. This fact should figure in real cost comparisons.

Photos of potential spot improvements for making bicycle travel continuous and eliminating barriers.

THE MOPED

Before going too far, let me introduce the moped because it relates to bicycle planning. The moped, a cross between bicycle and motor bike, has not yet become popular in America, but it fits to a tea the requirements of dealing with expensive and scarce fuel. The moped gets good mileage, up to 150 miles per gallon; can travel distances needed to satisfy most daily urban activities without exertion; can carry small packages; is not as demanding of space as the car; and is relatively inexpensive to buy and maintain. While it is a useful vehicle for a country entering a fuel tight situation, it has some disadvantages on our roads. It can be dangerous when mixed with faster moving cars because it can't accelerate quickly and can't brake well. Furthermore, it, like the bicycle, provides no weather protection. Yet, I believe we will see more and more mopeds, and that they will contribute to the transportation planner's challenge.

How should they be treated? As bicycles? Then bicycle routes would have to be wide enough to accommodate both bicycles and mopeds. Or should we treat them as cars, and try to slow down traffic to reduce safety problems. Mopeds can be as annoying to bicyclists as bicyclists can be to pedestrians. They travel faster than most bicycles, are noisier, and are often ridden by young people who enjoy the thrill of power (little as it is). Although the problems of dealing with mopeds are complex, its potential for future travel should be kept in mind as we are planning bicycle routes.

A few rules that have been developed by European countries where mopeds have been used for years are listed below.

- Mopeds are classified as vehicles and are subject to rules of the road.
- Mopeds may be ridden by people over 16.
- Mopeds may be used on bike-ways, but they must honor bicyclists' rights-of-way.
- Mopeds may not be ridden in any parks (unless cars are allowed).
- Mopeds may not be ridden on any sidewalk.
- Moped riders must wear a helmet (required for all motorized vehicles traveling over 15 m.p.h.)
- Mopeds must not be louder than 65 decibels.
- Mopeds may not be ridden by two people.
- Mopeds are classified as under 50 c.c. engine size. All vehicles larger are considered motorcycles, and are limited to street use.

MOPED

There are now more than one million mopeds in the United States, with expected growth to two and one-half million in four years. Because of difficulty of recording moped accidents, the number of accidents and fatalities is uncertain. However, projections are that the death rate could reach 1200 a year by 1984. (Source "National Highway Traffic Safety Administration")

TYPES OF BICYCLISTS

Each planning approach has its champion. While magazine articles tend to favor one and decry the other, both approaches have validity. Of significance to both camps is the establishment of priorities and implementing the most necessary thing first. In order to do that, we need to examine the different types of bicyclists (recreationists, learners, and commuters) to determine the actions that will benefit each and the best way to allocate funds over time.

Recreationists ride on holidays, weekends and occasionally during the week. They prefer safe, scenic routes such as parks and separate bikeways, often driving their cars to these places and then bicycling to another destination and back. They often use bicycling guides describing different safe, scenic places to ride. Recreationists' riding skills and stamina are as varied as their background, but since they can choose and drive to a selected bicycling place, they are able to avoid the dangers of the street. (This ignores the potential of recreational riding from one's own house, a topic to be discussed later.)

Learners, like recreationists are part-time riders, who may be the next wave of everyday riders. These bicyclists also seek safe, traffic-free areas for practice and seldom venture into busy streets. They may be satisfied to ride around quiet residential neighborhoods or drive to a nearby park, scenic rural location to use their bicycles.

Commuters are everyday riders who use the bicycle seriously to complete many daily tasks: to and from work, for errands, or to visit friends. While commuting, they also get the benefit of exercise and recreation. Children who bike to school and for other daily travel needs are also considered commuters. The bicycle commuter is an asset to the community in that he helps reduce the number of cars on the road, eases congestion, saves parking space, and keeps the air clean. The commuting bicyclist should, in turn, be helped by improved and safer roadways and should be encouraged to contribute to their planning.

Learners and recreationists, who are not as particular about destinations, would use a safe and attractive bikeway. On the other hand, the commuter needs to go to particular destinations that might not be served by bikeways. Separated bikeways, though safe and scenic, don't help if they don't go where the commuter wants to go. Thus, a planning dilemma is created: constructing separate bikeways or even bicycle lanes on existing streets is expensive, may disrupt the motorist or displace parking, yet may not serve the real needs of commuting bicyclists. Helping the commuter by correcting safety and functional problems on existing roadways is likely to be the most beneficial short-term effort. This involves identifying roads heavily used by bicyclists and correcting problems or unsafe conditions. Most improvements, which can be made inexpensively will be good short-term investments. As more funds are available, priority can shift to separating bikes from traffic on heavily used routes or where amenities are an attraction. All routes, whether existing roadways or separated bikeways should be continuous and obstacle-free.

BICYCLE SAFETY

With the increasing popularity of bicycling, bicycle-related accidents in the United States are on the rise, up 78 percent between 1960 and 1970 and deaths up 28% from 1970 to 1974. Each year, more than fifty thousand people suffer disabling injuries from bicycle accidents and approximately one thousand lose their lives. The United States Consumer Product Safety Commission has concluded that the bicycle is the most dangerous product in the American home, in large part because there aren't adequate facilities for its use.

Bicycle/Automobile Accidents One out of three bicycle accidents involves the automobile. The National Safety Council statistics suggests that the bicyclist may be at fault in as many as 75 percent of the collisions with cars. Two out of three riders killed or injured in accidents with cars have violated a law or safety rule such as turning improperly, disregarding traffic signs, riding double, or failing to yield the right-of-way. The bicyclist's greatest danger is in entering traffic from a driveway or sidewalk at right angles to the motorist.

Intersections are the most dangerous place on any bicycle, walking or automobile trip. The number of potential conflicts is high, and the confusion of multiple movements may cause drivers to not see bicyclists. Three intersection movements are the most hazardous for bicyclists, that is,

---

Bicycle riding has many advantages:

- Bicycles are the only means of vehicular transportation that create no noise or air pollution.
- The bicycle consumes no fossil fuel. A person on a bicycle is the most efficient traveler in energy consumption per distance. The rate of caloric energy expended by a cyclist is 1/5 that of walking for given distance.
- Bicycles offer reliable, convenient transportation at minimum cost.
- Bicycling can save time in urban areas, where the average auto speed during peak periods is often below 8 m.p.h., while average bicycle speed can be 10 to 12 m.p.h. In races between bicycles and automobiles in Boston and Atlanta, for example, bicycles won 17 times out of 20 over 2 to 3-mile downtown routes.
- Bicycles require no schedule to meet, no car to start, no traffic jam or parking problem to worry about.
- Bicycling is a pleasant way to maintain physical fitness. Bicycle ranks third behind running and swimming as the best means of exercise.
- Bicycling is an excellent, inexpensive and nonconsumptive recreational activity.
- Bicycles consume about 1/16 the space of the automobile, reducing the need for large parking facilities and relieving traffic congestion.
- Bicycles can help people perform many old jobs better. Police, mail delivery, meter-reading, neighborhood house calls, home maintenance, can serve many communities and neighborhoods on bicycles.

The State of California currently uses 287 bicycles to carry out various tasks at an annual fuel savings of $60,000.

bicyclists moving straight ahead and being threatened by *right or left turning vehicles;* bikers moving straight ahead and being threatened by *cross traffic;* and bikers making a *left turn* on multi-lane roads. (See sketch).

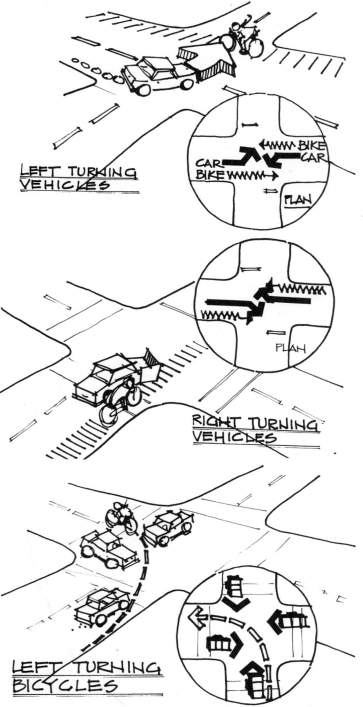

LEFT TURNING VEHICLES

RIGHT TURNING VEHICLES

LEFT TURNING BICYCLES

Potential automobile/bicycle conflict points for typical intersections. Note conflicts with left and right turning automobiles, with automobile cross traffic, and as bicycles make left turns.

There are unfortunately no physical improvements that will make these maneuvers totally safe. The best solutions involve a combination of improving rider *predictability* by educating bicyclists and motorists, concentrating bicyclists into lanes to make them more visible, and realigning the worst intersections. Making bicyclists more visible can be accomplished by restricting parking near intersections, improving lighting, reducing auto speed, and adding selective signage and traffic signals. Increasing the number of bicycles on main streets may do the greatest good, since continuous presence of riders stimulates driver awareness.

The cause of most car/bicycle accidents is *lack of cyclist predictability.* As we all know, predictability is the key to auto safety, with each motorist depending on other motorists to drive in a predictable manner, that is stopping for stop signs, moving with traffic, waiting until traffic is clear before entering a roadway, etc. However, many bicyclists ride erratically, avoiding stop signs, riding against traffic, or darting in front of traffic. These unpredictable actions can catch motorists off guard and may cause accidents. The following actions could result in situations where the motorist could not predict what the bicyclist would do:

- Darting out from driveways
- Riding against traffic
- Turning unexpectantly
- Failure to yield right-of-way
- Failure to stop for traffic signals.

There are several ways to make bicycle riding more predictable. One is to include bicycle safety in automobile education in schools and in driver education programs, raising the consciousness of motorists and bicyclists about what is legal and how bicyclists should ride for maximum safety. In addition, bicyclists should educate themselves about the rules of the road as well as equip their bicycles with safety equipment and wear reflective clothing and helmets. Lastly, the bicycles place on the road should be clarified. Should bicycles be classified as *vehicles* and thus be required to operate under all the rules of the road that motorists observe? The author feels that should be done.

The percentage of bicycle-caused accidents is greatest in the age groups of 12 and under. Children don't perceive dangers as well as older people, do not drive and are not familiar with the traffic rules, are less attentive to the dangers, and often ride improperly sized bikes. This suggests that providing safe bicycle routes to and from schools, parks, and other children activities is desirable and should be a high priority.

WHERE BICYCLE ROUTES ARE NEEDED.

Bicycle routes, that is, either separate bikeways or improved streets, are needed wherever bicyclists are subject to unsafe conditions, large volumes of traffic that produce dangerous fumes and road noises and unpleasant surroundings. While one street may be free of the problems, an adjoining street may have them all. Thus, the safety factor may change without a bicyclist realizing the change and the potential for an accident may increase. A planning goal should be for all streets to be safe while some, designated as bicycle routes serving the majority of bicycle traffic, should be *safe and attractive and convenient.*

Hierarchy Bicycle routes need to follow a similar hierarchy as our road system. Generally, there are three types of roads: *freeways,* with fast traffic moving over long distances; *arterials,* with the bulk of traffic moving over shorter distances between areas where people work, shop and play; *local roads* within residential neighborhoods or neighborhoods with residences and individual businesses. Equivalent *bicycle freeways* should be established for cross-town and inter-community routes, using abandoned railroad rights-of-way, utility and sewer easements, freeway service roads or secondary routes paralleling the freeways, courses of rivers, or along lightly traveled roads. While these through bikeways are best separated from automobiles, bicycle routes along arterials leading to areas of concentrated activity, might need separation only where traffic is heavy and the opportunities for auto/bicycle conflict abound. Local road access within neighborhoods could occur in the street, or on the sidewalk with improvements limited to curb cuts, and treatment of busy intersections.

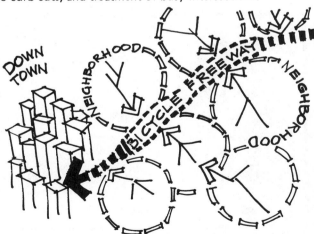

Standard practice is to begin the formal bicycle route at *destination points,* and work back toward neighborhoods, allowing the route to serve the most cyclists where competition with cars is the greatest. A typical bicycle trip might include a short ride on the sidewalk or street from home to the bicycle route, which would be separated from or raised above the road and which would lead to destination points,

Typical Destination Points

- Colleges and Universities
- Employment centers
- Grade schools
- Recreational facilities
- Large shopping complexes

such as shopping areas, schools, work places. Once in the immediate vicinity of one's destination, the bicyclist might again travel the last few blocks on the street or sidewalk.

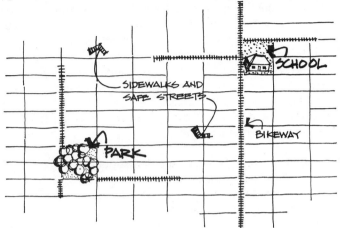

PLANNING FOR BICYCLE ROUTES.

Taking a Broad Approach. A comprehensive approach to integrating bicycle routes into a community might emphasize five concerns: road use, road improvement, bike parking, access to public transportation and education.

Road Use.

Since our road systems are the connectors within and between communities, they should be the backbone of bicycle circulation. Then they should be supplemented by bicycle routes that are separate from the roadway. On the other hand, some people feel free road access may be limited in the future by the automobile lobby in order to "improve safety" and car accessibility. That would be a fatal blow to bicycling and should be vigorously opposed. Classifying bicycles as vehicles can help prevent this.

An idealized grade separation with autos at lower level, bicycles in the middle and pedestrians crossing above all.

Road Improvements.

Increased bicycling has shifted the majority of ridership from childrens' recreation to commuting and utility riding by adults. The shift has moved the bicycle from neighborhoods to urban arterials, thus increasing bicycle hazards and need for bicycle-oriented facilities. The steadily increasing number of bicyclists as well as the confusion existing over their rights and riding conditions will continue to create safety problems. As a result, continual improvements in the roadway are necessary to make them safe and functional. These include minor patch and shoulder-widening efforts as well as extensive development of communitywide routes separated from vehicles.

In planning for improvement to the roadway, four factors must be kept in mind:

- Recognizable origins and destinations;
- Relatively level terrain;
- Space to accommodate the bicycle route; and
- Recreational and scenic amenities.

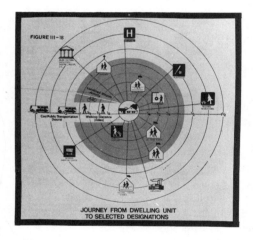

JOURNEY FROM DWELLING UNIT
TO SELECTED DESIGNATIONS

Access to Transportation.

Bicycle routes near transit routes and transit pick-up points can increase the distance bicyclists can cover and provide greater flexibility to the cyclist. Therefore, all buses and trains should have convenient bicycle storage on-board.

A bus-bicycle trip may be a great boon to bus use because one's car can be left at home while the bicycle is a vehicle used to reach the bus stop and the destination at the end of the bus trip.

Bicycle Parking.

A safe place to store the vehicle at the end of the journey is just as essential to bicyclists as it is to motorists. Parking should be simple, convenient and safe from thievery. Enclosed lockers should be available for long-term storage by commuters.

Education.

Education of motorists and bicyclists alike about bicycle safety is essential if bicycles are to share the roadway with cars. Combining bicycle safety with driver education programs and including a section on bicycle safety in State licensing publications and testing should be encouraged.

GATHERING INFORMATION.

Information to be used in planning bicycle routes can be gathered and organized in three categories:

1. Identifying principal routes along roadways that may need improvements to correct safety problems;
2. Identifying routes to be separated from motor vehicles; and
3. Identifying areas where spot improvements are needed.

Most principle routes follow arterials even though they may seem dangerous and unpleasant for bicycling. They should offer more through service than other nearby routes. They should have stop signs or signals on cross streets to give priority to the through street. On-street parking should be eliminated or controlled, and these streets should be maintained better than other streets.

The planner should observe *destination* areas where most bicyclists go, and the access routes used to get there. Places to look at are colleges and universities, employment centers (particularly whitecollar centers), grade schools, recreational facilities and large shopping complexes. Colleges and universities usually attract many bicycle commuters, particularly if neighborhoods for students and faculty are close. College enrollment should be checked to verify that sufficient students live close enough to commute by bicycle. Grade schools have bicycle commuting potential unless their busing program makes commuting by bicycle impossible.

Develop bicycle routes that connect homes with

- schools
- parks
- shopping
- bus stops
- places of work
- community services.

Next the planner should identify neighborhoods where large numbers of bicyclists may live, starting with denser neighborhoods close to destinations. It usually isn't necessary to develop routes within neighborhoods, as long as they are located near improved routes and access is easy.

All principal routes should be relatively level, and cover intermediate distances with a minimal number of stops. Each potential route should be compared with nearby routes to determine if there are safer parallel routes with fewer cars, fewer stops, and more level area. (There usually won't be, though there may be potential for making one.) Most commuting bicyclists are unwilling to shift from a fast-moving street just for the comfort of a neighborhood street. They know that neighborhood streets will reduce their speed because of uncontrolled intersections and a

slower pace to observe children at play, parked cars exiting from driveways, etc. Residents of less busy streets may also be wary of sharing their street with bicyclists, fearing a loss of parking and flexibility, and an increase in vandalism.

The planner should look for areas where bottlenecks occur: confusing intersections, bridges, tunnels, stretches of road with too many driveways, or a preponderance of trucks or buses. These areas may be targets for improve-

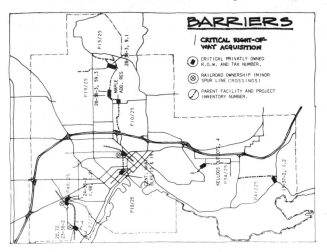

IDENTIFY BICYCLE BARRIERS

— Rivers	— Golf courses
— Freeways	— Institutional properties
— Tunnels	— Exclusive estates

ments. In addition, the planner should inventory potential routes for bikeways separated from traffic. These may serve predominantly recreation riders, unless they pass near universities, employment centers or shopping districts making proximity to destinations an advantage. Potential bikeway routes include: little used roads, flood plains, parks, school grounds, vacant or under used land, parking lots, industrial properties, abandoned railroad right-of-ways, power line easements, sidewalks, bridal trails, campuses, golf courses, cemeteries, etc. Publicly owned land is generally easier to use for bikeways since it may eliminate the need to purchase privately owned land or to obtain an easement. The planner should look for combinations of public and private land that can be linked together.

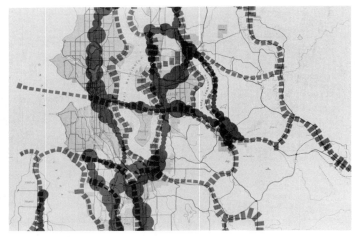

Develop diagramatic desire lines along the most logical corridors considering safety, grade, population density, activity generators and scenic resources.

69

Identifying spot improvements is easy and should be an on-going process. The planner might ask accomplished bicyclists from a local bicycle club to help by sponsoring a one-day "field planning/inventory." Ask one or two riders to cover each neighborhood, and mark all improvements that would make bicycle riding safer and easier. Give clear directions, such as "identify and mark on the map, described improvements on the attached form, and evaluate importance on a scale of one-ten (ten being high) of the following:

- Where ramps or curb cuts would allow continuous movement;
- Where shoulder widening would improve safety;
- Where traffic lanes are wide and could be narrowed, leaving space for a cycle lane:
- Where you feel unsafe, and feel improvement is needed, such as a bicycle ramp leading to a sidewalk that by-passes a busy intersection and then leading back into the street at the end;
- Where there is interference with bicycle travel, such as chuckholes, railroad tracks, gravel or glass on the shoulder, unpaved sections, etc.

Some suggestions given by these helpful bicyclists should be implemented immediately so they will sense the seriousness of the effort and will be willing to continue suggesting improvements.

User preference data might be obtained as part of an origin/destination interview. Locate interviewers on well-traveled routes, and question them about: trip origin and destination, length of trip, purpose of trip, frequency of trip, travel time, and any concerns, preferences or attitudes about traffic, amenity, safety, inexperienced riders, etc.

BICYCLE ROUTE PLANNING CHECK LIST

STREET_____ FROM_____ TO_____

- NUMBER OF DRIVING LANES: 1   2   3   4
  ONE OR TWO WAY: one   two
- SHOULDER WIDTH: none   3-5'   8'
  PAVED: yes   no
- SIDEWALK: none   both sides   one side
  PAVED: yes   no   OBSTRUCTIONS: yes   no
- GRADE: shallow   moderate   extreme
- LENGTH OF GRADE (specify)_____
- TRAFFIC VOLUME: light   moderate   heavy
- DESIGNATED SPEEDS (MPH) 20   25   30   35   40
- ARE SPEED LIMITS OBSERVED: yes   no   unsure
- PARKING: none   both sides   one side
- OBSERVED PARKING DENSITY: low   moderate   heavy
- PARKING RESTRICTIONS: (specify)_____

- PEDESTRIAN TRAFFIC: light   moderate   heavy
- DOES ROUTE PROVIDE SCENIC INTEREST: yes   no
- GREENERY ALONG ROUTE: yes   no
- REST STOPS/POINTS OF INTEREST: yes   no
- STREET LIGHTING: none   good   bad
- PROBLEM AREAS (INTERSECTIONS, BLIND SPOTS, PARK-ING, ETC.) specify_____

- SPECIAL INTEREST AREAS (specify)_____

- ADEQUATE ALTERNATIVE IF PARKING IS REMOVED: yes   no
- ALTERNATIVE ROUTES: (specify)_____

Predicting future bicycle demand is tricky, since little bicycle forecasting has ever been done. An alternate approach to forecasting is to determine the overall effect and quality of environment desired, and build facilities to match. This suggestion is based on the concept that transportation routes create their own demand. If routes are located and built with care, serving active destinations or scenic amenities and are convenient, safe and properly maintained, they will be used and will create increased demand.

IDENTIFY HAZZARDS ON ROADWAYS SUCH AS:

— Unsafe grates	— Shoulder rumble strips
— Debris	— Narrow traffic lanes
— Rough pavement	— Gravel shoulders
— High speed	— Excessive driveways
— High traffic volume	— Poorly set traffic signals

There are several logical ways to handle bicycle traffic:

- In places of low auto congestion and low bicycle demand, bicyclists can ride safely on the sidewalk or in the street. Most neighborhood streets fall into this category.
- When bicycle traffic increases and desired routes become obvious, certain streets may be designed as bicycle routes and made safe by keeping traffic to a maximum speed of 20 m.p.h. A 20 m.p.h. speed is compatible with bicycles, and often does not reduce automobile capacity or create major inconvenience.
- As bicycle volume increases, a special bicycle lane might be designated by eliminating one row of parked cars.
- A two-way street might be converted from one-way and the captured lane designated as a bicycle route. Costs are minimal since no new land must be purchased and no construction is necessary. One-way streets can satisfy the auto movement requirements of most neighborhoods. Bicycle routes should be located on the right-hand side of the street as drivers tend to pull to the left (their driving side). The one or two-way bikeway is appropriate, with extra care required for two-way travel (see following text).
- Narrowing the travel lanes of existing roads can provide more room for bicycle use. Many streets have 12 or 13-foot-wide travel lanes, which could be reduced to 10 feet. Car speed should be reduced on narrowed roads, making cars more compatible with bicycles. Two-way roads may be narrowed until it is impossible for two cars to pass, say, to 12 to 15 feet wide. This forces one car to pull into a driveway or parking space to allow another to pass. The remaining space can then be used for a bikeway, though it will have to be protected with a curb.
- Separate routes may be designated for the bicycle. Although finding vacant land may be difficult, design possibilities are varied and are limited only by planners' creative imaginations, political reality and budget.

DEFINITIONS

Bikeway Any road, path, or way which is designed to be open to bicycle travel, regardless of whether it is for the exclusive use of bicycles or shared with other transportation modes.

Bicycle Path A bike physically separated from motorized vehicular traffic by an open space or barrier and either within the highway right-of-way or within an independent right-of-way.

Bicycle Lane A portion of a roadway which has been designated for preferential or exclusive use by bicycles.

Bicycle Route A roadway designated for bicycles by signing only.

(Federal Highway Administration's "Guide for Bicycle Facilities" 1981)

SLOW DOWN TRAFFIC

ELIMINATE ONE PARKING LANE

CONVERT TO ONE-WAY STREET

NARROW TRAVEL LANES

DEVELOP SEPERATE ROUTES

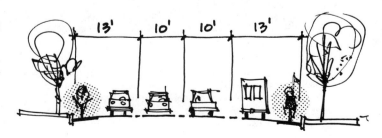

The BART Bicycle Study recommends that bicycles and motor vehicles:

1) can share the same roadway when auto traffic travels slower than 25 miles per hour and when the total traffic volume is less than 2000 vehicles per day or about 180 vehicles in the peak hour direction.

2) Utilize a striped bicycle lane where traffic does not exceed 40 miles per hour and the volume of traffic in the adjacent lane does not exceed 1000 vehicles per day and truck traffic does not exceed 5 percent of the vehicles.

3) that bicycle routes be separated from traffic by some physical barrier when traffic speeds exceed 40 miles per hour and traffic volumes exceed 1000 vehicles per day in the adjacent lane or when trucks comprise more than 5 percent of the vehicles on the road.

Providing safe and pleasant access to and through shopping centers is essential to expand bicycle usage.

Summary Objective and Criteria.

User objectives include safety, access to many areas and facilities, convenience and pleasure. In the United States, the bicycle's principal use is for recreation during non-working hours, a situation that may soon change to use for functional needs as energy costs increase and availability decreases.

Planning objectives include maintaining flexibility, integrating with other transportation modes, optimizing investment, and assuring social equity in terms of access.

Management objectives include minimizing maintenance problems and simplifying surveillance.

Design considerations include purpose of routes, speed of travel, optimization of grade, pavement, drainage, civic protection and low cost.

Curb cut ramps originally constructed for wheelchair use are beneficial to bicyclists, as they allow riders to use the sidewalk where streets are too busy. A curb cut on each corner should be the goal of all neighborhoods.

Most arterial streets are perceived as too dangerous for average bicyclists. However, as they lead to necessary destinations and services, providing safe bicycle lanes, reducing the number of drive-in crossings, slowing down traffic, and providing adequate signage is essential. Bike-ways can be either a striped lane in the street or as part of a widened sidewalk.

All nearby recreation options such as lakes, parks, tree-lined streets, etc., should be available for bicycling and walking. All routes must have some pleasant features: good views, trees, parks or open space along the route.

The document: "Planning and Design Criteria for Bike-way in California" published by the State of California, Department of Transportation in 1978 is a current source of information on bicycle facility planning.

FINDING SPACE

Once potential bicycle routes are located, the planner should study each segment to determine if bicycles should ride in the roadway with cars, in lanes separated to some degree from traffic, or on completely separated routes. To make bicycle planning communication consistent: bicycle routes are classified according to their separation from the roadways: *Class I* routes are totally separated; *Class II* routes are lanes along side roads but separated by curbs or painted lines; and *Class III* routes share the roadway with cars.

Class I—a path alongside a road but completely separated from it, or a separate pathway not related to existing roads.

Class II—a lane set off with a stripe or curb on an existing road or street.

Class III—signposted road with no improved bike lanes.

Class I bicycle routes generally are thought to serve inexperienced or recreational riders best. They are usually located where land is available, not necessarily where riders want to travel, and share space with pedestrians and joggers who interfere with faster moving, commuting bicyclists. Class I bicycle routes are most appropriate in suburban areas, where distances are great, land is available, and traffic on roadways is heavy and fast moving. While these routes are expensive to develop, they can be used by a variety of people for a variety of purposes (walking, running, cross-country skiing, roller-skating).

Class II—Bicycle routes can help all bicyclists pass by hazardous portions of our roadways, particularly along arterials. Finding room in the roadway may be difficult, although parking may be eliminated or traffic lanes narrowed. Maintenance (keeping Class II lanes clear from gravel and broken glass pushed there by cars) is a problem that would need to be overcome.

Class III can work for experienced commuters if problem areas are corrected and automobile speeds are controlled. However, they are little more than a gesture for recreational riders unless car speeds are reduced to 20 m.p.h.

The planner should keep in mind that, while classification is useful for discussion, in practice, it is a little overly simplistic. The most serviceable bicycle routes are invariably those that are complex in nature and use all three classes according to the complexity of the situation, the availability of space and user demand.

Improvements For Commuters.

Most commuters prefer riding in the street, often following busy arterials. Although cars may travel at 30 to 35 m.p.h., an experienced bicyclist pedalling at 20 m.p.h. can feel relatively comfortable in this traffic. Commuters' main fear is that they might not be visible by overtaking traffic or traffic pulling into the arterial. Widening the outside lane by striping or adding new pavement allows enough room to reduce this danger and increase rider comfort. Restriping four lane roads to include narrow inner lanes and wider outside lanes leaves extra space on the right for bicyclists. A 13-foot wide outside lane is generally sufficient width for motorists and bicyclists in this lane. Long stretches of road where automobile traffic moves smoothly are ideal for this modification. If there are sufficient bicyclists, it might be appropriate to narrow all traffic lanes, and paint a white line separating bikes from auto traffic on the right side. The striped bike lane is helpful *if* bikes are regularly visible in that lane; otherwise drivers may unknowingly venture into the bicycle lane and cause an accident. It is helpful to post signs instructing motorists to move left and bicyclists to keep right. Intersections should be carefully planned.

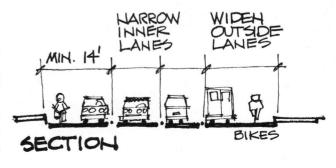

Two-way bicycle routes in a single lane are advantageous for commuters, as the extra width can be used by peak direction bikers flowing in the same direction. During non-commute hours, the 2-way route serves traffic traveling in both directions without conflict as traffic is lighter.

IMPROVEMENTS FOR SAFETY

A number of suggestions for enhancing safety on bicycle routes are given below.

- Prohibiting parking for at least 50 feet behind the intersection helps improve visibility of bicyclists. Although 50 feet is more than most municipalities require, it is necessary because of higher speed traveled on arterials.
- Relocating driveways from a through road to a less busy cross-street near an intersection reduces traffic congestion.
- Signs should be installed warning drivers of through bike traffic and directing them to *keep left*.

Signs, signals, and markings for bicycle facilities should meet the requirements of the "Manual on Uniform Traffic Control Devices" (MUTCD)"

- Motorists have a tendency to move right when making a right turn, and can usurp the space normally used by bicyclists, who may be forced to swerve left into traffic or go around the turning car and expose themselves to passing traffic. Actions to prevent this include installing a curb separating the bicycle lane or striping the bicycle lane at intersections. This may require widening the road slightly, but usually there is room since no parking is allowed near the intersection. (See sketch).

ADD SIGNS AND PAINTED LINES

INSTALL SAFE CROSS TO PROTECT BICYCLISTS

- Safety problems may have to be corrected by using a detour. Curb-cuts should be installed so that bicyclists can ride on the sidewalk past a problem area, and then through another curb-cut reenter traffic or note alternate routes with a direction sign to skirt problem areas or to avoid hills. Short cuts should be developed where possible, and made accessible with curb-cuts and a paved access path. Many block-to-block parking lots can become short cuts if just one part is opened up.
- Railroad tracks crossing bicycle routes are dangerous for narrow-wheeled bicycles. But they can be made crossable by being made level and by reducing the space between track and road. Abandoned tracks

can be temporarily paved over with asphalt until they are removed. Rubberized crossing pads to cover tracks are now available from several large tire manufacturers, and may be installed jointly by municipality and railroad. To reduce cost, they may be installed only on the right five-foot segment where most bicyclists ride, or only between the tracks, paving the outside portion tight against the tracks with asphalt. Since the train wheels ride on the inside of the tracks, the rubber with its compressible characteristics is important there, while the outside portion can be inexpensively asphalted right to the track, eliminating all gaps.

- Capable bicyclists can usually move from the right into the left-turning lane early enough to merge smoothly and safely with traffic. If there is a separate bikeway, curb-cuts should be provided or the curb eliminated about 150-200 feet from the intersection, allowing bicyclists to move smoothly into traffic and merge left. Children, elderly and others who are not experienced in making left turns may be better off demounting and crossing with pedestrians. They will benefit from any pedestrian improvements, especially curb-cuts in both directions to ride on and off the sidewalk, and traffic signals that favor pedestrians. If there are no sidewalks, a safe-cross should be installed at the intersection with wide curb-cuts and waiting space (see sketch).

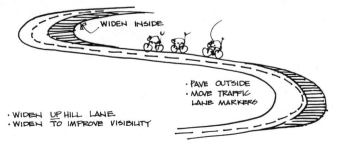

- Adding an asphalt apron or paving a shoulder to widen the pavement at a curve allows the bicyclist to move farther right.

IDENTIFY BICYCLE ACCIDENT LOCATIONS

- — Identify the physical hazard
- — Note recreational versus utilitarian rider
- — Note age and rider experience

WIDEN INSIDE

· PAVE OUTSIDE
· MOVE TRAFFIC LANE MARKERS

· WIDEN UP HILL LANE.
· WIDEN TO IMPROVE VISIBILITY

- Single routes carrying two-way bicycle traffic should be avoided on short blocks. They are dangerous at intersections since half the riders come from the "wrong" direction. For instance, a right-turning motorist may look left, and then right: in the meantime, an unseen bike from the left may move directly in the motorist's way. Additionally, bicyclists entering, leaving or turning from a two-way bike route must cross all lanes of traffic, making themselves vulnerable to accidents. (See diagram).

Intersections. Most accidents involving cars and bicycles occur at the intersection. If alternative bike-way locations are available, the one with the most favorable intersections should be selected. Favorable intersections are relatively compact, clearly channelized and without large, undefined paved spaces. Intersections should be tested for bicycle safety with emphasis on impact potentials from through, and left and right-turning vehicles. Right-turning vehicles can easily interfere with straight-ahead bicyclists, and cause an accident, or instill fear. Left-turning bicyclists must weave through traffic twice, one to reach the left turn lane, and then to reach the right side through lane. Both weaves are subject to accidents. At bicycle lane intersections with traffic signals, install looped signal detectors that are sensitive enough to change with the weight of the bicycle and rider. Installation of a sensitive loop detector well in advance of the intersection is desirable as it may allow continuous riding. Push-button signal activators are unsatisfactory as bicyclists must always stop to actuate the signal.

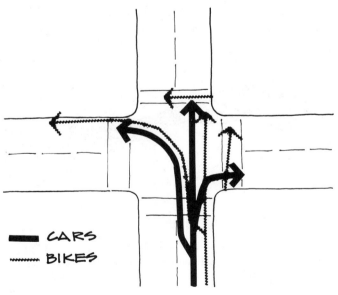

CARS
BIKES

Diagram depicting typical conflicts between bicycles and vehicles at intersections.

Identify and map all reported bicycle/auto collisions and develop corrective measures where possible.

- Turning bicyclists should be able to wait safely for a break in oncoming traffic. If the left turn is wide enough, a 4-foot wide lane should be indicated by a stripe on the right for bikers. If the left turn has a signal activator, it should be sensitive enough to be operated by a bicyclist's weight. If no room exists for a separate lane, the auto turn should be indicated, so that bicyclists can wait in front of the turning car. It is essential to make sure there is enough room so that oncoming left-turning traffic doesn't endanger waiting bicyclists.

Protecting bicycles from right-turning vehicles. Right-turning vehicles can cause bicycle accidents and care must be exercised to achieve safety. Two approachs are possible—

the safest may be to prohibit motorists from entering the bicycle lane with a raised curb; while the other attempt is to make both bicyclists and motorists realize that the intersection space will be jointly shared. Safety depends on individual conditions—keeping cars out of the bicycle way can set up a potential accident when the car actually turns right, while auto merging into the unprotected bikeway can cause an accident.

Protected bikeways can be separated from the road with a raised curb (see sketch). States requiring right-turning vehicles in turn from the right lane may prohibit this type of protected bicycle intersection since it occupies the turn

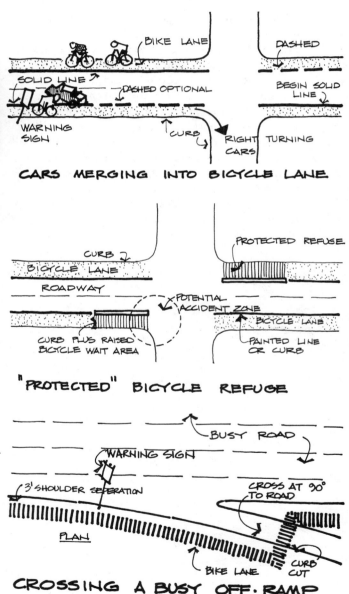

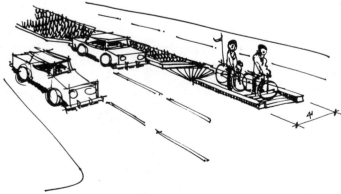

Where insufficient space for a refuge exists, provide a left turn pocket (minimum 4' width) on the RIGHT side as shown. This location places riders on the right side of the road following their turn, eliminating the need to weave through left-turning vehicles.

If room exists for a pedestrian refuge, ramp up for protection, and then back down at the other side. Since bicyclists in this position are left of their destination, they will likely remain on the refuge until cars have turned, and then proceed themselves.

lane. Unprotected bikeways can be designated with dash lines and warning signs at busy right-turning intersections. Right hand lanes should *not* be designated or signed for right turns along bike routes. Bikeways along freeways or fast moving roads should cross at 90% to the vehicle turn lane, with bollards or signs to warn of the danger.

The pedestrian refuge is ramped so bicyclists can cross it easily and safely. The curbed area before and after the crosswalk better defines the pedestrian zone, and adds visual scale to the crosswalks. Note also that the traffic lights are compact and on low poles to appear comfortable for those on foot.

Bikeway grade separation is attractive for riders. This underpass along a drainage channel uses a retaining wall to hold the earth back. Unfortunately, the line of sight doesn't allow riders to see bicyclists coming from the other direction. A convex mirror, similar to those used in department stores, placed on the opposite structure would improve views of approaching bicyclists.

Bikeways paralleling one-way streets can be made safer at the intersections by installing traffic islands as shown. The stop sign on the island directs vehicles to stop, allowing safe, through bicycle movement. Since traffic is one-way, vehicles may turn right or move through behind the island. The island can be landscaped and developed into a pleasant neighborhood visual element.

Correct Signal Timing Extend the clearance interval between the yellow and red light on wide-laned streets. The clearance can be extended by lengthening the yellow light or by adding an all-red clearance interval. Utilize an average bicycle speed of ten miles per hour and a perception/breaking time of 1.8 seconds. Make sure that any traffic actuated signal is sensitive to bicycles and located where bicycles will activate them.

• Most safety improvements can only be effective where there are sufficient bicyclists so drivers become accustomed to them. On roads with occasional bicycle use, the best way to insure safety is to construct a separate bypass bikeway skirting dangerous intersections. Unfortunately, this isn't always politically or uneconomically possible.

MAKING BICYCLISTS VISIBLE

Restrict parking near intersections

— Improve night lighting
— Reduce auto speeds
— Add signage and traffic signals
— Increase the number of bicyclists.

SEPARATE BIKEWAYS.

Separate bicycle routes have a significant place in bicycle planning. Recently, however, existing bikeways built during the 1960's and 1970's have been criticized because they were poorly constructed and were not planned to go where bicyclists want to go. Early, experimental routes were hastily constructed in many cities at minimum cost and often by traffic engineers, planners and landscape architects with little bicycling experience. However, bikeways that are properly constructed, separated from traffic, and connect to destinations where people want to go are fun to ride and are well used.

Where to Locate

There are many different places a bikeway can go. The planner can take different approaches by varying travel lane, parking space and sidewalk. The exact location of a bikeway may vary from block to block, without affecting the quality of the ride, as long as each change is carefully designed. On roads with light traffic, the bikeway adjacent to traffic may be comfortable for bicyclists. As traffic increases and noise, fumes and perceived dangers make riding next to the street uncomfortable, more separation between road and bikeway should be provided.

If the sidewalk is not heavily used, a bikeway abutting it is safe. The walk next to the bike path allows bicyclists to pass on the sidewalk and even ride two abreast. When the sidewalk is congested, pedestrians may ignore the line between sidewalk and bikeway causing a collision.

Level or Raised Bikeways

The bikeway may be raised six inches above the road or be level with it. Raising the bikeway assures separation, prevents cars from driving or parking on it, and keeps much dirt, gravel and broken glass from reaching it. Bikeways flush with the road and separated by a painted line are less expensive to construct and provide more flexibility. Cars can use the bikeways in emergencies and bicyclists can move into traffic easily to pass a slow bicycle or turn left. Regular maintenance is needed to keep the bikeway clean and its stripes freshly painted.

Directions of Bikeways.

Should bikeways be one or two-way? A two-way bikeway works well if the route is long and relatively uninterrupted by cross streets and driveways. It is ideal in many suburban locations. In addition, bikeways separated from the road should almost always be two-way, and can be safe if they are at least eight feet wide. On the other hand, in urban areas, a single two-way bikeway located within the road right-of-way, while easiest to plan and implement, can be dangerous. The "ride to the right" rule places the outside rider facing oncoming vehicular traffic. These single two-way routes are also more difficult for riders to reach or leave, and are more dangerous at the intersection because drivers waiting to enter an intersection may not see a bicyclist coming from the "wrong" direction. Thus, on the roadway in urban areas, it is better to have two, single direction lanes flowing with vehicular traffic if complete separation is not possible.

Types of Separation.

There are a number of different ways to separate bicycles from automobile traffic. They can be divided into two groups, one using *parked cars* as a barrier between bicycles and cars and the other using the *road side* for the bikeway.

Without Parked Cars.

- Separation can be achieved by placing planters between the street and bikeway and sidewalk. Although the bicycleway is pleasantly located, the bicyclist does not have use of the street or sidewalk to pass another bicycle. (Photo)
- If space is tight, a bikeway can be located adjacent to the street, but separated from the sidewalk by a planter strip. Bicyclists are subjected to the problems of the street, while they gain easy access to the street for passing and turning.
- A path on the roadside of parked cars is easy to construct, since just a painted line is required. The route can't be raised above the roadway since cars must cross it to park. Also, there is danger to bicyclists when cars park or leave, or open their door to get in or out. (Photo)
- A combined sidewalk and pathway with no parked cars or planter strip to protect users from moving cars is a possibility. Because the route is part of the road, it makes the road appear enlarged which decreases its pedestrian quality. (Photo)

If either of the last two solutions is implemented, it is important to protect bicyclists from oncoming traffic with either a curb or a stripe. The curb is preferred, because it provides physical protection although it does create some maintenance and construction problems. The bikeway should be widened at least 12 inches if only stripes are used, and the stripes should be painted in the roadway.

Potential Bikeway Routes

- Little used roads
- Flood plains
- Parks, school grounds
- Vacant or underused land
- Parking lots, industrial properties
- Abandoned railroads
- Utility line easements
- Campuses, golf courses, cemeteries

With Parked Cars.

- A bikeway completely separated from cars affords a clear and pleasant ride, though often at considerable cost. Suburban or rural areas, where few people walk or land is available, as along a canal or abandoned railroad are good locations for such bike routes. In urban areas, heavy bicycle traffic may justify the expense for one or two separate bikeways running the length of a community. Pedestrians, joggers and roller skaters would also use such a path. (See photo).

- A bikeway can be separated by planter strips from both parked cars and pedestrians. While parked cars provide an additional barrier between bikes and moving traffic, the planter prevents bicyclists from running into car doors being opened, and prevents conflicts between pedestrians and bicycles. However, bicyclists would not have easy access to the roadway or sidewalk for passing, or room for riding side by side. (Photo)

- A bikeway can abutt a sidewalk but be separated from parked cars by a planter strip, which visually separates the road from the bicycle pedestrian domain and enhances the roadscape. Bikeway and sidewalk should be paved differently, preferably asphalt for bikeway and concrete for sidewalks. (Photo)

- A combined bike and pedestrian path can be placed next to parked cars but with no planter strip. Parked cars protect bicyclists and pedestrians, though separation between them is lacking. The street appears wider since no planter strip visually divides it. However, there are problems created by car doors, pedestrians, children, etc. (Photo)

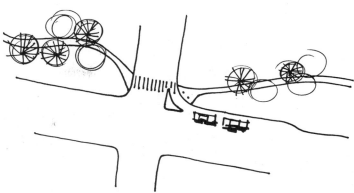

↑ 2" RISE

PAINTED LINE

INTERSECTING ROADS.

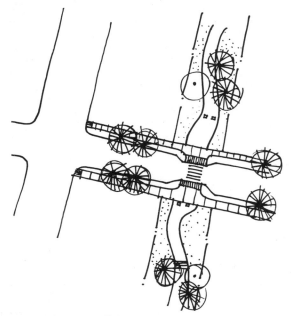

Move bike-way crossings away from the intersection whenever possible. A separate mid-block crossing improves bicycle flow, as cyclists may not have to stop, and there may be fewer cars at the mid-block location. Additionally, the mid-block location is generally more attractive to wait at or to cross. Place trees and shrubs carefully to not block visibility from vehicles.

Eliminate free right turns for vehicles at the junction of bike-ways and road intersections. Drivers and bicyclists simply do not have enough time to see each other, which creates a serious safety problem. Forcing vehicles to stop before turning, or to slow sufficiently to turn a sharp radius helps correct this problem.

Each trail and road intersection is a key design focus. This example is not well-resolved. The bollards are placed too close forcing an inexperienced rider to slow or even demount to move through, which may cause an automobile collision on the street side. They are also *not perpendicular* to the trail so cyclists have difficulty perceiving the exact spacing. The trail is also too narrow, causing waiting bicyclists to stack up at a place where visibility should be high. Lastly, there is little night light from the street pole on the far right.

One way to call attention to cross streets is to jog the route around a planter and then back at the street crossing. The jog—about 30 feet before the intersection—alerts the cyclists to the intersection becoming a congregating space that is removed from the intersection. Congregating space at the intersection makes it difficult for other cyclists to pass through or to be seen by motorists. Most bicyclists will *not* stop at intersections unless the danger is evident, and therefore, a clear view of the roadway is essential. Note the street light, the warning sign, and wooden bollards to prevent motorists from riding on the traio.

A 2-way entrance separates bicycle traffic and is less confusing. Each entrance lane can be narrowed to 5' wide, thus prohibiting motor vehicle access. Installing a removal bollard off the route (as shown) with a curb cut ramp allows emergency and service vehicles access by removing the bollard and using the combined ramps.

Bikeways on Boulevards

The median divider in the street has served many uses historically from horse trail to rapid transit to walkway with tree canopy. Why not a bikeway? The median bikeway could be an excuse to develop a boulevard with tree planting, lighting and other amenities. Such a bikeway should be two-way with a minimum of 12 feet of paving, with extra room needed for pedestrians, planting and buffer. The main disadvantages are access and egress and intersections, especially on fast moving roads. Cars trying to cross the boulevard at an intersection must worry about pedestrians, a lane of traffic in one direction, the bikeway (traveling in two directions), the traffic lane in the other direction, and finally pedestrians crossing the street on the far side. Eliminating cross streets along boulevards creates a safer street and also improves visual continuity. Eliminating trees and vegetation from the intersection also helps. Where streets do cross the boulevard, signals may be necessary. Furthermore, the bikeway should be paved differently (that is in brick or concrete) to contrast with the road's asphalt.

An alternative to the median planting strip location is striping a lane on each side immediately adjacent to the median. This location is visible for vehicles, away from parked cars, and pleasant because of the nearby trees and planting. Additionally, it saves the center area for trees and grass.

The Bay Area Rapid Transit recommends that bicycle access to transit stations be 2-way routes located on 1-way streets. This permits space for a physical divider between bicycles and cars, while retaining parking on 1 side of the street. A 2-way bicycle route's wider width can accommodate additional peak hour traffic which generally flows toward or away from the transit stop in morning or evenings. Two-way movement occurs throughout the rest of the day or weekends when travel demand is lower, while the 2-way route, using only 1 side of the street is easier to implement.

STRIPED BIKE-WAYS

Assigning a travel lane for bicycles within the roadway, but separated by a painted white line can enhance the ride quality and bicyclist safety. The striped lane helps establish orderly flow of traffic, keeping cars to the left, and making most bicyclists feel that they belong on the roadway. Lanes are demarked by painted stripes and signs painted on the roadway or installed alongside it. One-way directions are preferred for short blocks, with each lane a minimum of 4' wide or wider if traffic moves fast, or trucks are present. Painted stripes should be solid white and at least 6'' wide. Avoid raised buttons or bars as they may cause a cyclist to fall, and restrict maintenance equipment.

Locate striped lanes on the *right* side of 1-way streets to ease turning movements and duplicate a normal bike-way location.

This low cost striped bicycle lane is shared by all modes of non-motorized circulation—roller skates, runners, skate boards, walkers, prams and wheelchairs.

TYPICAL BIKE LANE CROSS SECTIONS

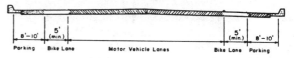

(a) CURBED STREET WITH PARKING

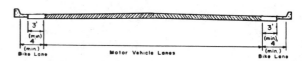

(b) CURBED STREET WITHOUT PARKING

(c) STREET WITHOUT CURB OR GUTTER
(Metric Conversion : 1 ft. = 0.3m)

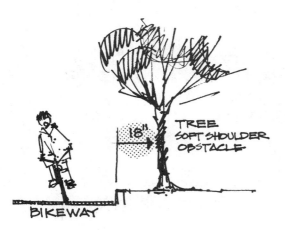

Minimum distance from a bike-way to stationary objects or soft shoulder is 18''.

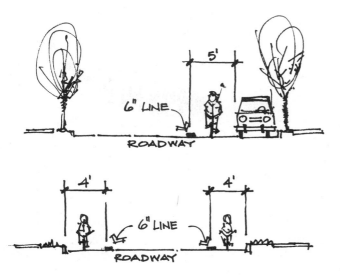

Widen striped lanes to a minimum of 5' if parking is allowed to reduce the danger of car doors being opened.

The sketch depicts bicycle lanes as proposed by the new Federal Highway Administration Bicycle Guidelines. Bicycle lanes located between the motor vehicle lanes and the roadway shoulders have a minimum width of 4 feet (1.2 meters). Additional widths are desired when substantial truck traffic is present or when vehicles speeds exceed 35 miles per hour. When bicycle lanes are delineated on the shoulder, a width of 5 feet or greater is desirable. Lighting where bicycles and automobiles conflict and to allow riders to see the path direction and surface condition is important for encouraging riders. It should be considered where riding at night is likely, particularly around colleges and along commuter routes, through underpasses and tunnels. Light level of between 1/2 and 2-foot candles should be provided where possible. Most handicapped access codes require illumination of one foot candle which might be considered the reasonable standard providing potential use for people in wheelchairs.

Pros and Cons of Bikeways

Several early trial bikeway designs have received negative reviews, and are now prejudiced against by planners who have not made their own evaluations. One such bikeway is the type that is sandwiched between the sidewalk and a row of parked cars. Early critics noted that access was difficult, that leaving it at mid-block was difficult, that passing was difficult because one couldn't ride into the street, and that drivers had difficulty seeing bicyclists at intersections. I believe that all except the intersection safety problem are exaggerated. Access between intersections is difficult, but how many people are really bothered by it and how often? Those who need access or egress between intersections can slow down and move between parked cars to the streets with some minor inconvenience. Passing is usually possible if the bicyclists is patient. The intersection safety problem can also be addressed. Problems can be lessened by prohibiting parking about 30-50 feet on each side of the intersection. The parking lane area should be ideally curbed to prevent parking and may be an area for bikes and pedestrians to wait for their time to cross the street. Free right turns should be prohibited, and an intersection stop sign provides the time for motorists to look in both directions.

In addition, this type of bikeway does work better on streets where there are few driveways and intersections. It also serves bicyclists better if it is *wider than eight feet.*

Bottle Bills—Requiring deposits and refunds on all bottles reduces bicycle tire punctures and decreases maintenance. The State of Oregon's bottle law has virtually eliminated bottles from the landscape as the refund is attractive for many.

Note: The new Federal Highway Administration Guidelines suggest that bicycle lanes should *never* be placed between the parking area and sidewalk, contrary to this previous paragraph. Their rationale is that that location would create hazards for bicyclists from opening car doors and poor visibility intersections.

SPECIAL BIKEWAYS.

Recreational Bikeways

Bicycle routes through a park, around a pond or lake, along a river, and near populated neighborhoods will be well used, based on experience of communities that have built them. They tend to be used by pedestrians, joggers and skaters as well as bicyclists. Conflicts can and do occur. Skaters' pushing movement makes them sway back and forth over a six foot wide area, while pedestrians and joggers may accidentally step in the way of a bicyclist trying to pass another person on foot. (Photo)

There are several approaches to sorting out the conflicts, and allowing each group access to the pleasures of the route. Assigning each a special day or time, reduces spontaneity and may eliminate users not free at that time. That should be the last resort. A route as wide as a small street has a capacity to handle people engaged in the different activities. Its principal disadvantage is its large scale which isn't intimate or pedestrian in nature. Separating wheeled vehicle, bicycles and skates, from others has advantages such as freedom from some conflicts and a small-scale feeling. The walker could be closest to the water or amenity, and on a packed gravel path, while bicycles could use an asphalt path separated by some distance (minimum of ten feet) from the pedestrian. This solution does not solve the problem of conflict between skaters and bicyclists, however, and, the cost of separate paths is slightly higher than a single wide path and more maintenance is required.

Converting a route to one-way tends to increase the route's capacity. Striping to designate separate lane for bicyclists and pedestrians with occasional signs to point out their lane is of some benefit. Installing pull out rest areas can ease pressure on the route. To enhance the experience add benches, picnic tables, viewpoints, etc.

Many transmission corridors make excellent cross-town circulation routes for nonmotorized travel.

Highway Bikeways

In 1973, the Federal Aid Highway Act authorized the use of Federal funds for design and construction of pedestrians and bicycle facilities on or in conjunction with highway rights-of-way. The Act is quite broad, allowing construction both on highway rights-of-way, and outside of the normal highway right-of-way. Bikeways along highways can be designed to serve long distance riding safely. They should be wide, completely separated from traffic, free from exhaust fumes, noise and dust, and properly landscaped. The cost of adding a proper freeway bikeway is relatively cheap compared with the total cost of constructing a freeway, so these routes should be sought. If a Federally funded bikeway won't fit into the freeway's right-of-way, the planner should advocate a transfer of funds to acquire space nearby.

Many new freeways have cut off former bicycle roads. Realizing this, several States allow bicycles on selected and signed portions of freeways, where the shoulder is wide enough or there are no other alternative routes. In many places, the alternative is a narrow two-lane road where vehicles travel fast, and even less attractive routes than riding along the freeway.

Where room exists, locate the highway bike-way above and separated from the roadway. Where room does not exist, provide an adequate paved shoulder with a striped line to visually separate riders from vehicles. Add frequent signs warning motorists of the bikeway.

Since freeway bikeways will normally serve long distance bicycling and there will no cross streets, a single, two-way route is best. It simplifies construction and diminishes problems with access and interchanges. Highway and freeway bikeways should be aligned on the windward side of the road to minimize exposure to exhaust fumes. While studies suggest that cycling along heavily traveled roads does not subject bicyclists to air pollution health hazards any greater than those to which motorists are exposed, no one wants even that level of exposure. (ii)

Bikeways in Subdivisions

New subdivisions and short plats should be required to provide bicycle ways. Most subdivision ordinances require developers to install proper roads, buffers and recreational spaces. Bikeways could be added to these requirements and might be implemented in some of the following ways:

- Short cuts for walking and bicycling midway on long block;
- Paved five-foot-wide sidewalks with curb-cuts on residential streets;
- Pedestrian/bike short cuts from each cul-de-sac to the nearest next street. This can be a narrow easement (eight feet wide) fenced to assure privacy for adjacent homes, and possibly used for sewers or other utilities;
- Short cut access to all schools, parks and community facilities;
- Short cut access to nearby shopping facilities;
- Bike paths along major arterials or through streets; and
- Bike or pedestrian trails along slope easements or buffers (all easements should include language defining public access rights, so they can be developed at the time the subdivision is developed or later.)

iii *Study of the Health Effects of Bicycling in an Urban Atmosphere: U.S. Dept. of Transportation Nov. 1977.*

The most important step is to secure space for a network of bike and pedestrian routes. Development (the more expensive part) can be constructed in phases over the years to meet demand.

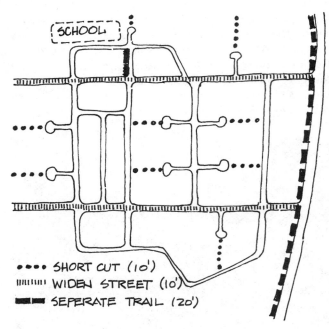

•••• SHORT CUT (10')
||||||| WIDEN STREET (10')
■■■ SEPERATE TRAIL (20')

Bikeways in existing suburban subdivisions are usually easy to construct. Streets are wide, front yards set back generous and double driveways insure adequate off-street automobile parking. The planner should develop routes that connect the most homes with schools, parks, shopping, bus stops, places of work and community service. The choice of approaches is open: Add sidewalks and curb-cuts, eliminate one row of parking along principal streets, narrow traffic lanes (ten feet wide is usually adequate), or decrease the size of front yards. The approaches might vary throughout the track. There is *no need* for bikeways on cul-de-sacs, short loop streets or lightly traveled roads.

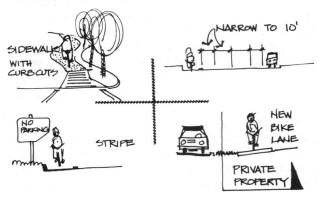

Bicycle underpasses can be constructed relatively simply during initial road construction. An eight-foot clearance is high enough, and grading can be gentle and blend into the landscape for a pleasant ride. For the route is to be wheelchair accessible, the grade must not exceed 8%.

Competitive Bikeways

Biking 100 or more miles in a day at speeds of 20 m.p.h. is typical for an avid or competitive biker. Devising continuous, safe and scenic routes for this interest group is nearly impossible. Once devised, the route will attract less skilled riders, and will likely be avoided by competitive riders seeking open, uninterrupted riding. However, these experienced riders are usually capable of bucking traffic, and can find their own way. They are best served by widening of shoulders on county and State roads, by striping to warn of visibility problems and to allow safe passage on uphill grades where riders slow down and by removing other safety hazards. Installing grates with openings perpendicular to the line of direction, correcting pavement problems, and installing direction signs also helps long-distance riding routes.

Temporary Bikeways

It is possible temporarily to close roads or reduce traffic speeds for long distances on specific days, say Sundays, allowing a carefree, easy ride. Freeway bypasses with limited access, scenic roads along the water, routes through a park, boulevards or other limited access routes are easily closed by the installation of temporary signs at each crossroad.

DESIGN DETAILS

Speed. Three ranges of speeds are common for most bicyclists. When cycling is leisurely, bicyclists travel at six to eight m.p.h. (about twice the speed of walking). Average cycling produces speeds of about 12 to 15 m.p.h., a rate sustainable for long time periods. Short bursts of speed up to 25 m.p.h. are possible, but can be dangerous unless the way is clear for several hundred feet ahead.

Normal design speed should be 20 m.p.h. in open level country and 25 m.p.h. for downhill grades over 5 percent. In urban conditions, a design speed of 20 m.p.h. is adequate except where steep downhill grades require 25 m.p.h. Sight distances for bicyclists need to be longer than for cars, since bicycles cannot stop as quickly as cars. Bicycles can stop at the rate of 16 feet per second. The typical reaction time for most bicyclers is about 1.8 seconds. Given these figures, at 10 miles per hour, stopping time is 3 plus seconds. At 15 miles per hour, 4.5 seconds. These figures are good weather average stopping time, and would need extension for wet weather or for gravel or dirt conditions that would allow slipping instead of gripping.

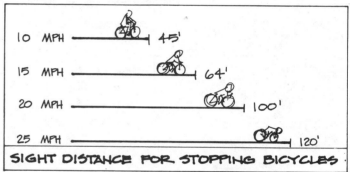

SIGHT DISTANCE FOR STOPPING BICYCLES

Curve Radii. Bicycles have the same turning characteristics as automobiles, since the dynamics and friction factors are the same. However, the standard formula (1.25 times the speed of travel plus 1.4 feet) is likely to produce curves that are too tight for many occasions and may be dangerous. For instance, travel during wet weather, during busy bicycle times, during heavy traffic times, or when pedestrian conflicts occur are likely to create safety problems. The Federal Highway Administration has developed design radii that account for these variables as follows:

MILES PER HOUR	MINIMUM CURVE RADIUS
15	35
20	70
25	90
30	125

If the radius must be smaller to avoid an obstacle or meet existing conditions, bicyclists should be warned with signs placed 30 feet before the reduced speed area.

Width. An absolute minimum width for a one-direction bikeway is 3 feet 6 inches. This includes a 2-foot handlebar width plus 9 inches on each side for bicycle sway. Three feet-six inches is tight; the recommended minimum width is 5 feet, allowing 18 inches of sway on each side, or enough space for another bike to pass carefully.

Two-way routes are slightly less efficient and require a little more space because of the dangers of oncoming bicycles. The minimum two-way width is double the one-way width or 8 feet, while a comfortable minimum is 10 feet. An extra 18 inch space is desirable between parked cars and bikeways to allow cars to open their doors without causing an accident.

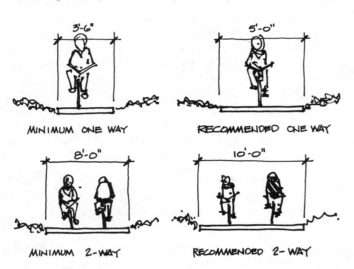

These dimensions are for average, even-flow conditions. If a bikeway is to be heavily used or used during peak periods, additional width will be required for rider comfort. If users are to be mixed (i.e., recreationists, slow riders, commuters, joggers, skaters and pedestrians), additional width is required. Optimally, the planner should try to obtain as much space as is possible to accommodate increased numbers of cyclists as bicycling becomes more popular.

Grade

The steepness of grade is to be decided by the planner although the average grade of a bikeway should not exceed seven percent. While multispeed bikes ease the problem of steepness, other types of bikes that handle hills with less ease are also commonly used. Grades 100 feet long or less can be up to 15 percent, though this is not desirable. For each additional 50 feet of slope length, subtract one percent of grade: therefore, a 400-foot grade would not be over 9

percent. Grades over 700 feet long should be kept at 5 percent or less, if at all possible. Here are some suggested grades for length of distance:

Bikeway Gradient	Desirable Length of Grade
5%	700'
7%	500'
9%	400'
11%	300'
13%	200'
15%	100'

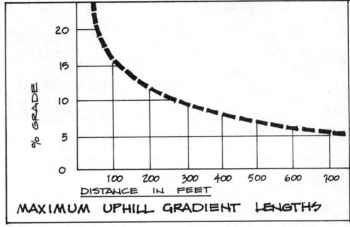

MAXIMUM UPHILL GRADIENT LENGTHS

Acceptable grades are determined in large part by the local terrain which cyclists become used to. In flat locales, a three percent grade may seem excessively steep, while in hilly communities, seven percent may be acceptable.

Moving over steep terrain can be accomplished either by a long, shallow ramp, or by a short, relatively steep ramp. Psychologically, the short steep ramp may not be preferred, since many bicyclists may not be able to ride it and may have to push their bikes.

Steeper Routes

Many scenic spots and quiet drives are along roads too steep for every day bicycle travel and so should not be part of the bike route. However, it is possible to have several routes of differing degrees of difficulty. Principal routes should be under seven percent, should serve the most important community functions and should be the most developed. Steeper routes, serving scenic or cultural facilities could be designated on a map but not developed.

Railings.

Railings are necessary to protect bicyclists on bridges and when the bike routes abutts a steep dropoff. Generally, they should conform to local handrail codes, except that they must be higher when there is a road beneath. How much higher than the standard 42-inch for a handrail is still being debated. Urban designers tend to favor lower railings that let people see over. They favor raising the protective rail 6 inches to 48 inches, an amount approximately equivalent to the bicyclist's height on his bicycle.

An opposite view is reflected in the new AASHTO Standard Specifications (Highway Bridges 1.1.8 railings) that require a 4 foot 6 inch high bridge railing on all bridges along bicycle routes. The regulation also requires a 4 foot 6 inch railing between traffic and two-way bicycle routes. A railing this high may cause more problems than it prevents, such as boxing in pedestrians, blocking views, or trapping a bicyclist riding on the road between the railing and a car. If the railing were lower, the bicyclist might have a chance to jump over the railing onto the sidewalk or bikeway if an accident were imminent. It may be possible for the planner to avoid these standards by *not* calling the space a bikeway, or by striping a do-not-use area 30 inches wide next to the railing.

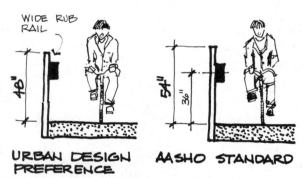

URBAN DESIGN PREFERENCE   AASHO STANDARD

Install on all railings a wide, (minimum 12'), continuous and smooth rub rail at handlebar height. This rail covers upright posts that may cause a bicycle to swerve or the handlebars caught in the parts.

A railing should be smooth at handlebar height between 32 and 38 inches. Protrusions such as decorations or posts should be kept out of the way. Wood is a material that works well for such railings. ASHTO standards require horizontal rails to have a maximum clearing of 15 inches and vertical rails to have a maximum spacing of 6 inches.

It may be possible to avoid railings by extending the terrain 30 inches to each side of a bike route and planting the intervening space (see sketch). This can be done with fill dirt and/or a retaining wall, and has the benefit of eliminating intrusive handrails from the landscape.

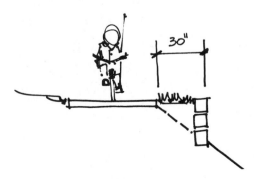

Isolated bridges that can't be policed or are near parks and schools should have a mesh enclosure to reduce the chance of people throwing objects at the roadway below.

Obstacles

Obstacles such as curbs and grates increase the danger to cyclists. Storm drain gradings adjacent to curbs, with widely spaced bars that a wheel can drop in, must be eliminated. Grading should run *perpendicular* to the direction of travel and should have openings narrower than one inch. Welding flat cross-bars perpendicular to the line of travel every 4 inches works fairly well. Cracks in pavement, loose dirt and gravel should be eliminated by regular maintenance. Narrow slots in the surface of the pavement that could catch a bicycle wheel should be eliminated. Gaps should not exceed 3/4 of an inch in width. At the same time, ridges in pavement that could cause a bicyclist to jar and lose control, such as expansion joints, gutters or utility covers should not protrude more than 3/8 of an inch above the road's surface. In addition to drainage grate inlets being perpendicular to the line of travel, it is important that the grates be flush with the roadway surface, particularly following road resurfacing.

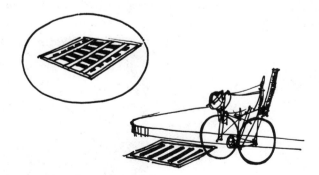

Sweep bike-ways regularly. Bike-ways located at the road edge collect dirt, dust, gravel, broken glass and other debris pushed there by passing vehicles. This debris is slippery, dusty and may cause flat tires unless regularly swept or washed.

This rubberized railroad crossing pad eliminates the gaps between the street and the railroad track and makes crossing it pleasant. To save funds, the pad was installed only on the shoulder where most bike riders cross.

Signs and Other Warnings

The past trend of using green signs to identify bike routes actually did very little to enhance bicycling. They should be replaced with a series of signs that give warnings, directions or commands to both motorists and bicyclists. Standard vehicle signs should be used to warn motorists of and to instruct motorists (as to more left, allowing more room on the right for bicyclists). Signs should be shaped and color coded to match other traffic signs, so motorist will recognize and respect them. The only difference is the use of a bicycle symbol to clarify the action where necessary. Bicyclists' direction signs can be green, but should state precise warnings, directions, or commands as STOP, YIELD TO CARS, MOVE RIGHT, etc. The shapes required in the Federal *Manual of Uniform Traffic Control Devices* used for bicycle signs: 1) the circle, designating mandatory rules; 2) the rectangle, offering guidance, speed regulations, and curb usage; and 3) the diamond, providing warnings. Two conforming signs are the octagonal stop signs and the triangular yield sign. The colors indicates specific classes of message. The red typically is used for prohibiting, the green for permitting, the yellow to indicate warning, and the blue to give guidance locally.

Use signs to provide specific directions to both driver and bicyclists.

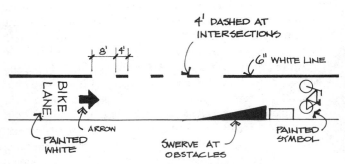

Bicycles on separate bikeways should be warned to slow down when they approach a busy street crossing. Unless there is a stop sign, it isn't always necessary for bicyclists to stop completely, but he must be able to see whether the street is safe to cross. Several physical changes from the traditional linear street are necessary: a warning placed about 50 feet before the intersection and again within 20 feet, and additional waiting space at the intersection. Vegetation should be limited so that bicyclists are visible to motorists and vice versa. The curb-cut should be at least 7 feet wide to accommodate two riders (and maintenance

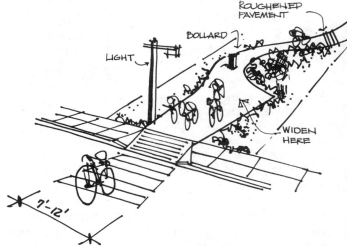

Keep intersections free of shrubbery and other view-blocking obstacles so passing vehicles can clearly see bicyclists.

vehicles as well). Narrower curb-cuts may cause delay and confusion between oncoming riders. A strip of rough concrete 5 to 10 feet wide placed perpendicular to the bicycle route can warn riders of an upcoming street.

One bollard placed across the bikeway near the intersection can further warn riders to keep cars from using the bikeway. Bollards are upright posts about 3 feet high and 10 inches in diameter that warn cyclists and force them to slow down to negotiate a narrow passage. Where more than one bollard is used, they should be perpendicular to the bikeway to avoid visual distortion as riders approach, and should be set back from the cross street 10 feet to allow maneuvering room and to reduce confusion at the street crossing. Relative danger of a street crossing should determine bollards' spacing, but in any case, they should be wide enough for all bicyclists to pass through safely. Spaced a maximum of 5 feet prevents cars from driving or parking on the bikeway. A removeable bollard allows police and maintenance vehicles to enter.

Road Stripes

Striping is typically used to indicate that a priority is given to certain modes of travel, or to warn about potential problems ahead. This author believes striping should be used with care so that its importance is recognized, as well as because it is costly to maintain. Striping should be used only on well-traveled routes. Striping to delineate a shoulder used by bicyclists is appropriate only if it is well-traveled. Striping the lanes of a two-way bike route is not necessary except in the first 50 feet from an intersection to alert bicyclists to the fact that the bike route is two-way. Stripes perpendicular to a bike route are effective indicators of upcoming danger. Striping to delineate a bikeway from a pedestrian portion of a wide sidewalk is also necessary, particularly in low light conditions.

When painted lines are used, each line should be at least 8 to 12 inches wide. Typical road colors, white or yellow should be used and green should be avoided since it isn't readily recognized by drivers. If possible, the bulk of the line should be painted *outside* of the bike route, thereby symbolically widening it.

Storage

Wherever bicyclists congregate or work, compact storage racks should be installed. Provision of secure, dry and visible bicycle storage is a major part of improving every day commuting and errand running. Places most often visited by bicyclists (schools, libraries, city halls, theaters, convenience stores) need an appropriate number of conveniently located bicycle parking places. Their use should be monitored and new racks added as usage increases.

The most efficient bicycle rack is a standard, galvanized pipe rack serving two rows of bikes. (Single-loaded rack is also available). The space between bars needs to be narrowed to 1 1/2-inch to support the narrow wheels of modern ten-speed bicycles. A "V"-shaped wheel holder that can

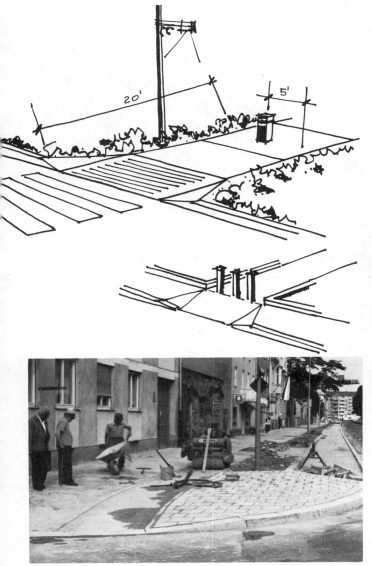

accommodate wheels of all sizes also works. The rider simply pushes in the wheel until it fits tightly and locks the bike. Cast concrete racks look attractive since they are flush with the ground. However, they fill easily with dirt, are difficult to clean, can freeze and have no posts to which a bike can be chained. A simple three-foot-tall pole inbedded in concrete with two chains welded on is an effective rack to serve two bicycles. Bicyclists lean their bikes against it, slip the chain through their wheel and frame and lock it with their own lock. Two bikes can lean against one post and maneuvering is simple. It is recommended that all newly installed bicycle racks provide strong chains or cables for each slot so that bicyclists will not have to carry their own chains. In addition, towns could have a special chain or cable installed on parking meters. (See Sketch)

Up to 10 bicycles can be stored in the space occupied by one car. Public garages might install racks and several car spaces, or where ground space is unavailable, install hooks on the wall to allow vertical storage. A pipe rail mounted horizontally eight feet off the floor, with movable hooks works well. (See Sketch)

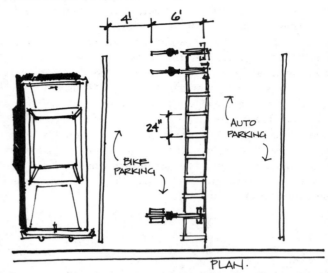

An alternative to organized bicycle racks is paved space out of the pedestrian flow with objects to lean bicycles against. This arrangement is less formal-looking, though also less efficient.

Bicycle racks must be located in lighted, visible spaces, so bicyclists can easily see them and so that vandalism and thievery can be avoided. Installing a token bicycle rack inconveniently in the basement or a great distance from bicycle destinations will not do. Ideally, each location would have a sufficient number of parking spaces in clear view, near a door, and unexposed to weather.

Lockers.

Businesses with daily bicycle commuters could provide bicycle lockers for protection and as an incentive to commute by bicycle instead of by car. Lockers are inexpensive, guaranteed security, and can be installed ten to twenty in the space occupied by one car. (See Sketch)

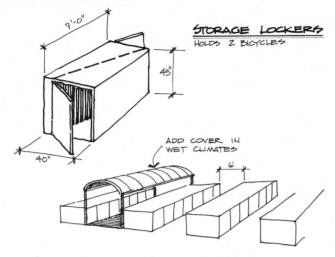

STORAGE LOCKERS
HOLDS 2 BICYCLES

9'-0"

45"

40"

ADD COVER IN WET CLIMATES

6'

Bicycle Storage. Many newer bicycle racks designed to secure the bike from theft involve complex hinged arrangements that are difficult to operate, and require agility to properly secure the bike. Some are large and bulky, others require all parts of the bike to be properly lined up before it will work, while others have spring-loaded hooks like an animal trap that can fly up and may cause injury. Most consume more space than conventional bike racks which is a disadvantage. The only real way to evaluate them is to test each to see if people can use it quickly and safely. If a rack will be used by the same person every day, they will get used to using it, however, if it is used by different people on rare occasions, it may look confusing and not be used. If theft is high, it will be used. If theft isn't, their use is questionable. I have seen complex theft-proof racks empty, while easy-to-use old-fashioned racks nearby were full.

Check the lock enclosure to make sure it's possible and easy for riders to insert their hands and lock the lock. Some have holes that are too small for standard bike locks and others are so difficult that people with low finger dexterity will not be able to manipulate them. Some racks are not galvanized and may rust quickly, requiring additional maintenance.

Shopping Centers.

Shopping center management should be encouraged to develop a number of bicycle parking locations, with one at each entry to the center closely aligned with bike routes leading to it. One assumes that bicyclists can park and walk into the center itself as do motorists. The easiest way to accommodate bicyclists at shopping centers is by converting several car-parking spaces to bicycle parking. As moped use for shopping increases, convenient space for their parking should be included. Mopeds can use older bicycle racks with wide spaces for wheels since their tires are approxi-

mately 3 inches in width. A double bike rack, with one side for mopeds and the other for bicycles might work.

Eight to ten bicycles can be parked in one car space. They can be arranged either parallel or perpendicular to the street with a parallel arrangement yielding slightly more spaces, but with less room for maneuvering. Using two adjoining parallel parking spaces can increase the efficiency of perpendicular configuration. (Converting diagonal parking spaces to bicycle parking isn't as efficient, and works best when the bicycle racks are oriented parallel or perpendicular to the road). A curb should be installed between the street and the parked bicycles to protect them from cars. Permanent commuter storage can also be handled by replacing several parking spaces. Storage should be near an entry door to increase visibility and decrease vandalism, and should be covered. Garage storage should also be near an entrance or elevator and well lit.

Round bicycle racks, with a V-shape rail holder are easier to use as the V support holds the wheel tightly, and as the space between bikes increases, making locking them relatively easy. The stand looks attractive and isn't as bulky as the linear racks when empty.

Bikeway Paving.

Asphalt is a preferred paving material for most bike paths. All-weather asphalt has the best properties for bicycling: smooth, even, quick-draining surface. Its dark color is easy on cyclists' eyes, and it can be laid to conform to many variations in terrain. Concrete has most of these same properties and is interchangeable, although it is often more expensive, harder on the eyes and more difficult to patch.

The principal criticism of asphalt is that it may look like a road surface. The looks are partly dependent on the design: For instance, a 12-foot wide, perfectly straight path laid with a paving machine may look bad. But a narrower path with curves and variations in width and planting can look as good as one surfaced with any other paving material. Colored gravel finds can be rolled into the top course to add a bit of variety. Installing bollards or barriers and signs at problem locations prevents motorists from mistaking the bikeway for a road.

Water locked gravels and gravel fines are suitable for recreational riding and in places where cyclists won't ride in the rain. Gravel does not hold up on grades of over four percent but may be appropriate in areas with high water tables. Gravel paths become rough and rocky after prolonged use, which slows down riders and can cause skidding. Ongoing maintenance which includes raking, rolling and adding gravel is greater than for concrete or asphalt trails. Gravel is *not* preferred by cyclists since gravel dust causes wear to sensitive parts of good bikes and soils clothing during wet weather.

Bicycle paths need not be designed for heavy truck traffic and therefore, the construction section can be minimized to save expense. For most walks, a six-inch base of crushed stone, plus a two-inch asphalt course works well. The surface course should be a fine mix: 100 percent passing the ½-inch screen. In areas of heavy frost, the recommended base depth needs to be verified in order to minimize frost heat damage. Asphalt will work well only if a proper base is installed. Pick a construction time coinciding with the best weather. Drainage, height of water table and soil conditions are important design considerations. Drainage requirements are:

- Pitched two percent to one side or crowned at two percent.
- On cut sections, it is necessary to pitch to the hill to catch runoff in ditches.
- Wide planted swales are preferred for dissipating run-off.
- At cross streets, catch basins should be located on the uphill side of the bikeway to reduce the quantity of water in the gutter.
- Colder regions must drain sufficiently to avoid standing water that can freeze.

The bike lane of this facility is paved with asphalt to distinguish it from the concrete sidewalk. A slight curb keeps bicyclists on their side, while allowing use of the sidewalk for passing when safe. NOTE: the 18" concrete strip on the left to protect bicyclists from car door openings.

The same principle that assures quality control for sidewalks should be used for concrete bike paths: They include: firm subgrade, five-sack mix (slightly more cement and air entrainment for frost-thaw areas), a maximum slump of four inches, and compressive strength in 28 days of 3500 psi. Four-inch pavement thickness is recommended unless heavy vehicles will use the path. The surface should be roughened with a broom to reduce slipperyness and expansion and isolation joints used to prevent cracking.

BICYCLE IMPROVEMENT SELECTION SHOULD CONSIDER THE FOLLOWING:

- Removal of barriers
- Correction of accident problems
- Follow direct routes
- Provide varied access
- Be attractive, incorporate scenic sights
- Be secure against criminal acts
- Minimize delays
- Reduce bicycle/motor vehicle conflicts
- Ease of maintenance
- Smooth, hard pavement
- Avoid truck and bus trafficked streets
- Avoid streets with extensive parking
- Avoid streets with high traffic volumes and speeds

Maintenance of Bicycle Routes.

Bikeways and streets used for bicycle routes need to be cleaned, patched and cleared of vegetation with some regularity. Dirt, gravel, broken glass tends to get pushed to the edge of the road where bicyclists usually ride. Maintenance of the road's edge must be included in planning for bicycle routes. Some bicycle routes get less dirty than others; for instance, separated bikeways do not have dirt generated by cars. Curbs separating the road from the bikeway keep some debris from reaching the bikeway, but they also have limited potential for use of street cleaning equipment. Consequently, bikeways should be at least six feet wide, and have curb-cuts as wide so motorized cleaning equipment can be used.

Raised roadway buttons or bars should not be used to identify bikeways since they are dangerous for bicycles to drive over. Bars or buttons with raised walls should especially be avoided. Flat, four-inch in diameter buttons may be used if they are located on the roadside with painted lines and are used primarily to warn motorists. They should be no closer than three feet apart so bicyclists can move freely around them.

Parking bicycles on the sidewalk conflicts with pedestrians and is an awkward intrusion on narrow, busy walks. One auto parking space can serve ten bicycles and is an efficient method to reduce the sidewalk clutter.

LEGAL ASPECTS OF BICYCLING.

Bicycle as Vehicle. Should a bike be officially classified as a vehicle? Classifying bicycles as vehicles assigns them all the rights and responsibilities of motor vehicles. Many motorists don't want bicycles to be classified as vehicles because they believe bicycles should ride only on sidewalks or special paths and cross streets as pedestrians. If the bicycle is treated as a vehicle, the traffic code should include language *allowing* bicycles to use bikeways and sidewalks (which cars can't) and to ride on the right as safety and purpose permits. Bicyclists would have to obey all automobile rules and regulations, and would receive traffic tickets for any violations. If the bicycle is treated as a non-vehicle, the traffic code should have language describing how and where bikes are allowed in the road, if at all.

The author recommends that bicycles be classified as *vehicles,* since this regularizes bicyclists' behavior and makes their actions more predictable. As mentioned earlier, studies indicate that bicyclists' unpredictability is the greatest cause of accidents.

Passing on the Right. One legal question to be raised is: Should bicyclists be allowed to pass on the right side of slow-moving cars traveling in the same lane? This often occurs at intersections when cars are stopped, and the bicyclist can ride carefully alongside to the head of the line of traffic. With care, this movement can be safe and *should* be allowed, though many motorists argue against it. The reciprocal suggesting that cars should *not* be allowed to pass slow-moving bicycles in the same lane, may shed fairness on prohibiting bikes from passing cars on the right. This usually causes motorist opponents to back down on their objections.

Bicycling on Sidewalks. For years, the subject of whether to allow bicycle riding on sidewalks has been discussed. No clear-cut decision has been made, but this author suggests that common sense should prevail; where it benefits the bicyclist and is not detrimental to pedestrians, sidewalk riding should be allowed. Allowing sidewalk riding on dangerous streets when there is no bikeway alternative aids inexperienced bicyclists. Suburban track development with few pedestrians, no bikeway, and fast moving trafffic makes bicycling on the sidewalk reasonable. However, pedestrians on a crowded downtown sidewalk could be endangered if bicyclists were allowed to ride there. Because policing bicyclists is difficult, some communities have banned sidewalk cycling. To solve these problems, bicyclists and pedestrians should develop peer-pressure policing to keep sidewalks safe.

Bicycling in Malls. Bicycle riding should be prohibited in pedestrian malls if they are busy and attract many pedestrians. Bicycles create problems for pedestrians unless they are ridden slowly and carefully. It is better for bicyclists to park their bicycles and walk. To encourage bicycle use, provide frequent bicycle parking racks and signs showing bicyclists how to move around the mall area.

The Department of Transportation, Federal Highway Administration document entitled: "Guide for Bike Facilities" contains criteria to be followed for developing bike programs funded under the Federal Highway Program. This document does not set strict standards, but rather contains guidelines to provide general program directions. The Guide also includes information on planning, operating and maintaining bicycle facilities.

ADAPTING ESTABLISHED NEIGHBORHOODS FOR WALKING AND BICYCLING

Inner-city neighborhoods surrounding downtown areas, which were developed along trolley routes from city centers may have the best chance of being adapted to serve bicyclists and pedestrians. Originally, circulation through these neighborhoods was primarily on foot, with trolleys providing transportation for longer trips. The original layout of inner-city neighborhoods included main trolley routes radiating from downtown with most development clustered around them. Every mile or so, a small neighborhood shopping district could be found. Houses were clustered around these convenience districts which often included library, grocery, hardware, drugs, and five-and-dime stores, as well as other services. People could walk from their homes to their shopping, in the friendly atmosphere of a small town.

These older neighborhoods were usually platted in a grid pattern, with uniform street, lot, and sidewalk widths, and a school and park forming neighborhood focus. Since many of these neighborhoods still have the same physical form, they are easily readapted for foot travel. Since World War II as modes of travel have changed from foot and trolley to automobile, neighborhoods have changed too. Whereas the focus of shopping was in a district where businesses were clustered and easy to reach on foot or bicycle, now the focus is on strips of businesses, long and linear and not easily accessible without a car.

Further changes were made to streets to accommodate increased numbers of cars and higher travel speeds: streets were widened and designated as arterials. These arterials are now generally considered unsafe and unpleasant for walking and bicycling. Along arterials, land uses have often been changed from single-family residences to auto-oriented apartments and commercial developments layed out along a strip, thus the term strip development. This type of development generally reflects little concern for the street's quality: that is, the street is often unattractive, dirty, cluttered with parked cars, and devoid of vegetation and appealing shop fronts.

Many residents of inner-city neighborhoods have found that, while automobiles are convenient for long distance travel, they create problems around home. Cars are noisy, polluting, hazardous to bicyclists and to children playing along the street and visually degrading to the streetscape.

Older neighborhoods were not planned to accommodate the large number of cars found there today. Two cars may be parked in front of individual houses on small lots for which parking was not intended. Parking on planting strips along sidewalks is even more commonplace. Alleys that can be used for parking instead of the street, do not even have sufficient space to accommodate all the cars used in city neighborhoods today.

Perpendicular parking increases parking efficiency and is acceptable to create more parking in older neighborhoods. However, these cars are parked too close to the building for comfortable walking and should be set back at least another 3 to 5 feet for a planting strip or wider sidewalk. Second-floor units overviewing cars, and parking noise would also be improved.

Apartments constructed before the 1940's usually lack parking spaces, because residents relied on bus transportation and nearby shopping. Even newer apartments often provide insufficient parking space. Now the street must absorb parking for residents of these apartments. In addition to cars, boats and recreational vehicles, visitor and service personnel also compete for parking space. Although parking is a critical problem, we cannot be sure just how long it will continue, considering rising fuel costs and its scarcity, reduced car sizes and increased options in nonmotorized transportation.

Newer apartment buildings with parking that crosses the sidewalk area for a long length makes walking uncomfortable. A single entry, internal driveway and a new pedestrian streetscape would improve the walk's quality, enhance safety, and help convert an auto neighborhood to accommodate pedestrian activities.

Although most neighborhoods considered in this section were constructed prior to 1950, many blocks and arterial streets constructed after 1950 have no sidewalks. While sidewalks were typical in early times, the shift to auto transportation reduced the need for them. Competition with the car often reduced or curtailed bus transportation, so that bus stops are probably inadequate. *In summary,* the conversion of older neighborhoods from communities where people walked or used public transit, to communities dependant on cars has created the following pedestrian circulation conflicts:

- loss of convenience shopping
- increased speed and volume of vehicular traffic
- widened streets developed especially for the car
- increased parking congestion and decreased pedestrian comfort
- decreased public transportation.

PLANNING BY LOOKING AT THE PAST.

In principle, changes to accommodate pedestrians would involve returning to less dependence on the automobile as well as land-use configurations of the pre-1940's. In practice, there are many pre-1940 conditions that are impossible (and maybe undesirable) to achieve, because of seemingly irreversible changes that have occurred. For instance, jobs that previously were located downtown may now be located outside the city where public transit service may be poor compared with service to center city. Reinstitution of neighborhood convenience shopping may not be feasible, given the present merchandising practices of high volume sales and centralized control. Car ownership isn't going to decrease immediately. Even with reduced usage, cars will still create parking and congestion problems.

Another approach is towards reducing the need to rely on cars for every activity, shifting some activities to bikes, others to foot, and still others to public transit. The procedure is to survey neighborhoods for nonmotorized circulation problems and opportunities, and to develop solutions and priorities to implement them. Solutions should concentrate on:

- reducing the impact of automobiles,
- improving the neighborhood for walking and biking, and
- changing some land uses to make these activities possible.

Solutions should run the gamut of easily implementable projects such as new sidewalks, curb cuts, benches, rest areas, bus stops, etc., to dreams such as covered areas, street closing, expanded bus service, zoning changes, etc. Projects should include short-term capital improvement projects and long-term land use and transportation changes that foster pedestrian activity. Opportunities for changes in the sale of merchandise, zoning, and public transportation that may seem difficult to implement should be studied and discussed publicly.

European service station scaled for pedestrians could work in many older American neighborhoods. The pumps are mounted on an expanded sidewalk area and cars parked in a drop-off zone, eliminating sidewalk crossing and the barren scale of large service stations.

GATHERING INFORMATION.

The planner should survey neighborhoods for problems and opportunities related to pedestrian and bicycle circulation. The process involves gathering and locating information on:

- different pedestrian activities,
- places used by people in the neighborhood,
- types of people who walk and cycle,
- attractive places,
- problems that make walking and biking difficult.

Identify car-oriented places where lack of sidewalks and parking lots make walking uncomfortable.

Specific steps for the planner to follow are listed below.

1. Obtain maps of each neighborhood at two scales: One no larger than 100 feet in one inch and the other at 20 feet in one inch. Use the larger scale for showing broad relationships and the smaller scale to show the conditions of specific blocks in detail. Define the neighborhood by selecting boundaries that limit foot and bicycle use, such as freeways, topographic relief, and known edges of the community.

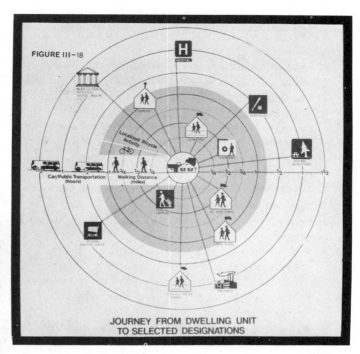

FIGURE III-18

JOURNEY FROM DWELLING UNIT
TO SELECTED DESIGNATIONS

2. Locate on the map all the schools, parks, convenience shopping areas, dense residential neighborhoods, active employment centers (even if just several buildings), public facilities such as meeting halls, churches, libraries, museums, etc.

3. In each place listed above, check connections to the neighborhood via bus, foot, or bicycle. Note the availability, usefulness, and condition of sidewalk. Also note areas where auto speeds *exceed* 20 m.p.h. Do this within a radius of 1/2 mile, which is roughly equivalent to a ten-minute walk. Suggest measures necessary to correct problems observed. These might include capital improvements, such as construction of sidewalks, benches, transit stops, overpasses, underpasses; zoning and land-use changes to help shorten walking distances; public transit improvements; merchandising practices to improve the appearance and function of the area for

A sidewalk with garage doors and landscaping or a reduction in numbers of driveways with internal circulation would improve the condition.

99

pedestrians.

4. Identify pedestrians and bicyclists typical of the neighborhood. These are likely to be older people who have free time but limited access to cars and carry out many activities on foot; younger people who also don't drive and must use public or non-motorized transportation; commuters who can travel from home to work without a car relatively easily; recreationists, who in walking or bicycling, use the neighborhood for exercise and relaxation; and service people who shop and carry out other activities on foot.

5. Locate all sidewalks on the map. Divide them into three categories:
   • Existing sidewalks that are continuous with sufficient widths and planting areas and that function well;
   • No sidewalks or sidewalks in poor repair with obstacles; and
   • Existing sidewalks that are not convenient or safe and therefore are not well-used.

Bus stops without benches, shelter, light, or landscaping detract from pedestrian circulation and should be improved. Benches should be the first addition.

Sidewalks totally surrounded by the car, a parking lot on one side and street on the other side, offer no pedestrian protection or quality to make walking pleasant. Each spot should be identified and corrected.

6. Identify car-oriented places, particularly arterials and streets that carry heavy volumes of traffic at relatively high speeds. Note drive-in businesses where cars cross well used sidewalks and parking lots and wide driveways adjacent to sidewalks.

7. Locate accident areas where pedestrians or bicyclists were injured. This information can be obtained from police accident reports. Also note areas where people perceive dangers to exist such as busy intersections, arterials, areas without sidewalks.

8. Mark bus routes and all stops that do *not* have benches, shelters, schedules, bike racks, and sidewalks leading from bus stops into the neighborhood.

Identify all sidewalks that are too narrow for 2 people to walk abreast of each other, or where they are not separated from busy traffic by parking or a planter strip with trees or shrubbery (above). Extensive drive-ins, no-parking zones, fast-moving traffic, lack of vegetation, and absence of pedestrian scale, should be identified and noted for redevelopment. Note the small size, identification, and detail design of this parking lot entry (below).

This drive-in bank, located off a side street is designed to be seen by pedestrians. The drive is narrow, the sidewalk and drive pavements are different colors, the granite bollards act as a gateway, and it is well-landscaped. Note the parking meter at the *back of the walk*. Note also the driveway depression extends too far into the sidewalk area and creates a potential tripping spot for unwary pedestrians.

Specialty planting such as espaliered trees and patterned vines adds visual interest to relieve the boredom of walking. They also soften the garden senses and show concern for the walker.

9. Mark all areas that are visually attractive and are potential pedestrian routes.

10. Do a bicycle survey. (See Page 70).

11. Note any of the following problem areas as: places unable to be reached on foot, particularly employment, shopping and school areas; barriers or obstacles along routes; large parking lots; drive-in businesses; wide intersections with fast moving traffic; wide and busy streets. Suggest measures that might correct these problems.

12. Note opportunity areas such as potential short-cuts (such as alleys or public property); views; attractive places where people might walk, bicycle or rest.

13. Check immediately outside the boundaries you have established to see if there are activities, uses or events of interest to people in the neighborhood. Find any problems that people traveling on foot, bicycle or bus are likely to encounter reaching them and propose corrective solutions.

14. Encourage as many different people to help in information gathering as is possible. The more people who can report their observations as well as successes and difficulties encountered, the more real and useful the survey is likely to be. Develop a simple questionnaire (see Page 99) and map of the area.

Extensively used shortcuts should be properly developed.

People on foot and moving cars can share the same space. The design secret seems to lie in first solving the scale problems for the walker, and then integrating the car. If the reverse occurs, that is if the space and speed requirements of the car are satisfied and then the pedestrian integrated, they will always be more comfortable for the motorist. The apartment complex shown has a roadway narrowed to the point that drivers travel slowly. It is bordered on one side with a sidewalk, and separated a slight amount with the garden. The interior is nicely landscaped and detailed for viewing at a very low speed, preferably on foot. The whole feeling of the place is one of tranquility and motorists sense upon entry that they should drive slowly and be on their best manners.

Identify shopping places with poor connection to the sidewalk. Large parking lots between the sidewalk and the buildings, or businesses with no pedestrian walkway adjacent to them should be noted.

Arterials with fast moving traffic, no parking, and center dividers that prevent street crossing should be identified.

Some Planning Solutions.

A number of planning solutions will be discussed in detail in the following pages. They will be presented in the order of ease of implementation from methods for widening sidewalks, changing streets and slowing down automobile traffic to methods for reorganizing street layouts. Then, methods are presented for including the bicycle in planning for older neighborhoods. Finally, suggestions are made for ways to revitalize neighborhood business districts and to adapt arterials for pedestrian use. A study of inner-city neighborhoods should concentrate on identifying four conditions:

- Activities involving large numbers of pedestrians;
- Dangerous areas for pedestrians or those with perceived safety problems;
- Discontinuous pedestrian routes;
- Unique attractions of interest to pedestrians.

The old engineering rule of thumb that sidewalks should equal ten percent of the road's width is simply not enough for comfortable walking.

TO IMPROVE THE PEDESTRIAN/BICYCLE EXPERIENCE:

Vehicular traffic "friction" problems are the same ones felt by most walkers and need to be corrected. They include delay, congestion, poor accessibility, low visibility, discomfort and fear of accidents. To ease these:

- Reduce vehicular speed limits to 20 m.p.h.
- Add parking to busy streets to buffer sidewalks and reduce vehicular speed.
- Reduce curb radii at corners to 5-10 feet.
- Eliminate free right turns at traffic lights.
- Eliminate time delays on pedestrian WALK signals.
- Guarantee pedestrian rights when in the street (California does).
- Switch pedestrian accident from civil to criminal proceedings (Germany does, and drivers are more careful).
- Add sidewalks everywhere.

WIDENING SIDEWALKS.

The sidewalk, the realm of the pedestrian, tends to be most pleasant if it is safe, uncluttered, continuous and regularly maintained. Of these four factors, crowding is the one that most affects how much, how fast and how often the pedestrian walks. While on residential sidewalks, crowding is seldom a problem, on busy sidewalks in business and recreational districts, congestion can restrict a pedestrian's free movement and sense of comfort. Since the object of this section is to help improve neighborhoods so that more people will want to walk, rather than drive, solutions are offered for eliminating sidewalk congestion and for enhancing the experience of walking.

How does a planner determine if the sidewalk needs to be widened? The planner must observe sidewalks at different times of day and consult people who use these sidewalks about safety and crowding problems. Areas where crowding is most likely to occur are: intersections, busy streets where people have to wait; streets where people are involved in different activities; and spaces in front of schools or buildings where many people congregate.

Not all places need wide sidewalks. Small scale neighborhood roads may be comfortable with narrow walks protected by parked cars and planting on the other side.

In addition to crowding, there are sometimes other reasons why a sidewalk should be widened. The extra width may make the sidewalk more pleasant or attractive and it may afford additional protection from the street. Times when sidewalks feel crowded may not be times when they are used by the most people. Although morning and evening commuting hours may generate the greatest numbers of people on sidewalks, their purpose for being there is generally the same, that is going to or returning from work. During rush hours, there tends to be fewer interruptions such as people window-shopping or stopping to talk, or mothers pushing strollers. The times then when congestion presents the greatest problem is during the mid-morning and mid-afternoon when people engaged in different activities are moving at different speeds.

The first priority for sidewalk widening should be given to intersections where improvements increase safety. Sidewalks abutting the intersection could be expanded into the parking lane (see sketch). This allows waiting pedestrians to be spread out rather than crowded and allows fast walkers to move to the curb's edge and cross first when the signal changes. Expanding the sidewalk in this way also makes the intersection safer by decreasing the distance across the street.

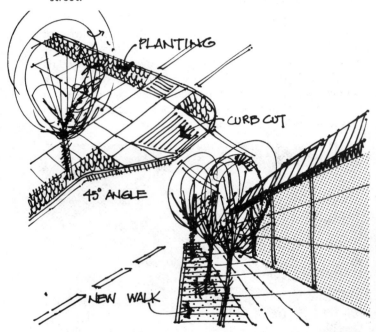

Widen the pedestrian area at intersections to narrow the street, slow traffic and reduce perceived and real safety problems.

After sidewalk widening at the intersection, widening along the street for safety should be considered. For instance, sidewalks abutting busy streets, particularly streets without parked cars, could be widened to insure an extra measure of actual and perceived safety. The extra width may allow pedestrians to pass each other without feeling the proximity of passing traffic or parents to walk with children without feeling a hazard. A narrow planter could be incorporated into the sidewalk's street edge and could provide an additional measure of safety.

Finally, sidewalks should be widened in places to allow space for people to wait, rest, talk and people watch. Most sidewalks are constructed to serve as channels for through movement. The actual sidewalk width required to handle pedestrian traffic is often less than is required to allow for other social functions. Since narrow sidewalks by their very nature are suggestive of movement, they don't function well for people who want to wait, rest, talk or watch other people. Since the latter is an enjoyable pastime for many older people, it should be made comfortable and easy. A solution that would serve all these activities is to widen the sidewalk in some places, so that those people who want to stop can do so without disturbing those who want to keep moving (see sketch). These resting places

should provide some seating: benches, raised planters with wide edges, walks or steps. They should also be sited for sun and protection from wind.

Some questions need to be considered in the widening of sidewalks. Should sidewalks be widened on one or both sides of the street? If one side, which side? How wide should sidewalks be?

In some neighborhoods, it may prove more advantageous for a sidewalk on one side of a street to be widened substantially than for sidewalks on two sides to be widened only a small amount. At least 26 inches of walk width has to be added to create one new lane of walking space. Twenty six inches is the width of the space required for a pedestrian carrying a small item such as a purse or briefcase. Unless the amount of space gained on two sides allows at least one lane of traffic each, it could be better for the planner to incorporate all the available space on one side, thereby saving expenses for extra curbing and utilities. To decide which side, the planner should decide which side will provide the greatest benefit to pedestrians. For instance, widening should be done on the side of the street with the most businesses, on the side with the most sun or the most weather protection, or the side where the most pedestrian activities are concentrated (transit stops, schools, places of employment, stores).

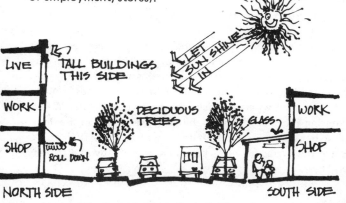

NORTH SIDE   SOUTH SIDE

How wide should sidewalks be? There's an old engineering rule of thumb that states sidewalks should equal 10 percent of the road's width. A 60 foot wide street would thus have 6 feet of sidewalks or 3 feet on each side. Unfortunately, hard and fast rules don't work for every situation. It has been proven that 10 percent of street width is likely not to provide appropriate sidewalks for pedestrians in urban areas. Most small-town neighborhoods and business districts use a sidewalk width of 8 or 9 feet in the business area and a 5 foot sidewalk in residential areas. Often residential sidewalks are separated from the street by a 5 foot planter strip. These two sidewalk widths are minimum, and may leave something to be desired in making walking truly pleasurable, as they do not allow for congestion, for passing or meandering or varying one's course, or for the pleasure of sharing a walk with several other people.

On 8 foot-wide sidewalks, some space is lost adjacent to the stores where people browse and window-shop, and some is lost on the street side for parking meters, street furniture, fire hydrants, light poles, etc. The space left is about 4 feet, just enough for two people to pass, though not comfortably. Adjustments, which are inconvenient and tend to make a walk trip less pleasant, would have to be made for more than two people to pass each other. (See sketch).

A 5 foot sidewalk has enough space for two pedestrians to pass but does not allow a couple to pass a single pedestrian without some adjustment. Furthermore, it does not allow convenient passing of people with wheeled vehicles (that is, with bicycle, wheelchair or grocery basket). However, as long as use is light, 5 feet of width is inexpensive to construct, is not overbearing visually, and is sufficient for casual walking and bicycling.

As foot traffic increases, this author recommends a minimum width for business district sidewalks of 12 feet, and for residential sidewalks of 7 feet. These widths would increase the flexibility of the street, allowing more freedom and ease of movement for people walking, bicycling or riding in wheelchairs.

With some adjustments, sidewalks can be made effectively wider by moving street furniture. For instance, moving parking meters, sign posts and light poles to the back of the sidewalk next to shops. The street furniture is moved to the area used by slower-moving pedestrians, e.g., those who are window-shopping or waiting. This frees space near the curb, improving pedestrian flow for faster moving people. Mail boxes and news stands can be removed from busy sidewalks to less busy side streets.

Many older neighborhoods have grid street patterns that run long distances without any variation. The quality of walking along the street can be very boring because of the lack of variety and lack indication that suggests you are getting someplace. More variety in the walk and in the detail is necessary before this will be a comfortable place to walk.

Urban sidewalks have traditionally paralleled the street. While they may visually unify the neighborhood from the perspective of motorists, parallel sidewalks provide a boring walking experience for pedestrians. There is no reason why sidewalks should not curve, narrow in places or widen in others, or be separated from the street by walks, hedges, or trees, and in general, be more random. This author expects that most people would not mind the varied course, but would appreciate the enhanced walking experience. With design care, the streetscape could still appear uniform when viewed from passing vehicles. (See photo).

Straight sidewalks that parallel the street are boring to walk along unless they are treated differently by the neighbors. This garden, crossing over into the traditional lawn strip with different tree types provides walker interests and eases the travel distance.

Sidewalks with a wide planter strip may benefit from the addition of a narrow strip of concrete behind the street-side curb to serve as a hard surface for people to walk across as they get in or out of their cars. Scoring patterns of lines on a sidewalk guards against random cracking and reduce the scale of the sidewalk as well. It has been observed that people, especially children, enjoy the experience of walking on or between the lines. Score lines closely spaced increase the texture and visual diversity. The pattern can be either uniformly or randomly spaced without bothering pedestrians, though most designers seem to prefer the uniform spacing.

Vary the sidewalk in parks and where there is a wide enough set-back so the end destination is less visible to relieve boredom.

When plans are being made for widening a sidewalk, the planner should be careful to solve or correct drainage problems. Although this may be expensive in the short run, good drainage is worth the cost in the long-run because it makes the sidewalk usable and extends its life. Typically, sidewalks and roads slope to the gutter where run-off is collected from both surfaces. In sidewalk widening, there is seldom sufficient room to extend the sidewalk grade toward the street without the new curb being below street grade. Therefore, widening a sidewalk may require developing a new drainage swale, or excavating the roadway to accommodate a walk that slopes uniformly to the curb and gutter. Because most roads have been carelessly and repeatedly overpaved, it may not be possible to merely excavate them. It may be necessary to resurface them. (See sketch).

One alternative to repaving is using catch basins or continuous drains installed within the sidewalk area. The sidewalk is sloped so that water drains towards the grates. The continuous drain pipes are generally ten inches in diameter, and have a narrow neck with a removable grate. Water, entering the drain through the grate, is carried in the drain pipe beneath the sidewalk to a central collection point. Since the surface is neat, the drain doesn't adversely affect any users.

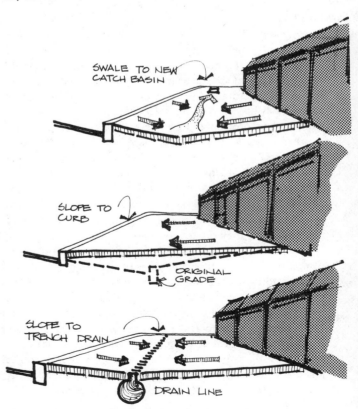

SIDEWALK WIDENING DRAINAGE

CHANGING STREETS

New space for pedestrians and bicyclists is generally gained only with considerable bargaining by concerned citizens and planners. Traditionally, the planner's first responsibility was to figure out how to accommodate the automobile. That responsibility should be reversed by questioning whether a designated street "must" or merely "should" serve its stated automobile purpose. If it "must," the decision to allocate space to pedestrian use may be a political one, that is the planner can't logically decide in favor of the pedestrians. If the traffic planner says a street "should" carry a certain amount of traffic, it can be assumed less effort will be made to maintain or extend space for the automobile. Thus, there is room for bargaining for the interest of pedestrians and bicyclists. The planner should look for precedence in the neighborhood to make the opponents' argument more difficult, that is, an existing narrow or one-way road that seems to work well.

The planner should not be afraid to suggest changing roadways, particularly in residential areas. Some of our most charming roads are tiny, narrow lanes which twist and bend around trees and other natural elements. Obviously, all residential roads should not be converted to narrow lanes, but some conversions would enhance a neighborhood. Since changes often imply reducing the speed limit on residential streets, it is helpful to note that this reduction usually will *not* affect the street's vehicle carrying capacity. This seeming paradox is true since the number of cars on most residential streets is below the road's capacity. Some conversion approaches include:

1. Converting a two-way street to a one-way street, and using the abandoned lane for pedestrian or bicycle traffic. Installing one-way signs is inexpensive initially. Converting the lane to pedestrian use may be expensive, since curbs, gutters, and pavement must be removed and relocated, but this can be phased over time. The planner should decide if the new space should be on one side or be divided between two sides of the street. It is possible to begin by using temporary rolled asphalt

curbs, shaped so run-off reaches existing storm drains. New walks, curbs, gutters, and planting can then be added. In most cases, the existing lighting can remain. Converting the lane to bicycle use can be relatively inexpensive if the bicycle lane remains in the roadway and only striping is needed. If the bicycle lane is raised, however, the expense will be similar to that for converting a lane to a sidewalk.

2. Eliminating one parking lane and converting it to pedestrian or bicycle use. This change can be accomplished inexpensively by installing signs and policing the street. Over a period of time, the new space will be treated as discussed in (1) above. (see sketch).

3. Eliminating one lane, but still allowing cars to travel in two directions. Streets like this exist, and they work quite well once people become used to them. (See sketch). No parking spaces are eliminated, but the cars are forced to travel slowly. When approaching an oncoming car, one car must pull into a driveway or empty parking space and let the other pass. Neighborhoods with garages or off-street parking work best, providing space into which passing cars can drive. It is interesting to note how courteous drivers can be; there is often a rush to see who can pull off the street first and usually a thank-you wave as the cars pass.

25' wide two way street

Streets that serve limited neighborhood access can be closed as this one was and converted to an informal play space. This particular street formerly separated a school and park, and was a logical space for a play facility. Without the roadway, access between the park and school is completely safe.

This street was closed with minor modifications to restrict auto traffic. The low cost planter in the center of the street gives it a pedestrian feel while still allowing emergency access. However, the resolution of the street at the intersection would benefit with the planter that conformed to the turning lane configuration.

4. Narrowing each travel lane, adding several feet to the pedestrian or bicycle domain. Most existing streets are wider than is actually necessary, with 12- or 13-foot-wide travel lanes. For neighborhood streets, lane widths greater than 10 feet are an unnecessary luxury, particularly with the decreasing size of American cars.

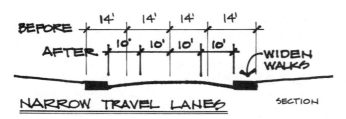

5. Reducing planter strips. Many streets have wide planting strips, which could be added to the sidewalk. This is not always the best solution, since most streets are visually oppressive because of extensive paving and lack of street trees. Thus, planting strips should be used only if:

   - The street can't be narrowed;
   - Existing trees can remain and be protected from abuse;
   - Sidewalk paving is small scale (that is, unit pavers, brick, scored concrete, sets). This eliminates the feeling of "acres of paving."

6. The roadway may be abandoned to automobiles, creating a traffic-free space for both bicycles and pedestrians. (See photo)

This former street leading to a neighborhood park has been closed to traffic and converted to a pedestrian street. The lighting fixtures, paving and the retaining wall that borders the new walk are all varied and intimate to relieve the mental boredom of walking. The houses are serviced off an alley.

RE-CHANNELING STREETS

Many street intersections have been indiscriminately widened and extensively paved, with little respect to actual vehicular needs or pedestrian quality. Some occur at angled street intersections, while others happened to accommodate the large turning radius of fast-moving traffic. Most occurred by randomly paving without considering the edge treatment. The planner should determine precise vehicular space needs, and channelize the street with curbs to match these needs. A reasonably slow speed should be assumed, coupled with smaller automobile turning radii, and an understanding of pedestrian requirements. The leftover space can be landscaped, paved for pedestrian or bicycle circulation, used for bus stops, or built on if it is large enough. Add curb cuts to ease wheelchair and bicycle movement. (NOTE: Channelization may squeeze bicycle space from the roadway, forcing them to use the pedestrian area—provided there is direct curb cut access.)

BEFORE   AFTER

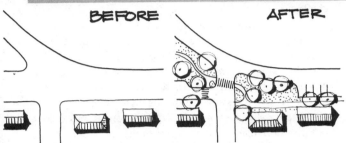

Islanding. These trees and walkway occupy a former intersection that was large and difficult to cross on foot. The street edge was channeled to direct cars, and the captured space converted to a pedestrian island. In addition to serving foot traffic, the little park creates a special feeling for this district.

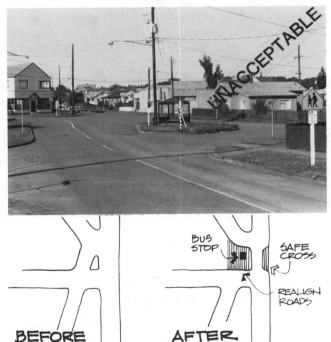

BEFORE   AFTER

Complicated angled intersections should be channelized to increase the walking space and make it difficult for traffic to travel fast. These intersections are generally accident-prone and channelization will decrease the size visually and provide pedestrian protection. Note the bus stop in the middle of the small island. It would be improved if the ''island'' were attached to a nearby neighborhood by closing one street. (See sketch.)

SLOWING DOWN THE AUTOMOBILE.

In certain neighborhoods, it may be desirable for the automobile speed limit to be reduced, for the sake of safety and amenity. Speed should be reduced near schools, parks, business districts, employment centers, residential neighborhoods, as well as along routes used by recreational walkers, joggers, skaters, or bicyclists and in any area with large numbers of pedestrians. Several ways of accomplishing this are listed from simplest to most complex as follows:

1. Installation of speed limit signs can theoretically reduce automobile speeds, preferably to 20 miles per hour.* However, designating reduced speeds is only half the job: local police must patrol the routes to assure that drivers obey the new speed limit. Reducing speed limits is inexpensive, quick, and not disruptive socially. The planner should remember, however, that restrictions in one area may affect traffic in another area and plan accordingly.

The police should be encouraged to enforce rules that aid pedestrians. Frequent violations include: speeding, careless driving, and failure to stop for pedestrians in the crosswalk. Cars parking on the sidewalk or planter strips should be discouraged. Many police departments do not do this. Issuance of traffic citations in Seattle, Washington, illustrates this point. A pedestrian safety study shows that 56 percent of pedestrian accidents are the fault of motorists who fail to yield or who are speeding or driving erratically. The remaining 44 percent of accidents are either the pedestrian's fault or indeterminable (many are violations of restrictive pedestrians laws that should not be on the books). It is interesting to compare the number of traffic citations issued annually to motorists for violating pedestrians' rights and issued to pedestrians for violating motorists' rights. Of the 11,500 tickets issued yearly, 1,500 went to motorists (7.6 percent) while 10,000 (92.4 percent) went to pedestrians.

*At 20 miles per hour, atuomobile drivers are driving slow enough that they can see pedestrians and react quickly enough to stop if necessary. This speed is slow enough to discourage unnecessary through traffic. Vehicles traveling at 20 m.p.h. are not excessively noisy or frightening to most pedestrians. The perceived and actual safety for pedestrians increases considerably with the shift downward from 25 m.p.h. to 20 m.p.h.

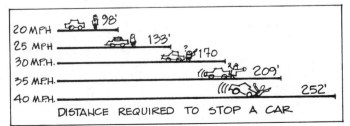

DISTANCE REQUIRED TO STOP A CAR

2. Rough pavement surfaces slow down automobiles. Old streets paved in cobblestone, brick, or rough concrete are uncomfortable to drive over. The simplest way to obtain rough pavement is not repairing a street and letting chuckholes develop. Another way is to add a skim coat of asphalt with coarse gravel that alternates with the smooth surface causing a bumpy ride. The most expensive method is to replace the street with cobblestone or brick pavement, or to remove asphalt exposing bricks or cobbles underneath. Consequently, rough paving reduces the car's speed and efficiency, while enhancing the visual quality of the street.

3. Speed bumps have traditionally been constructed only on private property (in apartment complexes, parking lots, shopping centers) where slow speed is expected. They have not been installed on public roadways where cars might hit them while traveling at a high speed and lose control. As the idea of slowing down the automobile is becoming more widely accepted, it is possible in some neighborhoods to locate speed bumps on public roads where drivers travel slowly. Many cities now place them on park roads and in residential neighborhoods where through and fast traffic is restricted with signage or closed streets. The British Road Department has found that a long, shallow speed bump serves to slow down traffic without creating dangerous driving conditions. Their recommended speed bump length is 12 feet long. When speed bumps are used on public roads, the planner should make sure that drivers are *already* traveling slowly and use speed bumps to discourage speeding up.

Speed bumps are prohibited in many communities because they slow down emergency vehicles. While this is true, careful planning can provide alternate through routes for emergency vehicles. If the local street with a speed bump is a final emergency vehicle destination, it will have slowed down already, and can negotiate the speed bump, particularly if it is a long, shallow one.

A speed bump can be either a bump or a depression. Bumps are easy to construct by forming an asphalt mound, but may cause snow plow blade damage in snowfall areas. A slight depression across the road is an acceptable substitute and doesn't damage snow plows. The depression should be five inches deep and eight to twelve feet across. It can even be made part of the drainage system. Both bump and depression should be long enough so cars traveling within the posted speed limit can negotiate them without slowing down. When a bump is extended over a 12-foot distance, it cannot be felt at 20 m.p.h. but the effect is objectionable at faster speeds.

4. Extend the sidewalk across the street with up and down auto ramps to create a large speed bump. The sidewalk should be carried across the street at its normal height, and ramps for the cars added in both directions with asphalt paving. (See sketch). For added warning, leave the curb flush where it crosses between the street and sidewalk, and pave the raised crossing with a different material such as brick or exposed concrete. This treatment requires driver and pedestrian awareness to insure safety, but if several raised crossings are installed throughout the city, users will become familiar with them. The raised sidewalk crossing eliminates the need for ramps serving the handicapped, and places the pedestrian in a superior position.

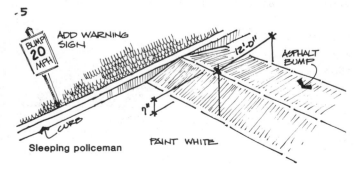

Sleeping policeman

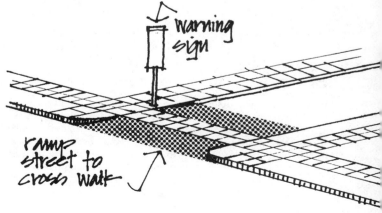

5. Streets converted to one-way traffic may be reconstructed with a roadway alignment weaving slightly to the left and right, forcing drivers to slow down and also creating a pleasant pedestrian and bicycle street, though at a high construction cost.

6. Traffic lanes on two-way streets may be narrowed to a point where it is impossible for two cars to pass another. Thus, both must slow down. When two cars come abreast of one another, one must pull into the parking lane to let the other by. A majority of residential streets in Seattle, Washington, achieve this. They are 25-feet-wide and serve two-way traffic with parking on both sides. Parking consumes 14 feet of the street, leaving 11 feet for two directions of traffic. There are few safety or user problems with these streets because motorists are forced by the very configuration to drive slowly. These narrow roads make pleasant places to live on. (See photo).

Typical 25-foot-wide residential street with parking on both sides. Speed of travel is reduced because of the narrowness of the street, and the potential of encountering a car traveling in the other direction.

Garages with doors set back slightly from the sidewalk with vines or other landscaped treatment provides a satisfactory integration of parking where cars must cross the sidewalk. Contrast the above photo with many potential hiding places for muggers and the uncertainty of where a car might back in or out, with the lower photo where it's clearly evident because of the open or closed door, and the chance of muggings are reduced.

Perpendicular parking reached directly from the street speeds up vehicular traffic as motorists can turn and reach their carports at relatively high speeds. Elimination of continuous driveways by replacing them with single drives and on-site service roads is preferred.

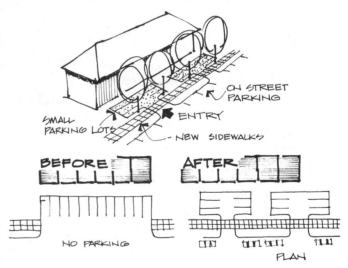

On-grade parking with continuous driveways should be prohibited. Convert existing units with a single driveway serving parallel parking. (See sketch).

REORGANIZING STREETS.

In older neighborhoods overrun with nonneighborhood, through-traffic, streets can be reorganized using layouts that redirect traffic to nearby arterials, thereby discouraging unnecessary through-traffic. This type of reorganized circulation plan can make the neighborhood safe and pleasant for pedestrians. *Local Access Zones* (also called Protected Residential Neighborhoods or Priority Neighborhoods) have been used successfully in many cities across the United States (San Francisco, Berkeley, Seattle, Boston, etc.) providing precedence for other cities.

A neighborhood of 12 to 20 blocks is first defined, then plans are made to divert unnecessary traffic by using different traffic controls such as diverters, culs-de-sac, safe-crosses, one-way streets (particularly exist streets), traffic circles and street crossings. Two conditions are necessary: a community will to recapture the peace and quiet of previous years; and existing arterial streets on the periphery which can absorb the diverted traffic. Raising community interest requires several concerned neighbors to convince others that the problem is acute enough and that there are alternatives to excess traffic.

Arterials exist every four to five blocks in most cities. Generally the percentage increase of cars diverted to arterials by Local Access Zone conversion is low enough not to overcrowd or worsen the environmental conditions of arterials, especially since the bulk of the traffic occurs during peak periods and not during the day. The percentage of traffic increase on the arterials compared with the percentage of decrease in residential streets is generally favorable. (For instance, the reorganization may increase arterial traffic from 8,000 vehicles per day to 8,350 or a five percent increase, while a residential street may lose 200 vehicles per day from 800 or a 25 percent reduction.)

POTENTIAL PROBLEMS

Most street organization schemes have merely shifted traffic from local roads to arterials without any compensation for those who live on the arterials. Thus, the best solution would be to reduce rather than redistribute the traffic. Reduction could be accomplished by adding traffic constraints to the arterials and enhancing opportunities for such other means of transport as bus, bicycle, car pool. One suggestion is to prohibit trucks, which contribute heavily to a poor street environment.

Reorganizing and reducing traffic in neighborhoods can change social conditions and opportunities, and these should be analyzed before proceeding. They may cause higher rents and market values of properties if living conditions become more desirable, and that may force poorer people to move out of the neighborhood. Those efforts may, too, help prevent neighborhood deterioration or increase the desirability of the place for children, thus stabilizing the neighborhood.

Let's look at several ways to convert existing auto-oriented neighborhoods. These suggestions *reduce, but do not eliminate,* auto efficiency and flexibility, while increasing pedestrian and bicycle safety, use and enjoyment. Three elements, the street diverter, the safe-cross, and the traffic circle, which make street crossing safer, are considered in detail in the following pages.

Street Diverter. The street diverter connects sidewalks at an intersection in a cater cornered fashion, eliminating through auto traffic. Automobile traffic is diverted to the right or the left in a loop. Cars can still travel on the street but are forced to slow down. At the same time, a continuous diagonal pedestrian route is created through the intersection. The street diverter works well on one-way streets, since only one lane needs to squeeze around a rather right

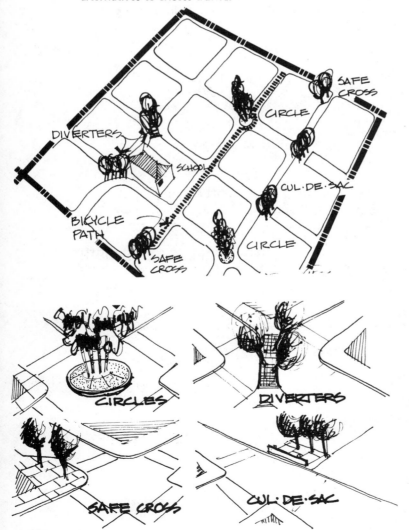

radius. However, it is possible to accommodate two lanes by enlarging the inside curb radius. Dimensions are critical: two lanes require 20 feet of roadway width as a comfortable minimum with an inside curb radius of 15 feet. With these minimum dimensions, average-sized cars can pass each other, while trucks may have to wait and turn the corner when the roadway is empty. However, this should cause little inconvenience since trucks should travel slowly in neighborhoods, and use arterials for through-circulation.

The diagonal walk across the intersection should be raised to at least a standard curb height of 6 to 9 inches and may be arched in the center to a height of 2 feet providing greater visual warning of the diverter to the approaching motorists. (See sketch). Since a street diverter may be unfamiliar to motorists, an unsuspecting driver might try to drive straight across it. Thus, it is essential that the design warn motorists of a change in route. Speed signs requiring drivers to slow to 15 m.p.h. should be installed before the approach to a street diverter, and Local Access Zone signs should be installed at entrances to the neighborhood from arterials.

Advocates of street diverters may face a major problem: convincing planning officials that emergency vehicle access is adequate with installation of a diverter. This problem may be solved by devising an alternative traffic route on parallel arterials, or may be argued as being unimportant since diverters were planned to reduce speed and minimize unnecessary auto intrusion. Since the police or fire vehicle traveling to a Local Access Zone would be within one or two blocks of its final destination, slowing down would not be a major problem. If a compromise can't be worked out, a rolled curb ramp could be installed across the street diverter for emergency crossing. (See photo). A fire or police car could drive over the street diverter and move on in a straight line.

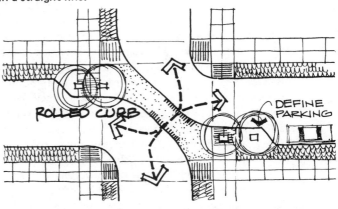

ROLLED CURB   DEFINE PARKING

street diverter

The street diverter in Vancouver, British Columbia of concrete planters is visible from a distance, and has a mounded center portion for emergency vehicle through access.

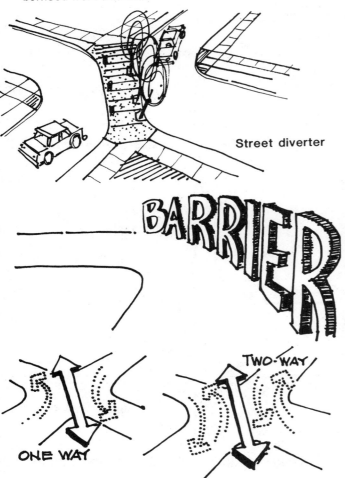

Street diverter

BARRIER

ONE WAY   TWO-WAY

Neighborhood support and cooperation is necessary. Many neighborhoods still value the right to use their automobiles freely and they're not yet willing to compromise. Without neighborhood support, changes such as street diverters would be difficult, but there is nothing to be lost by the planners suggesting the idea, outlining the costs and benefits, suggesting a temporary test and saying to the neighborhood; "You decide."

Street diverters serve two broad purposes:

1. Singly to improve access to pedestrian-oriented facilities along heavily traveled pedestrian routes (for instance, connecting a playground to a school, a shopping center to a pedestrian route, or an office building to a bus stop, and so on); and
2. Jointly as one of several traffic constraints designed as a coordinated effort to make a neighborhood safer for pedestrians.

Some design and construction suggestions are listed below.

1. A temporary street diverter, consisting of two extruded six-inch asphalt curbs with asphalt between and painted white, could be installed quickly and inexpensively and used on a trial basis. The diverter can be removed if it doesn't work or it can be replaced with a permanent, well-designed diverter if residents like it. The process is inexpensive; four or five test diverters can be built in a neighborhood over two or three days for several thousand dollars. Several "slow down" signs will need to be installed, and use of a diverter will need to be announced to people in the neighborhood.
2. The design opportunities for street diverters are many and include pedestrian protection, special paving details, tree planting, safety and decorative lighting and furniture such as fences, signs, fountains, benches, planters, trash containers, etc. Some design possibilities are:
   A. Narrowing the diverter toward the center, allowing a wider automobile turning radius and a varied experience for pedestrians;
   B. Removing existing corner curbs and pavement and replacing them with a new pavement design that carries across the intersection;
   C. Making the diverter pavement different, perhaps brick, stone or exposed aggregate concrete; (the expanded corner might be furnished with mail box, light fixture, information kiosk, drinking fountain or plantings.)
   D. Raising the protective curb in the gentle arch to a high point 24 inches above the road surface, providing protection for the pedestrian and making the diverter more visible to approaching motorists;
   E. Planting several trees in the walkway, further defining the crossing and protecting it. Depending on the intersection configuration, an additional catch basin may be required at each corner. A ramp for wheelchairs and bicycles should also be provided at each corner.

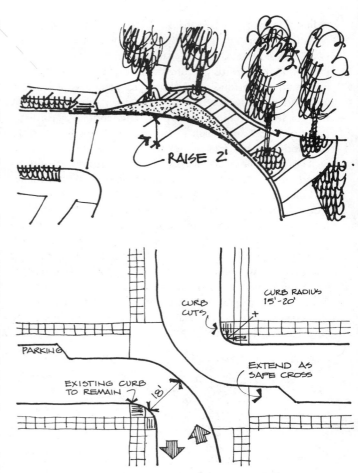

MINIMUM 2-WAY DIMENSIONS

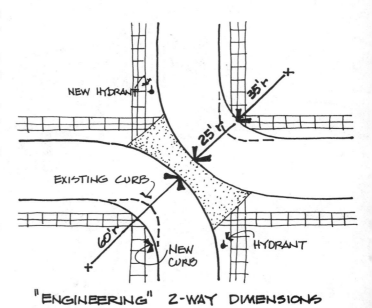

"ENGINEERING" 2-WAY DIMENSIONS

Pedestrian Safe-Cross. A pedestrian safe-cross lessens the danger of street crossing at intersections or mid-block locations. The safe-cross, essentially an expanded sidewalk, can be easily constructed in the unused parking lane at corners. (See sketch). This extension allows pedestrians to walk safely to the street side of parked cars in order to see if crossing is safe. As a side benefit, the safe-cross constricts the street, forcing cars to enter slowly, and defines the parking area eliminating the need for 'No Parking' signs. The safe-cross works well alone or in pairs. It can be installed as an isolated element or as part of a coordinated effort to pedestrianize a neighborhood.

Expand the intersection sidewalk into the parking lane to increase the pedestrian waiting area.

Safe-crosses do *not* work efficiently on narrow, busy streets or on clear zone streets where the parking lane is used for rush hour traffic. They are primarily designed for neighborhood streets or for commercial streets where traffic flows at a moderate pace and there is pedestrian traffic. Each safe-cross occupies a space approximately 6 feet wide by 20 feet long, replacing an unused portion of parking lane. Constructing a safe-cross involves removing and realigning the existing curb, modifying drainage structures, laying new sidewalks, planting, and installing necessary street furniture. Design considerations include the following:

- *Dimensions.* The exact dimensions of a safe-cross will vary according to the amount of room available, but should be at least 20 feet long. Since parking is usually not legal within 30 feet of the corner, no parking spaces will be lost. The width is also flexible. Since parking lanes are typically 7 or 8 feet wide, the safe-cross could be the same width or slightly narrower, say, 6 feet.
- *Return Angle.* The safe-cross should return to the street line at an angle to allow for cleaning by machine.

The angle also prevents collection of sediment and trash, facilitates drainage and looks better than a 90 degree corner. The exact angle is variable depending on the available space, with 45 degrees being common.

Safe Crosses can vary in design to fit the amount of available space— with different angles, radii, planting or paved conditions possible. The objective is to provide more wait space for pedestrians, to safely move pedestrians further into the street, to slow down through-traffic, and to develop the feeling of a "special place" at that intersection.

- *Paving.* The amount of paving should be determined by the number of people using the crossing and the route they desire to travel. Large volumes of pedestrian traffic require most of the safe-cross to be paved so pedestrians have ample space to walk and adequate stacking room while they wait to cross the street. Lighter pedestrian flows allow planting beds between desired travel lanes. The triangular area at either end of the safe-cross could be planted if it is not part of a desired travel lane, although planting may create additional maintenance. (See sketch).

For test purposes, a temporary raised asphalt area, painted a cheerful color (avoid green), can allow a neighborhood to see whether or not it likes the device.

If the neighborhood approves after a trial period, a permanent safe-cross may be constructed. If it doesn't approve, the asphalt can be removed.

- *Drainage.* Adding a safe-cross to an existing corner may create drainage problems. For instance, the existing sidewalk and street may slope toward the gutter in the shallow V-shape with the lowest point exactly where the safe-cross should begin. The proper way to handle drainage is to install new catch basins, grade the new safe-cross area to conform to existing roadway gradient, and warp the final grades to assure drainage.

Location Safe-crosses are typically used in 3 different situations, as either isolated elements, or part of a coordinated pedestrian improvement effort as follows:

- at intersections
- at mid-block crossings
- to define parking spaces.

Mid-block locations pose some dangers for pedestrians, since drivers expect street crossings to occur only at intersections, and are not as attentive to pedestrians crossing at mid-block. Increasing driver visibility by removing several trees, adding a sign, and delinating the crossing with paint of a different material helps. (see photo)

NO PARKING areas can be permanently eliminated from parking by converting them to a safe-cross form and planting trees. The legal area would then remain at street grade, and the sidewalk amenity improved. To discourage street crossing, don't pave places where people shouldn't cross, and plant it instead.

A double safe-cross serving pedestrians traveling in both directions has many advantages, and may not cost much more to install than a single one.

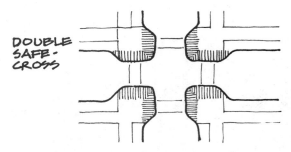

- *Street Furniture and Bus Stops.* Consider including a bus stop with benches, shelter, and kiosks in the safe-cross zone. Make sure road widths and turning radii are adequate so buses can travel easily and that a bus route would not conflict with diverters or safe-crosses. Buses may be too long to turn corners around street diverters and safe-crosses. If this is the case, the bus company may attempt to force their removal. Another problem is that buses usually load and unload in the parking lane, allowing traffic to pass in its own lane. Since the safe-cross occupies the parking lane, buses must stop in the traffic lane, causing cars behind the bus to wait. There are ways around this dilemma. The planner should verify the traffic volume of both buses and cars to determine if the problem occurs often enough to cause conflicts. If it does, the planner should look for alternative solutions: does the bus have to stop in this place? Can it stop across the street, or around the corner? Can people still wait on the safe-cross and move towards the bus when they see it coming? The planner should evaluate the advantages and disadvantages of each alternative and make a decision. For instance, an advantage might be that moving many people on the bus is reason enough to force several drivers to wait while passengers load and unload.
- *Plantings.* The planner should carefully determine new tree locations along the safe-cross to avoid blocking drivers' lines of sight. Trees should be selected to branch high, and they should be placed near the back of the sidewalk. The safe-cross may be made more distinctive by planting it with special trees, flowering or fruiting trees, trees with textured or colored foliage, special bark or a unique fruit.

This safe-cross was constructed without changing curbs or gutter configuration by constructing a new curb with steel grates to bridge the gap. The method is not totally successful as people can trip or twist an ankle.

Traffic Circle.

Traffic circles installed in the center of an intersection may be the most efficient way to discourage unnecessary through traffic. The circles force drivers to slow down enough to negotiate the circle, thus discouraging shortcutting. Circles allow drivers with neighborhood business to reach destination without driving out of their way as with traffic diverters, and they can be an attractive addition to the neighborhood as well.

The planner should make the circles as large as possible. They should be mounded in the center with dirt and planted with evergreen trees to make the circles more visible at nighttime. A curb should be installed around the circle to protect the planting and increase visibility. Since the circles would be installed primarily in residential neighborhoods, their use by emergency vehicles would be limited, and such use would not present a serious problem.

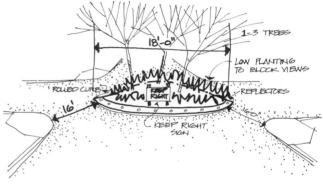

The circles should be large enough to slow down cars, but not so large as to constrict their movement. A minimum 18-foot diameter circle is sufficient to be in scale with the street intersection. For most residential neighborhoods, a 20-foot inside radius with a 16-foot travel lane around the circle is sufficient.

Construction costs increase considerably if an intersection's corners need to be widened to accommodate a large diameter circle. To reduce the cost, the planner may suggest using a smaller circle with a sloping curb backed by a row of concrete pavers, with holes for grass to grow through, to allow emergency vehicles to cross over them. The curb and concrete can be laid directly on the old road surface, except in areas where frost heave is a problem. A hole can be cut in the center portion of the street for penetration of the tree roots. The soil should be mounded at least two feet high. Low "Keep-right" signs mounted on heavy bollards should be included to alert unfamiliar motorists to the circle. This is especially important in winter when circles covered with snow may not be visible. (See sketch).

TRAFFIC CIRCLE DESIGN CRITERIA

The City of Seattle has developed design criteria for low cost traffic circles that will reduce traffic speed and accidents while allowing through movement for large trucks. The design criteria provides the largest possible traffic circle, thereby allowing maximum landscaping and visually warning drivers of the impending obstruction. The design criteria include the following:

1. The distance between the traffic circle and street curb projection (the offset distance) shall be a maximum of 5 feet.
2. The width between a traffic circle and a curb return shall be between 16 and 20 feet.
3. As the offset distance decreases from 5 feet, the opening width would increase.
4. The outside 2 feet of the traffic circle will be constructed with mountable monolithic concrete curb doweled to the existing pavement. The street will be broken and removed from the center of the curb for planting.
5. Traffic circles will be landscaped with one to three trees set back 4 feet from the curb.

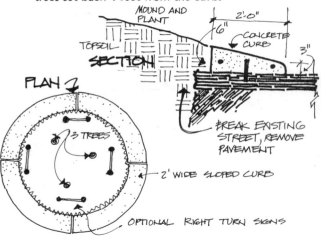

If there is enough money, the corner radius could be widened to enlarge the circle's size. This may require new drainage structures and perhaps a fire hydrant, and would therefore be expensive. But, a large traffic island that is well-planted and landscaped adds to the character of a neighborhood.

Irregular-shaped traffic islands can be constructed to fill the space created by multi-street intersections. Simply parallel the outside curb as closely as possible maintaining minimum distances.

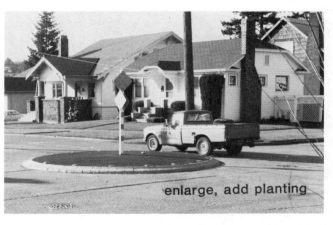

Constructing a traffic circle using precast "C" curbs and paved with asphalt gets the job done quickly and inexpensively, but adds little quality to the neighborhood. Additionally, this traffic circle is not readily visible during bad weather because of its flatness. Improve it by mounding soil and planting trees. The automobile opening shown here is too wide, allowing motorists to use them at a high speed, or to turn left improperly. Correct lane openings are shown in the chart.

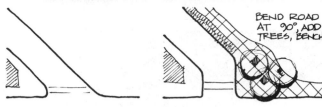

Streets that intersect on a diagonal are dangerous for pedestrians. They increase the distance necessary to cross the street, and allow cars to move through the intersection at a faster speed. Where possible, these spaces should be regularized and brought back to meet at 90 degrees, with the extra space provided for pedestrian protection. The throat of the road should be as narrow as possible and islands or peninsulas for pedestrian protection added (see sketch).

CUL-DE-SAC CONVERSION

The ultimate solution for reducing through traffic is to close the street entirely or to through traffic with a cul-de-sac. The additional space gained could be converted to pedestrian use. Since this treatment is so different, it may cause problems for drivers unless the beginning of the street is carefully signed. Construction costs can be reduced by planning the work over time and by using a simple, temporary barrier at the onset. Space that is gained from the street

This Vancouver neighborhood converted its grid pattern streets using street diverters, cul-de-sacs and closing streets to create small neighborhood parks.

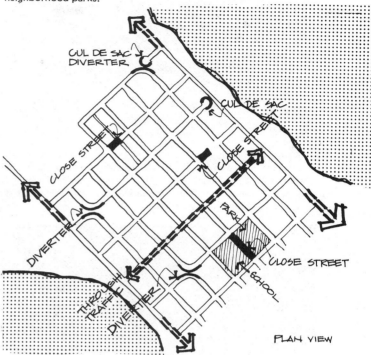

closure can be used for active or passive recreation, turned into a community garden or divided between uses (such as park and parking). Several configurations are shown below.

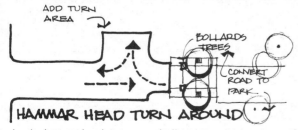

A simple hammerhead turnaround allows cars to turn around by backing into a turn space with the remaining street closed for pedestrian use. The street is narrowed and the turn around kept at a small scale to not destroy the neighborhood character.

This neighborhood park was a street closed at the alley, so street users can circulate without interference. The development is simple, with shuffleboards, seating, a small ampitheater, lights, drinking fountain and planters.

Vancouver Neighborhood, continued.

This former through-street was converted to a cul-de-sac by enlarging the turn area and constructing a planted separation between it and the old street. The change prevents fast-moving through-traffic, and creates a safe space that neighbors can play in. Note the curb cut and sign to warn against through travel.

Replacing the street with a pedestrian way and park reduces the noise for abutting residents, and makes walking more comfortable. Note the small scale paving, variety in edge treatment (it isn't all straight) and curb cut ramp.

In certain places, the sidewalk width and alignment can be varied to reduce boredom and enhance the walking pleasure.

URBAN GREENWAYS AND INTERIOR PEDESTRIAN SPACES

Just as vehicles have a variety of road types to choose from, so should pedestrians. The planner, in devising a network of routes, should plan a patchwork system of spaces and routes that are extra quiet, virtually safe, and pleasant to be in. These include the modified streets previously discussed plus interior spaces such as alleys, behind stores and apartments, shortcuts, streets with slow-moving traffic, and streets converted totally for pedestrian use. Look at the whole neighborhood to determine where some exist, and where more are needed.

Shortcut footpaths connecting two streets on a long block needn't be very wide. These walks are less than 4 feet in width which may be accomplished by narrowing the back yard on either side a small amount. Gates and some lower fences allow views from the apartments to the footpath, and reduce the danger and chance of vandalism. The walk should be maintained as other sidewalks with each abutting owner cleaning their strip—a service that spreads the load and provides for individual initiative of different plantings, color, variations in the degree of maintenance, etc.

Alleys are a forgotten part of our circulation system. However, the pedestrian's short-cut need may make alleys attractive again. The addition of street trees and planters creates a special feeling and makes it comfortable for walking.

The interior portions of older neighborhoods can be converted to living and shops, with courtyards for restaurants and small shops on the ground floor, and living above. Interior courtyards are quiet and peaceful even though it might be busy outside.

Narrowing the street in places to provide neighborhood entertainment such as this chess set brings people to the street at nighttime and is another form of stay-at-home recreation. The chess men are stored in nearby lockers while the neighbors bring their own chairs.

Add a raised sidewalk on narrow bridges to slow motor vehicles and guarantee pedestrian/bicycle safety. Ramp each end of the sidewalk for bicycle and wheelchair access.

Expand the walkway wherever it reaches a view or some amenity and add benches and planting. The space needn't be formal or extensively developed, as long as it is available, neat and has seating.

INCLUDING THE BICYCLE

Should older neighborhoods construct separate bikeways? In general, this author believes that assuring safe bicycling on every city street is better than spending large sums on construction of one or two separate routes. I favor installing good sidewalks with curb cuts at all intersections so bicyclists can ride away from traffic and cross street safely. In addition, I recommend eliminating all barriers to continuous bicycling.

A method for gathering information about bicycle-related problems and opportunities in the neighborhood could follow the steps listed below. Find two or three experienced riders, give each a map of the neighborhood, and ask each to independently find all the logical routes, potential short-cuts, problems and opportunities. The planner should analyze their findings for areas of agreement. Most problems that may be able to be easily corrected are:

- Filling chuckholes near the edge of the pavement;
- Constructing ramped access to and from shortcuts, and paving rough-surfaced shortcuts;
- Restriping the center lane of a street to allow a wider bicycle lane on one side;
- Widening the shoulder on busy roads to increase room between passing cars;
- Providing bicycle racks at key locations.

The bulk of work should begin at *destinations* (schools, parks, and shopping districts) and proceed toward residential areas. Problems should be fairly simple in all areas, except perhaps the business district where heavy traffic may make construction difficult.

If a major bicycle route is located near one edge of the neighborhood, the planner should connect internal bike traffic to it. If a community-wide bicycle route could pass through the neighborhood, making room for it would likely be worthwhile.

What should be done with bicycles in a neighborhood business district? The planner should decide whether bicyclists should ride in the shopping district, lock their bikes at a central location, and move around on foot; or if they should be allowed to move between stores on bicycles. The latter is preferred if the district is not overcrowded with pedestrians and cars, and if bicycles won't become a nuisance. Maintaining flexibility is a good way to encourage bicycle use. If bikes will be a nuisance, then a central bicycle parking location is preferred.

If bicycles are to be permitted access to stores, they should be able to park near the most frequently used stores. Replacing one or two car parking spaces with racks for 10 to 20 bicycles is a simple solution. Metal racks with chains are best. Preferably bicycle parking would be protected from bad weather. Access through dangerous parking lots should be avoided. Bicycles may be directed to the bicycle racks via a route without parked cars and with curb cuts, special paving, and signs. It may be necessary to have several paths leading to the racks.

Bicyclists benefit from a complete system of curb cut ramps as they can use them to mount the sidewalk to avoid dangerous places. Note the narrow radius and continuous curb cut in this photo.

REVITALIZING NEIGHBORHOOD SHOPPING DISTRICTS

Shopping. Compact, convenience retail shopping is essential for neighborhoods interested in promoting non-motorized circulation. Residents should be able to run daily errands on foot, by bicycle or bus or in some cases by car. A neighborhood district should include groceries, drugs, notions, hardware, beverages, baked goods, a restaurant and services such as post office, library, barber, etc. Without these conveniences, residents will travel by car to another neighborhood, increasing traffic and reinforcing past patterns of driving.

Each neighborhood will most likely be different. One may have a small business corner where 5 or 6 small stores operate, surrounded by housing; another may have several scattered single mom-and-pop stores that serve a smaller number of homes. But more than likely, most neighborhoods have auto-oriented stores located in strip patterns along an arterial and isolated from residential units.

Because strip developments are difficult for pedestrian circulation, they should be discouraged while compact, convenient business centers near residential units should be encouraged. Retail businesses on arterials can be discouraged by zoning the area for manufacturing or housing, or by reducing the ease of car access. At the same time, incentives could be provided for relocation in the compact neighborhood shopping districts. Incentives could include revitalization through beautification, improved foot travel with sidewalk treatment, additional bus service and bus stops, centralized parking, etc. It could also include professional assistance in moving to shopping organized for pedestrian convenience. Reducing the ease of shopping by car by increasing the convenience of shopping on foot is essential. At the very least, shoppers should be able to reach a number of stores on foot, even if reaching the district does require driving.

SETTING SPEED LIMITS

Radar tests of drivers in residential areas show that the speed actually traveled usually exceeds the posted speed limit by five miles per hour. That is, drivers tend to travel at speeds greater than are posted. To help assure driving within the required speed, post the speed limit five miles per hour under the desired speed. Assuming an acceptable speed of 15 to 20 miles per hour, the posted speed should be 10 to 15 miles per hour.

The success of a neighborhood shopping precinct is dependent on encouraging the greatest number of people to reach it on foot, or by bus or bicycle. If shoppers *must* drive to get there, it may be just as easy for them to drive beyond to a bigger store or to another shopping district where parking may be more convenient. Established neighborhood shopping districts catering to pedestrians can't increase the amount of parking spaces easily because of diverse ownerships, small land parcels and the negative impact of expanded parking on the pedestrian.

A small grocery store in an apartment building serves a pedestrian-oriented district. The arrangement benefits from an indoor-outdoor display, and a deep setback with sidewalks close to the building.

Most participating businessmen want their business districts to become more important than is possible, given a realistic assessment of their potential to attract shoppers. That's natural. Yet, without a full range of stores, offering competitive prices and easy access, shoppers will travel to the nearest shopping center. While that needn't discourage improvements, it is offered as a warning for the planner to question consultants' reports of the market potential for a newly pedestrianized business district. It is essential for the planner to seek realistic solutions that match the potential of the district. The planner, for instance, should insure that there are enough convenience stores to attract people to move around once they arrive at the neighborhood shopping center. Many older districts have converted to auto-oriented stores catering to infrequently made purchases, including furniture, appliances, pianos, auto or plumbing supplies. Because customer gain for these stores from pedestrian improvements is slight, business owners may be unwilling to join forces in making the area more comfortable for pedestrians. But, they might be willing to help attract new businesses, served by increased foot traffic, if they could be convinced that increased numbers of pedestrians might mean more customers for them.

Revitalizing of a neighborhood business district will be difficult if a combination of the following factors contribute to low market demand:

- Low residential densities with population levels less than businesses need to sustain themselves.
- Competition from downtown or nearby shopping centers that may keep business volume at marginal levels.
- Districts with most former stores boarded up or converted to nonbusiness uses with too few remaining stores.
- Shifts in residential populations which cause reduced neighborhood buying power. This might include an ethnic or income shift, forcing previously successful stores out of business.
- Too many small stores that can't carry the variety of merchandise or offer competitive prices with supermarkets.
- Seedy or poor visual character making shoppers feel unsafe.
- Increase in women workers who are employed elsewhere and may shop near their employment, causing a decrease in neighborhood shoppers.

These reasons all respond to market conditions of the last 25 years, and do not yet reflect changes in lifestyle, the economy or energy. One can accept past trends and project them forward, or one can look closely at each and assess the chance of overcoming them in light of changed times. Physical improvement of the business districts may eliminate safety and crime problems. Constantly increasing fuel costs may make decentralized shopping more attractive so new merchants will own small neighborhood stores. Lifestyle changes have encouraged some young people to seek a simpler life which a small store with living above might satisfy. The energy situation may cause people to move into close-in neighborhoods and revitalize their business districts.

The planner should try to link nearby supermarkets and variety stores to stores in the pedestrian shopping district. These stores may be overlooked by planners searching for the "old" district, since supermarkets may be on the fringe and since they have large, unattractive parking lots. Because supermarkets have strong shopper appeal, they can act as anchor stores in the traditional shopping center pattern. With the supermarket as an anchor, a link can be planned to attract users from it to other smaller stores. Pedestrian and bikeways can also be incorporated into the parking lot to make the connection.

The planner should minimize through auto traffic in the business district. Drivers traveling through a neighborhood business district generally stop only if parking is convenient or if they need to buy specific merchandise. While merchants may feel that cars traveling past their businesses are potential customers, this is probably an exaggeration. It may be unwise to count heavily on through traffic motorists as becoming principal customers for pedestrian business districts.

The planner should consider sun exposure to assure some sun for warmth on cold days. Sunshine is more important than shade in most northern climates and vice versa in the south. Trees on the south side of east/west streets, and on the west side of north/south streets assures that one side will have afternoon sun. (See diagram).

Intersections in business districts should be strengthened and enhanced visually for pedestrians. Many business districts, laid out around a busy cross street, will benefit by making the street crossing safer and easier and the corner more attractive. Each grouping of stores ideally should have an expanded pedestrian area for socializing and people watching. Adding a safe-cross to enlarge the pedestrian area at the intersection is necessary for safety, but can serve other purposes as well. The planner should consider locating a bus stop, benches and overhead protection, bulletin board kiosks, mail box, newspaper stand, bicycle racks, trees and lights.

Small supermarkets should connect to the neighborhood sidewalk system with a raised sidewalk and perhaps several trees. The concurrence of driveway immediately adjacent to the pedestrian access from the neighborhood should be avoided as is shown here.

To alert people to the best place to cross the street, develop a "gateway" that the pedestrians must pass through to cross the street. This example uses planting and a handrail to define the crosswalk, which can also be used by blind cane users. Note the extensive painted crosswalk to delineate the pedestrian space, and the continuous wheelchair ramp.

Street Trees A uniform row of street trees may *not* be appropriate for shopping districts. Trees may block views of unique store fronts and limit views of specific shops. Some vegetation is always pleasant, but several trees planted at a mid-block crossing and visible from surrounding blocks may be just enough. It isn't necessary to maintain uniformity in planting. The old-fashioned uniformity notion of many architectural schemes adds little to a pedestrian's world, where variety and differences may make it visually more appealing. If a street is wide in relation to building heights, trees can reduce the apparent width of the street, but a row of trees in the center may be better (see photo).

Streetscape. There have been so many business district streets redeveloped that a common streetscape treatment has emerged. Most paving, benches, lights, trees and other outdoor furniture detailing are now at a pedestrian scale and with perhaps a feeling of being borrowed from the suburban shopping center. Designers try to make each project unique by varying a standard range of detailing. (See photographs). The *paving pattern and pedestrian lights* are often assigned the role of creating a "unique place." In general, a street solution is likely to include a widened sidewalk with special exposed aggregate or brick paving, trees added where possible with low planting at the intersections. Benches are added and pedestrian-scaled lights line the street. If there are sufficient funds, a small fountain or sculpture might be included. The most vocal design discussion is usually over loss of parking, which may limit sidewalk widening to several mid-block crossings and a widened safe-cross at the intersection.

Achieving uniqueness by varying standard details can improve shopping comfort but the planner should make sure overall goals are met and that funds are wisely spent. Here are some architectural considerations for planners to use in evaluating proposed project details.

- Use pavement that can be duplicated as a sidewalk is repaired over the years.
- Provide variety, and a measure of randomness.
- Try to keep the intersections somewhat free of vegetation.
- Encourage variations and improvements for individual shops. Different pavements, awnings and facades add to the pedestrian's interest, and add distinctiveness to each merchant's business.
- Encourage shortcuts to parking behind stores. Shortcuts should go between shops when possible. The idea is to facilitate movement on foot.
- Accept merchants' preferences for vegetation, for instance, if they want no trees in front of their store.
- Keep tree planting space as large as possible. The more room for root growth, water and air, the better.
- Install as many benches as possible, because shoppers will use them.
- Avoid using very expensive street furniture. Light fixtures, planters, trash cans and benches can all be designed at lower costs. Typically, the average user usually does not know the difference, and the savings might as well be used elsewhere.
- Avoid planters unless they are to be maintained regularly. Large raised planting areas in closed streets are acceptable and is an inexpensive method to convert the street.
- Set back 3 to 5 feet, new shops constructed in older downtowns to allow room for window shopping and provide widened sidewalks. (See photos).
- Have trees planted in the ground rather than in planters, unless there is a basement beneath the planting strip. Although many architects prefer to use planters, they aren't good for trees (they restrict roots and dry out quickly).
- Don't overemphasize the strip next to the curb. Many architects suggest that because this area includes trees, light poles, parking meters, fire hydrants, etc.,

it can't be walked upon and should be accented with a band of special rougher pavement. However, it seems more logical to use special pavement on places where people walk, and where there is little likelihood of it being removed to service underground utilities.

An 8 foot wide business district sidewalk is not wide enough for window shoppers and through-walkers to comfortably pass.

New businesses or stores should be sited back from the original building to allow a wider sidewalk area for congregating or relaxed strolling. All stores needn't do this, as long as it occurs occasionally.

This temporary wall used to bridge the gap caused by a building torn down in an older business district and to screen the parking lot behind provides continuity and minimizes the disruption of the neighborhood of the business district.

Widen walkways where parking is prohibited to define where parking is allowed, thereby eliminating NO PARKING signs. Add trees, especially where no retail shops exist to avoid blocking shoppers' view in. Note that the 2 light poles at the crosswalk direct pedestrians to the best crossing place.

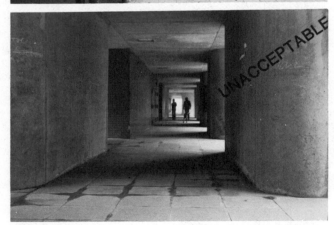

Keep arcade support structures light and airy so pedestrians can see ahead and avoid muggings and problems. The bulky columns, plus the low ceiling height make it an uncomfortable and unused space subject to vandalism, while the other affords weather protection with no visible danger.

Ground level shops in neighborhood business should *not* be replaced with parking as is shown here. The parking replacement conflicts with pedestrians along the sidewalk, reduces the size and usefulness of the shopping and creates an unpleasant edge to walk along.

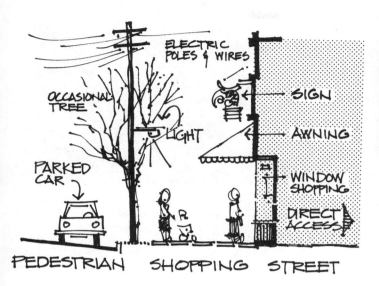

PEDESTRIAN SHOPPING STREET

Housing should not displace retail shops. This retail street, closed to vehicular traffic, is now quiet enough to live on comfortable. The arrangement of small apartments over retail shops is an idealized small business district housing model. Retail shops on the ground floor eliminate residential privacy problems, and upper floor apartments can have adequate access to light and air. Apartment dwellers can carry out many activities on foot, provide street life, and be a moderating voice in public decisions. Entry to these apartments are through small doors on the main street, with parking located some distance away.

Housing Pressure for in-town housing is causing some developers to construct apartments in older business districts. This is occurring because the business district is also zoned for apartments and there is little citizen complaint against construction. Residential units in and around a shopping precinct are good; however, the exact mix and location needs to be carefully considered. Too many residential units can overpower businesses by usurping much of the land. This can leave the business district disbursed instead of concentrated, and lacking in vitality and mix.

Residential units should *not* be on the ground level. That space should be reserved for businesses. Housing over shops is fine though. Higher density housing behind the shopping may be even better as street noise won't bother residents there. Residential parking should be separated from shopping and detached from units by as much as a block.

Older apartments with parking that crosses the sidewalk (see photo) should be encouraged to construct private garages with overhead doors. The closed door is not only pleasant to walk past, but affords more safety since open garage doors warn pedestrians that a car is about to enter or exit. Much of San Francisco's parking is treated this way, and the effect is very pleasant. (See photo). Additionally, garages with doors give residents more enclosed space to store personal belongings. Moreover, San Francisco is limiting the number of sidewalk crossings by allowing no more than one 10-foot-wide driveway every 30 feet. This increases on-street parking, and prevents cars from overwhelming the sidewalk.

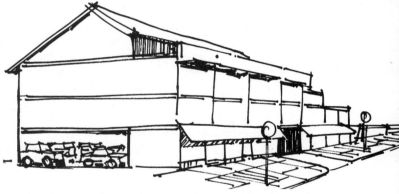

American business districts can solve the parking problem by using wide but shallow shop space with parking located behind. Residential units can then be added to the floors above.

Focus retail district housing on interior courts or pedestrian streets to reduce noise and increase personal safety.

In fill buildings constructed in older neighborhoods during the last 20 years might include parking that drives across the sidewalk as shown here. They are unattractive and dangerous for walking. The open garage allows cars to drive in and out with undue speed. The continuous driveway is glaring and boring for the walker, and the sense of entry or connection between the building and a streetscape is obscure, making those walkers and residents feel detached from the surrounding.

Parking Neighborhoods with many apartments most likely suffer parking problems. This encourages illegal parking, elimination of trees and planter strips, and reduction of street quality. To solve this problem, it may be possible to convert some neighborhood streets to parking lots. With careful location of walks, landscaping and privacy screening for residents, the block can be quite a pleasant place.

The actual gain in parking space depends on the amount of space available for conversion. If parallel parking exists on both sides of a street and the street is converted to accommodate single, perpendicular parking bay, there is no gain. If an existing street is not 40 feet wide, conversion will require construction to provide enough room. If two perpendicular bays are necessary, 60 feet of cross-street space is required. A single-bay parking lot may be preferred as accommodation of street and adjacent sidewalk forms a pleasant space for walking and game playing (street games, frisbee, basketball).

Parking can often be increased by converting the street to one-way and using the captured space for perpendicular parking. Design the streetscape so it is attractive for pedestrians with pavement variations from asphalt to cobbles, and trees between the parking spaces. Keep the sidewalk wide to insure pedestrian comfort.

Lot sizes should be kept to a minimum to accommodate smaller cars. Suggested dimensions for each parking space are: 8 feet wide by 40 feet for back out and through travel space. Trees can be planted between every other car, and the sidewalk constructed at the inside end of the space. Bicycles could travel in the street on a signed route.

New buildings constructed in older neighborhoods should have parking access off the side streets or alleys. Ideally, parking should be underground or in garages from an alley. Alley parking should be in garages rather than open lots. Garages can enhance pedestrian safety, as an open door warns that a car is about to enter or leave. When parking is behind the main street, the pedestrian character of that street is enhanced because there are no curb cuts.

Entries overpowered by the need to park and difficult to reach from the sidewalk should be raised so the walk way cannot be parked on. Separating the sidewalk and entry with a curb or step increases its sense of territory, though it makes handicapped access difficult. Varying each door treatment enhances the pedestrian's view and reduces the walker's boredom. The entry need not be located a great distance from the street, though should be clear, handicap-accessible, and not violated by automobiles.

Apartments on arterials with parking between the street and building create an unpleasant sidewalk environment. Parking should be screened with planting and a fence or could be replaced with a one-story commercial building with underground parking. The businesses could serve apartment residents, could provide an attractive window shopping experience for pedestrians, and could serve as a noise buffer between the street and the apartments (see photo).

ADAPTING ARTERIALS FOR PEDESTRIANS.

Arterials are usually classified depending on their ability to carry volumes of vehicular traffic, the speed of travel and the distance traveled. The faster and farther large volumes of traffic can travel, the more important the road is considered. *Principal arterials* are the most heavily traveled and link several communities. *Neighborhood collector arterials,* at the opposite end, are often residential streets designated to serve local residents access to a Principal Arterial or to link two neighborhoods. Unfortunately, arterial design standards deal principally with moving cars and ignore measures that make nearby residents and pedestrians comfortable. There is discussion of speed limits, road surface and width, parking restrictions and stop signs, but no mention of noise, street crossing safety or amenity.

Collector arterials are easier to adapt to pedestrians since they are usually residential streets serving a relatively small number of people traveling a short distance. Collectors should *not* be widened and parking should not be limited. They should be allowed all the normal design options used to curtail traffic problems on local streets. These design options, that is, stop signs, traffic islands, raised crosswalks, and reduced speed limits, should be used to slow traffic when necessary but not to eliminate it. While this is departue from normal practice, it would enhance pedestrian circulation. Slowed traffic would benefit pedestrians, bicyclists and adjacent residents. Because motorists are not using collector arterials for through travel, slower speeds should pose little problem and lengthen the trip by only a short time.

Most arterial design standards are too large scale for pedestrian comfort: Four traffic lanes with lane widths 12 feet and wide intersection curve radius, increase the speed of traffic and make street crossing difficult. Many of these standards are set by Federal or State highway agencies and the availability of construction subsidies makes them look attractive. However, using one wide lane and limiting parking and driveways, may be an acceptable alternative. One good, 14-foot-wide lane can carry a large

traffic volume (up to 1200 vehicles per hour) may fit into the existing road system, may allow for a parallel access road, and most likely will not cause pedestrian crossing or walking problems.

A row of parked cars plus planted setback for the parking lot improves pedestrian safety on busy arterials. However, if a parking continues for more than about 100 feet, it becomes uncomfortable, unattractive, and boring to walk along.

Alleys or narrow streets parallel to busy arterials can be converted to pedestrian walkways, with wide, midblock crosswalks such as this one in Portland, Oregon.

Urban arterials present a real dilemma for the pedestrian planner. On the one hand, they are crowded with cars and buses, with little room left for bicycles and pedestrians. Motorists tend to be interested in driving through quickly. The noise level is likely to be high. On the other hand, main pedestrian and cultural spots where pedestrians and bicyclists would be likely to go, are located on the arterials. Moreover, arterials usually are lined with apartments, which means there is much potential for pedestrian-oriented improvements.

The dilemma has no simple solutions, so that a combination of approaches is appropriate. If the neighborhood arterial is also a *main shopping street* it may be best to re-route through traffic and widen the sidewalks for pedestrian use. Cars could still use the street, but under speed restrictions. Wider pedestrian walks would benefit most retail stores, though some merchants may feel their sales will drop because fewer motorists will see their shops. However, unless the street is closed to traffic, passersby can still see stores.

Principal arterials can either be enhanced or abandoned. If improved, one approach is to adopt boulevard standards of wide sidewalk areas, with walks separated from the street, and regularly spaced trees. Parking can be eliminated to make room for pedestrian amenities. (Conversely, a row of parked cars can protect pedestrians from fast-moving traffic). Traffic flow can be improved by removal of driveways and elimination of stop-and-go traffic.

The other option for principal arterials is to abandon the road to cars and trucks, and to develop a new pedestrian route elsewhere in the nearby community. If there are parking lots along the arterial with stores set back and virtually no street amenities for pedestrians or if the arterial has primarily auto-oriented stores, the chances of improving the streets for pedestrians are small. The planner should seek a quieter, parallel street nearby or combine portions of a parallel street and the arterial where businesses serve pedestrians (see sketch). A parallel street might be zoned for pedestrian businesses, and have more room to accommodate pedestrians and bicycles. It may be possible to develop a complete pedestrian street with higher density residential, commercial shopping and public transit, leaving the nearby arterial exclusively for auto use. If just a small part of the arterial is convenience store/business-oriented, that part could be converted to pedestrian use by slowing traffic, removing parking and widening sidewalks. Pedestrian access points could be from adjacent parallel streets, so the arterial is avoided except at the business district.

Highway agencies should fund pedestrian improvements along arterials. However, at the present time, most highway agencies pay only for auto-oriented improvements to the street itself. Ways to get around this narrow approach by the agency is to call a pedestrian improvement by a name that sounds auto-related: for instance, calling a tree-planted center divider a *safety island* may slip past the anti-beautification bureaucracy. Some municipalities have used state monies to pave and drain the curb-to-curb section of the street, then added "temporary" pedestrian improvements at municipal expense to corners and other places. (p. 117) While there are some functional (drainage) and aesthetic problems with these temporary improvements, they are a step in the direction of more improvements for pedestrians.

Street-use permits that give administrative permission for such nontransportation uses as placement of fences in unused right-of-ways, parades, outdoor restaurants, temporary street closings, could also be used to legitimize changes along arterials to make living there more comfortable. Apartments constructed in the pre-1940s with little setbacks and now suffering from lack of outdoor space and street noise, might benefit from construction of balconies projecting over the sidewalk. (See sketch). These balconies would form an arcade for the ground level. The balconies would muffle street noises somewhat, provide private garden space and make the units more attractive for long-term tenancy. A covered arcade over the sidewalk might allow people waiting for buses to keep dry, or for the first floor to be converted to stores with protection to window shoppers. Shop additions could extend into the parking bay with the owners renting the parking-space from the city. That would allow some planting and better pedestrian protection on the sidewalk.

Separate pedestrians from busy roads on bridges with substantial low rails. Note the small, pedestrian-scaled light fixtures and open metal rail on the water side for viewing out.

Delineate major crosswalks on arterials with warning signs, wide striped walkways, and lighted overhead CROSSWALK signs.

Service stations with wide driveways and no separation between street and sidewalk or between the sidewalk and the parking area are unsafe and unpleasant for pedestrians.

PEDESTRIAN PLACES ARE ENHANCED BY:

- Unique environments: water, river, natural amenity, etc.
- Variety of stores—inexpensive to exclusive, automotive to zoological
- Eating, dining, and drinking establishments
- Subtle or dramatic views
- Sense of history
- Amusements, especially for kids
- Well-maintained environments
- Protection from the elements
- Shopping near subway or bus stops or other traffic generators—major employment, shopping, etc.
- Presence of vegetation—trees, shrubs, flowers
- Convenient parking
- Clean restrooms
- Entertainment, activity, sound
- Places to rest—sitting areas, benches, lawns, etc.
- Extensive window shopping
- Other people—if only to look at
- Something to do—preferably at low costs
- Freedom from auto intrusion
- Safety for children
- Bright, colorful spaces
- Tactile quality—variation in paving, patterns
- Unique elements—clocks, play areas, change in levels

ADAPTING DOWNTOWNS

ADAPTING DOWNTOWNS

Pedestrian improvements in downtowns are constructed for many reasons. The most common is competition, with an older downtown installing pedestrian amenities to compete for business with suburban shopping centers. Some downtowns use pedestrian improvements to control traffic or as a positive answer to urban problems, be they economic, social or environmental such as reducing noise and exhaust fumes. Some downtowns, whose identity has been lost in metropolitan growth, use pedestrian improvements to give themselves an updated identity. Improvements, too, may be used to emphasize historic landmarks or unique settings in order to increase a downtown's attractiveness to tourists.

Planning for pedestrian-oriented streets is not an easy task. Communities considering such improvements are wise to assess their willingness and stamina to see them to completion. Sometimes the number of opinions about "where", "how big", "whose parking will be lost", and more seem limitless. Conflicts surface between large and small stores with different financial, merchandising and customer drawing abilities. Opponents are likely to be merchants who fear loss of business and taxpayers who don't want increased taxes. Both groups are often well organized and financed. Those in a community who seek pedestrian improvements for their downtown should be even more organized, prepared to deal with inevitable conflicts, and be able to see that small efforts, as well as large, can prove beneficial.

Improving pedestrian comfort doesn't necessarily mean a massive project costing large sums of money. There is a wide range of options from reducing traffic speed and volume, widening sidewalks, improving parking, adding benches, cover, and planting to the creation of "pedestrian precincts" and on to complete street closing and the creation of plazas.

PEDESTRIAN PRECINCT, as used in this text, describes a zone where pedestrians are given precedence over automobiles and other motorized transportation. Although it is not necessarily a traffic-free zone, a variety of measures make walking more comfortable: reducing speed limits, widening sidewalks, restricting traffic during certain hours, encouraging pedestrian-scaled retail spaces, organizing parking, enhancing buses, adding benches, covered areas, landscaping and possibly closing some streets.

HISTORY OF DOWNTOWN IMPROVEMENT PROJECTS

Many people associate downtown improvements with the 1956 proposal by Victor Gruen for an enormous mall for Fort Worth, Texas. Though never built, it was well publicized and prejudiced many people against malls. Gruen's "Save Downtown" approach was simple and rational. It attacked the car as "downtown Enemy No. 1", proposing closure of the central core to traffic and conversion of former roads to pedestrian streets. People would drive to the edge of town or around the center city on an express ringroad, and then park in large garages. All movement in center city would be by foot in a beautified auto-free zone, while goods and services would be moved underground in special tunnels. The project was enormously expensive and required a large development organization. However, no such organization exists in most downtowns, where small property ownership is the rule and most merchants are not able (or don't want to) invest in schemes whose results are uncertain.

Since the Fort Worth plan, several dozen cities have developed pedestrian streets and others have explored the idea but decided not to proceed. Typically the cost is thought to be too high, the need for such a radical step is thought not to exist, or the need for car access is thought to outweigh pedestrian needs. Tax revolts and the problems of completing complex downtown projects have diminished some projects.

Many successful pedestrian precincts, areas closed to traffic and reserved for pedestrians, have been constructed in Europe, so lessons and precedents are available. Over 500 German cities and towns have converted portions of their downtowns to foot traffic. Most were accomplished without construction of bypassing streets and with better organization of existing streets. Many of these cities have closed their main street to traffic and have restricted truck deliveries to morning and evening hours with handcart deliveries during the day. Almost all these cities have experienced a sharp rise in the number of visitors and a substantial rise in sales reported by merchants. Private storefront improvements have followed in almost all these cities with many merchants restoring buildings with historical accuracy. Parking has generally been handled by constructing small parking lots or structures on the periphery of the city, though most European cities rely on buses to transport employees and shoppers. Bus transportation doesn't hamper German shoppers, who come downtown in droves to shop and willingly carry their packages home on the bus. However, buses run regularly and are usually more convenient than driving.

Most towns have extended pedestrian improvements beyond the main street to side streets, allowing pedestrian penetration from many places and extending pedestrian access to new shops. Because of the visual diversity of historic buildings, European landscape treatment is usually minimal, consisting of simple but rich textured concrete pavers interspersed with granite pavers. Trees are used sparingly and plants are almost always in movable containers.

There are never enough benches, though some towns provide movable chairs. Small fountains are placed in odd-shaped spaces. (See Photo). The overall appearance is extremely simple; however when these downtowns are filled with people, vendors and musicians, the need for street furniture disappears.

Unlike improvements to American downtowns, European counterparts have *not* been constructed to compete with shopping centers, because their development has been restricted by land use controls. Rather, downtowns were redeveloped to correct impossible traffic-congestions problems and to aid shoppers and city residents.

Pedestrian-oriented towns in Great Britain are fewer in number than in Germany and in many ways not as pleasant. Some British towns have constructed a ring road encircling a walking zone. This road resembles a small freeway with mini on- and off-ramps. It allows too many cars to reach downtown, creating traffic jams and congestion. Reaching the center on foot from outlying areas is all but impossible and not very pleasant. Because the ring road allows freer movement, more cars use it, and eventually spill over to other streets inside the ring. The ring degrades the neighborhood where it was constructed, as it imposes high speed traffic on an old road pattern. Adjacent to the ring road development is slow because of noise created by the road. Landscape treatment of British malls are more American in character with extensive use of decorative elements, such as planters, trees, benches, sculpture, and drinking fountains.

Both German and English cities have downtown residents. Munich, Germany has over 1200 people living in the inner-city, (down from an earlier 60,000 residents). Proximity to center city eliminated the need to travel for shopping, allows much activity at night and provides for a moderating voice in city-planning matters that has helped humanize new development. Munich has had a slight backlash from residents of nearby communities who claim that evening noise from entertainment, tourists and musicians is bothersome. The popularity of downtown living has driven up rents so that poorer residents are forced to move farther out. Most of those problems can be corrected. In comparison with what Munich was like before pedestrian improvements were made, today's problems seem small, indeed. A more serious problem is the danger that residents of other towns will be prejudiced by complaints and mount pressure against converting streets in their towns for pedestrian use.

Higher densities and mixed land-use boost European communities pedestrian success. Housing above the ground floor shops provides close-by workers and shoppers.

The charge that rents increase in pedestrianized downtowns is substantiated, but rents everywhere, including those in shopping centers, have increased. Some small downtown businesses have failed to succeed, but no one knows if these stores would have failed anyway without the pedestrian improvements. European economies are able to support small shops, but when there are many large and successful competitors, it is difficult for these shops to compete. However, survival of small shops is essential for the economic strength of these cities and their citizens. Munich, for instance, has passed laws preventing major department stores from expanding and has limited their business hours to aid small shops. Likewise, Quincy Market in Boston has a rent structure based on a percentage of sales which allows the small shops to compete with department stores.

There are some merchants who do not benefit from the pedestrian improvements. The most common example is that of a shop which relies on foot traffic but which is located away from proposed mall. Since pedestrian traffic on busy auto-oriented streets falls off considerably following mall construction, such shops may have to move into the pedestrian zone or go out of business. However, many such bypassed merchants have been leaders in efforts to extend the pedestrian zone to include their shops.

Pedestrianized towns also benfit from tourism. Local and foreign tourists are attracted to towns with beauty. Towns can increase the number of visitors by improving their appearance, designating pedestrian areas, opening museums and creating a festival spirit. The addition of an outdoor restaurant, coffee house or beergarden provides an additional attraction.

WHY PEDESTRIANIZE DOWNTOWN

- To "Save Downtown", countering the trend toward suburbia by improving downtown access, parking and environment.
- To improve pedestrian safety and enhance shopping comfort by separating shoppers from traffic.
- To control increasing traffic and reduce traffic jams that interfere with shopping.
- To improve the city's image and identity.
- To reduce noise (by up to one-half of the previous level).
- To reduce air pollution (and aid conformance with the 1970 Clean Air Act).
- To increase tourism and leisure opportunities Munich's walking zone is visited by about 20,000 tourists per day during the tourist season).
- To promote social relations within the town. Pedestrian spaces serve public events and activities that bring people together in a positive way.
- To promote the conservation of historic buildings, monuments and towns.

UNDERSTANDING EFFORTS TO IMPROVE DOWNTOWNS

Pedestrian improvements can be understood by defining their *purpose* and *configuration*. Most are done for a commercial reason and focus on the heart of the shopping district. However, they can also serve other purposes such as government, historic, university or residential. In Boston, pedestrian-oriented streets unite local, state and federal offices focusing on the new city hall. Pedestrians can safely continue to a restored historic district with outdoor markets, shopping and food and then farther to the heart of down-

town. College and university shopping streets are excellent locations for pedestrian improvements since students generally have no cars, travel exclusively on foot and are partial to a pedestrian street atmosphere. Historic or architecturally important districts are often too small and fragile to serve large volumes of auto traffic and may be served by pedestrian-only streets. A river or lake edge can be developed as focus for a pedestrian precincts, as was done in San Antonio, Texas. Mini-pedestrian districts can be organized with neighborhood shopping districts focusing attention on themselves.

Configurations of pedestrian improvements vary from complete street closings with new paving, trees, benches, fountains and other features, to a street closed to traffic for several hours a day. With the latter approach the street remains in all respects a street but is used at separate times by shoppers and traffic. Sidewalks are widened for pedestrians with cars driving at slow speeds in narrowed traffic lanes; a portion of the road is used exclusively for bus and taxi traffic. Pedestrian-oriented streets can be planned in isolated locations throughout the city, or in a comprehensive arrangement with many linkages over a larger area.

Pedestrian Precinct

The term "pedestrian precinct" describes a zone where pedestrians are given precedence over automobiles and other motorized transportation. The precinct may have some streets with wider sidewalks, parking restrictions, limited or no car access, slower speed limits, all contributing to improved pedestrian circulation. These may also be called "traffic-free zones", "auto-restricted zones" or "pedestrian precincts".

A community might want to develop a Pedestrian Precinct ordinance that would allow certain areas to adopt the designation as a guide to development in a positive and orderly way. The ordinance should set down guidelines on areas that could be designated as pedestrian precincts, and on the conditions that should be met once the ordinance is adopted. Passage of the ordinance would allow for evaluation of all new developments within the community, as well as implementation of improvements to older areas.

Appropriate areas for a pedestrian precinct are probably no less than four square blocks in size and include:

- the essential core of the business district;
- areas with a preponderance of street-related shops;
- areas with minimal parking along the streets;
- areas with a high proportion of retail and service trades;
- areas with limited warehousing and manufacturing;

- areas with cultural facilities and historic landmarks; and
- areas with unique landscape and natural conditions (such as lakes, rivers, streams)

General guidelines for future development in the precinct might include:

- prohibition of drive-in businesses;
- widening of certain sidewalks;
- closing of certain streets to motorized traffic;
- parking restrictions to favor short-term shoppers;
- fee in lieu of parking for shop owners for centralized parking;
- low speed limits to restrict pedestrian conflict;
- expanded intersection treatment to ease street crossing;
- establishment of bus priority;
- construction of high density housing nearby;
- parking restricted to the perimeter; and
- requirements for landscape treatment, etc.

Widening sidewalks may be the first step toward eventual street closing. This may be a perfect solution for small towns with light traffic and many pedestrians.

Transit malls may have the advantage of Federal D.O.T. aid for construction. However, it would be a mistake to seek federal money if the malls are inappropriate, as buses may hinder walkers and create noise, fumes and safety problems.

Enclosing pedestrian streets is seldom considered as costs are high and construction problems large. However, where weather is poor much of the year towns should partially enclose sidewalks with awnings and covered intersections, bus stops and other places. (See photo). The argument

A covered arcade unifies the streetscape and provides pedestrian protection. Each arcade section was built by the merchant and the variety between stores is visually attractive for pedestrians. The sidewalk should be at least 11 feet wide, with 8 feet between building and post and three feet between post and street.

This small downtown was converted to enhance pedestrian circulation by closing one cross street, repaving the sidewalks, widening sidewalks at the intersection, paving the intersection with bricks, and adding street trees. Parking spaces are delineated by the expanded sidewalk at the intersection. Note the curb is depressed along its entire length at each corner for wheelchair access. The permanently closed street is barren and underused at most times, and the frequency of shop vacancies is higher than on other nearby streets. It may have been better left as a street or treated with a lawn or large planter to absorb some of the space.

that an enclosure is necessary to complete with shopping centers is unfounded in all but the worst weather areas of the country. Most people enjoy the out-of-doors, as demonstrated by the number of pedestrians on the streets in bad weather.

Some businesses do not work well in pedestrian areas. First, some stores are too spread out, lacking the compactness necessary for walking. Then too, some merchandise is large and bulky and thus can't be transported easily by those on foot. In this category also are stores whose merchandise is purchased so infrequently that the store is not used by pedestrians. It is also necessary to distinguish between businesses that are appropriate on streets closed to motor vehicles, and those that are appropriate on streets used by cars, but given preference to pedestrians. Many businesses that can't survive on a street closed to traffic can flourish on a street partially closed to traffic and with widened sidewalks.

Businesses that are clearly inappropriate for pedestrian streets are car dealers, drive-ins, lumber yards, furniture stores and other large merchandising outlets. However, there are ways that these could be scaled down to fit in. For instance, an auto dealership might have a small storefront displaying several models, particularly sports or other unique cars. Supermarkets could be scaled down, could offer a fine delicatessen and sell carry-home food and even provide home delivery. Banks and post offices too may be smaller scale to fit a pedestrian street.

The quietness of pedestrian zones makes them ideal hotel locations. If handling of luggage and cars are a problem, there are several solutions: use of electric and handcarts if the distance from the street is not too great; a double entry to the hotel, one on a car-oriented street and the other on the pedestrian street.

Expensive, luxury stores selling jewelry, furs and art may claim that their clientele come only by car and that they can't, therefore, survive on pedestrian streets. That just hasn't proven true. In Munich, Germany, a compromise solution works well: the "luxury" merchandise are near the perimeter road of the pedestrian precinct, allowing shoppers to be driven to within 100 yards of their destination.

Restaurants because they attract many people are appropriate for pedestrianized downtowns. Using the street for outdoor dining enhances their business and vitalizes the downtown. (See photo). In addition, specialty shops seem to succeed in pedestrianized downtowns, while they can't survive in suburban shopping centers.

Past Failures

Not all pedestrian conversions are successes, and there are lessons to be learned from each failure. Some never get off the ground, like the University Avenue proposal in Seattle, Washington. The idea seemed perfect: closing the main university-district shopping avenue would cause no traffic problems since adjacent streets could handle the diverted traffic. Large numbers of students traverse the avenue on foot making it a lively place. The avenue has also become a popular entertainment and shopping street for many suburban users who find it unique. After an elaborate study and handsome plan were prepared, the debate began. Development was to be financed by merchants and, though most neighbors, politicians and users approved, one large landowner mounted a campaign against the project which eventually killed it. The argument he used was that business was booming and long-term outlooks were bright so why change the situation.

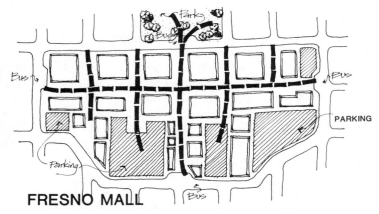

FRESNO MALL

Fresno's mall covers 6 blocks along Fulton Street and portions of 2 cross streets. Like many other downtown projects, it was staged over several years, with more parking added and improvements to shop facades.

Tacoma, Washington, an industrial city of 157,000 population, suffered from the usual 1960's flight to the suburbs and construction of several large shopping centers. Shopping downtown decreased and finally, after most downtown department stores had closed, the remaining merchants and the city decided it was time to reverse the trend. Extensive renewal was undertaken: new parking garages were constructed, traffic was reorganized and a four-block long shopping street was converted to a land-

scaped pedestrian street. But there were too few merchants left, and the conversion was too late. Hopefully, this may prove to be a short-term problem for now with organized traffic, parking and increased amenity, Tacoma's downtown is starting to grow. A number of specialty merchants have appeared (those who are well financed will undoubtedly most likely succeed). The Old City Hall, located on one end of the pedestrian street, has been recycled as a center for small shops and other historic buildings are being remodeled. While original sponsoring merchants may be out of business by the time the area is healthy, a turnabout is possible. (See Photo)

Tacoma's downtown Broadway Mall, constructed *after* major department stores had moved to suburban shopping malls.
Tacoma's Broadway Mall extends for 1300 feet, and is 80 feet wide. The mall includes new paving, covered waiting areas, seating for over 1000 people, and planting. It was funded by a joint merchant, city and federal government effort.

Other early malls suffered a similar slow startup but were more fortunate than Tacoma. Eugene, Oregon, constructed an extensive downtown mall in 1971 to counter the impact of new suburban shopping centers. Its downtown is now stable, though many of the original shops have been replaced. Two timing quirks caused unforeseen problems: 1) because renewal occurred at the beginning of the youth movement of the 1970's, the area was immediately taken over because the renewal area is near a large university; and 2) some original merchants, weakened by several years of slow business failed. Fresno, California, one of the first downtowns to convert Main Street to pedestrian use (designed by Victor Guren and constructed in 1964), suffered similar problems, as well as an improper mix of stores. It should have had, but did not, a mixture of department stores, shops for comparative shopping and specialty shops. After years of struggling by merchants, these problems have worked themselves out, and both downtowns are now financially healthy and popular shopping spots.

Pomona, California, failed for slightly different reasons. Since its architectural design was stark and unfriendly,

This handsome retail building was constructed *in the roadway* near the Quincy Market, Boston. Other streets around the Market were closed to traffic, and converted to pedestrian use. In the background is the new City Hall, with a plaza that extends the pedestrian area further into the Government Center.

Boston's Washington Street Mall was accomplished with minimal construction consisting of only a sidewalk awning. The street was not replaced, and few traditional mall amenities such as trees, benches, planters, etc. were added. Still because of the numbers of users, it is vital and successful.

The Eugene pedestrian precinct covers 8 square blocks with half the streets closed to automobiles. The central cross street has an enlarged plaza, replacing a former store, and includes a fountain, benches, trees, special paving, play areas, and a unique covered intersection crossing. Eugene has 80,000 residents and a major university.

shoppers were uncomfortable. Poor merchandising limited comparative shopping, and an unsupportive community failed to promote the pedestrian mall. It has more recently been converted to predominantly office use, a different but successful use.

Conversion of Boston's main shopping street, Washington Street, to pedestrian use was advocated by planners for over ten years, while the merchants and traffic engineers fought it. The engineers, claiming conversion would cause massive traffic jams downtown, proposed a major bypass to handle through traffic. Washington Street's closure was finally accomplished due to the success of Quincy Market, a nearby planned pedestrian area built around four historic market buildings, which was a success the day it opened. After Washington Street merchants saw their trade shift to the Quincy Market, they agreed to close their street to traffic *without* a bypass. It has worked well for three years. Visitors and merchants alike love the change and businesses are thriving. Deliveries to shops are actually easier because vans can park in the street during set hours, an impossibility before the street closure.

Some factors that make downtowns appropriate for pedestrian improvements are:

• Changes in cost and availability of gasoline that may make America's "shop anywhere, any time" pattern obsolete. Instead, we may have to shop in places close to home that offer a complete range of goods and services. The energy crisis favors bus travel and older business districts and downtowns are often served by bus.

• Growth management solutions being applied at many levels of government are concentrating development in and around existing business centers. These centers are often older business districts that offer increased vitality if surrounding land uses are developed properly. High costs of home ownership and changes life styles encourage apartment living around older business districts.

• Shopping is more satisfying if the character and quality of the shopping district is unique. Older, unique shopping districts can often serve this purpose.

• Existing ownerships and land use patterns that include shopping and commercial uses are now important for development. Obtaining building and other permits for a shopping center may be almost impossible in many areas, while it may be easy to obtain permits for development in an existing older district.

• Changed merchandising methods now allow small stores to compete with the larger ones. These include group purchasing, computerized management and a younger population of merchants who want to be their own bosses.

• The character of older business districts, with small scale, individual appearance and unique older buildings, contributes to the appeal of these as shopping areas.

IMPROVEMENTS TO MAIN STREETS

Closing the main street to traffic may or may not be necessary to adapt a downtown for pedestrians. Some small districts feel alive and busy because of the traffic, and people are able to park near shops during nonpeak traffic periods. Drivers with handicaps enjoy shopping on trafficed main streets since they can drive to the store of their choice. Before the planner draws conclusions about the appropriateness of closing a main street, the following points should be considered.

1. Is it *possible* to close the street? Are there alternative ways for traffic to circulate in and around the business district? Will shoppers and delivery people be able to reach business with ease?

2. Would large utilities have to be moved or undergrounded in order to close the street? The money spent on moving or undergrounding utilities is staggering, and would be an invisible contributor to the cost of the project. If there are large utilities, can new pavement be designed to allow access so the utilities will *not* have to be moved?

3. Are there enough people to utilize a pedestrian-oriented street? In most cases, the absence of automobile traffic makes streets very quiet. Would widening the sidewalks, instead of a full street closure, accomplish what is needed?

4. Are there alternatives? Would arcades or small courtyards provide adequate pedestrian space? A plan with interior pedestrian areas on private property, away from traffic has advantages. It may require fewer permits and approvals, could be done incrementally by interested merchants, could be constructed less expensively than public work and would likely be more varied because of individual efforts. Shoppers should be able to walk between stores with as many shortcuts as possible. It isn't important how architecturally developed each part is, as long as each is comfortable to walk through, has visual diversity, and provides places to sit as well as shelter.

5. What is the minimum size for a street closure in order for it to create a special character, a gathering area or a focus for the business community? Will closing a cross-street or only one block of Main Street provide enough focus? It may be advantageous to try a small project first and expand it if it succeeds.

PRELIMINARY PLANNING

With so many choices, what is the best thing to do? That can be answered by addressing several questions:

- *Determine the need.* If the reason for making improvements is civic pride with a mandate to create downtown identity, the planner should think about beautification efforts and pedestrian treatment. If the reason is to "save downtown", the planner should think in larger scale. He should make sure there is good car and bus access, that parking is adequate or can be improved, and that there are sufficient shops and department stores to compete with nearby shopping centers. Development of pedestrian streets or widened sidewalks may not be enough to attract shoppers if the types of shops are not appealing or if access and parking is too difficult.

- *Determine the will.* Is there interest and willingness to fund and implement a large-scale effort or should smaller, incremental projects be undertaken. Some immediate success, such as a quick, small improvement, is important since participants become discouraged if they don't see some results for their efforts.

OPTIONS

Organizing for the pedestrian doesn't necessarily mean closing streets to traffic. There are in-between steps that may be better. For instance, increase customer parking by organizing employee parking, or improving bus transportation. Add awnings to make winter shopping comfortable .Increase customer service with package checking and delivery so shoppers don't have to carry packages home. Improved window displays make the scene attractive, while new restaurants or cafes add another reason for the shopping trip. Benches, planting and other pedestrian amenities help make shoppers' visits more pleasant.

The most important improvement is providing a balance of stores to fit all shoppers' needs. It may be necessary to relax zoning rules to help stores that want to improve the shopping environment. These include allowing small stores to modernize without meeting all parking requirements, allowing owners to pay a fee in lieu of parking space, or providing a jointly owned lot elsewhere. The heart of downtown should be as intensely developed as suburban shopping malls, and stores there should have *no* open parking on the premises.

Widening the center-block sidewalk to provide more room for walking, display and community focus can be accomplished with little traffic disruption. A one-block widening may remove only 15 parking spaces which can probably be replaced elsewhere. Sidewalks can be enlarged at intersections with safe-crosses and mid-block crossings to ease street crossing and to define parking. Sidewalk widening can be done on the main street the length of the business district, or on several side streets.

A downtown that may be too large for complete pedestrianization, could be divided into small shopping areas, which would cater to either pedestrians or drivers. Mer-

The heart of a small downtown can be pedestrianized by eliminating a lane of traffic or parking and widening the sidewalk. Through traffic remains, while the enlarged pedestrian space with its gazebo, fancy lighting, special paving and trees symbolizes the heart of downtown.

chandise shopped for on a regular and frequent basis (such as groceries, clothes, drugs, etc.) should be available to pedestrians. Stores carrying larger or infrequently purchased merchandise (such as furniture, large appliances, car parts, etc.) should cater to those with cars.

The planner should try to determine where a pedestrian precinct should begin and end, and concentrate development efforts within the most used areas. The area where retail gives way to commercial development, offices, parking lots, used car lots, large item merchandising or warehousing usually marks the end of the best zone for pedestrians. The actual distance is difficult to pinpoint. While some 200-foot-long retail areas are so uninteresting that the length is excessive, others can hold a pedestrian's attention for 2,000 feet. The planner might consider the possibility of having more than one pedestrian district, perhaps one focusing on medical facilities, specialty shops or a financial district.

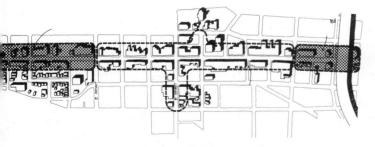

Many smaller downtowns are active for one block on either side of the main cross-street and can support a pedestrian precinct of 800 to 1,000 feet. Most shoppers can walk these distances, assuming parking is in a peripheral but central place. (Surburban mall shoppers may walk two to three times as far without realizing it.)

If a decision is made *not* to convert a main street to pedestrian use, there are several improvements that will make it more pleasant for pedestrians.

• *Reduce traffic speed and volume.* If drivers have business on the street, the time lost through a reduced speed will be minimal. A 20 m.p.h. speed recommended as comfortable for drivers and pedestrians and enforceable. Drivers traveling at that speed can anticipate conflicts and have enough time to stop for pedestrians at crosswalks.

• *Eliminate through traffic.* Traffic with no shopping purpose should be channeled elsewhere or slowed to 20 m.p.h. That's easier said than done. If a bypass is developed, or if traffic is diverted to parallel streets, these streets may suffer from the extra traffic. A bypass may work effectively enough to draw traffic to other shopping districts, discouraging shoppers from stopping downtown. A bypass on the next parallel street may diminish the effective size of the pedestrian precinct. It would be better to locate it several blocks away from the main street. Sidewalks, special parking, landscaping, noise barriers and other amenities should be added to the diverted road to reduce the impact of traffic.

Dispersing traffic over several roads including the main street may be most appropriate politically. Established traffic patterns are difficult to change, and residents of a street proposed for increased traffic will surely protest. If all streets in a downtown share the traffic load and are landscaped to make pedestrians feel comfortable, this solution may work.

Signs announcing the pedestrian zone should be low enough to be read by pedestrians and suggest low-speed driving. Installation *in the street* defines parking and narrows the traffic lane. Temporary curbing with the old gutter remaining allows drainage at low cost. When the sidewalk is reconstructed, this area can be properly integrated.

• *Provide convenient parking on periphery.* Shopping districts without good public transportation or with high-density housing have to rely on shoppers reaching them by car. Convenient parking on the periphery of the shopping area is a must. Ideally, parking would be at the rear of shops and bordered on all sides by them. Multi-storied parking should be considered for all lots except those close to the downtown core. The reason for not having large parking structures downtown is that the space they require is valuable and may need to be converted in the future. The cost of replacing a parking structure to another use would be prohibitive. Each parking area should be linked to the downtown core with direct walkways that are landscaped and lighted. (See Photo)

Converting one or several streets from parallel parking to angle or perpendicular parking eliminates the cost of purchasing land for parking lots. And more cars can be accommodated.

Set fees should be charged for parking meters and parking lots so that drivers are not encouraged to drive around looking for the least expensive parking space. In addition, if walking is convenient and comfortable, drivers will become accustomed to taking the first vacant space.

Jane Jacobs, the noted urbanist, believes that cars should *not* be excluded from most downtowns. She stresses that wider sidewalks and slower moving traffic are more appropriate. Her rationale is that many towns do *not* have sufficient pedestrian traffic to feel urban, and that the presence of cars helps create a lively feeling. Small towns can easily follow this advice, converting a two-way street to one-way, eliminating a lane of parking or narrowing the travel lanes, and using the captured space for sidewalk widening.

San Francisco, though not a small town, probably represents the epitome of this approach. San Francisco is a city, laid out on grid pattern, with enough flexibility to solve any traffic or parking problems that would ordinarily require street closures. San Francisco has instead widened selected sidewalks, such as along Market Street and encouraged the development of privately-owned pedestrian precincts including Giradelli Square, The Cannary, The Golden Gateway, Embarcadero Center and others. Furthermore, the city has encouraged perpendicular extensions of walkways through private arcades, lengthening store frontages and increasing window shopping. Its foggy, wet weather has much to do with this approach, since these small spaces feel more comfortable under such conditions.

• *Leave the main street* for through traffic and develop an internal shopping arrangement. This may be appropriate for a main street which is very short and for which there are no alternatives. (See plans of Kirkland.)

• *Selectively widen portions of the sidewalk.* Towns wanting to improve pedestrian comfort but unsure of their commitment can concentrate on improving their intersections. Since intersections become crowded easily pedestrians appreciate any improvements there. Widening intersection sidewalks at the parking lane causes no problems for motorists and can make the corner more distinctive. The entire space can be paved and part of it planted, depending on the amount of crowding. Benches and special light fixtures can be added if space permits. Construction for these improvements is relatively easy and inexpensive and requires little cooperation or agreement among merchants. (See photo).

A major sculpture identifies the place. This sculpture—depicting a sawblade in a logging community—is bold and serves that purpose well. It occupies a former parking and traffic lane and serves congregating and waiting needs.

• *Mid-block crossings* may be the next best, least expensive improvement for pedestrians. Mid-block crossings occupy one to two parking spaces per side, allowing pedestrians a safe place to cross between intersections. (See photo). Although loss of parking may be opposed by some merchants, stores located adjacent to mid-block crossings usually benefit from increased exposure and thus, their owners may be a force advocating approval. The entire

crosswalk can be depressed to form a wide ramp serving wheelchairs, prams and bicycles. Because mid-block crossings may not be expected by motorists, they should be well marked.

It should be noted that expanding sidewalks at intersections may cause drainage problems, since the gutter and curb are already at the lowest point. It's best to extend the sidewalk out at the same grade and install a new curb. If this is impossible, the expanded sidewalk should be graded up from the curb at the same slope as the street, using a trench drain for runoff, or the old sidewalk should be removed and the new sidewalk sloped at a shallower grade, using swales if necessary. This may work if the existing sidewalk is quite steep and can be regraded to 1½ percent slope. (See sketch).

SIDEWALK WIDENING

There is no pleasure for pedestrians in struggling to walk on sidewalks that are too crowded. If people have to dodge other people frequently on a given walk, it may need to be widened. If the number of cars parked or traveling in the lanes adjacent to a sidewalk is substantially less than the number of pedestrians using the sidewalk, it may be time to eliminate the traffic or parking and widen the sidewalk. Particularly if auto traffic is heavy and fast, more pedestrian room on the sidewalk can buffer and increase their perceived sense of safety.

Widening sidewalks is expensive and should be done only if the gain in width is substantial, unless, of course, the walk is in need of repair anyway. The minimum a sidewalk should be widened is 24 inches, equivalent to a narrow pedestrian lane. For sidewalk widening, drainage may be the biggest problem. Typically, roadway catch basins have to be relocated and the present street gradient may prohibit extension of the sidewalk. In addition to drainage, lights, hydrants, parking meters, and trees may have to be relocated.

The pavement can designate areas used for walking, window shopping, and street furniture. In this photo, the trees, benches, signs, street lights, fire poles, etc. are located in a three-foot-wide brick paved strip, while the walking course is paved with concrete. A narrow band for window shoppers parallels the buildings.

To save costs, the sidewalk widening might be confined to the blocks on either side of the town's main cross-street. The heart of many small downtowns is essentially that two-block portion, where development is concentrated. Sidewalk widening could be extended later to the adjacent blocks if it proves successful.

Which side of the street should have the newly widened sidewalk? One approach, the one that is likely to satisfy more merchants and landowners is to divide the sidewalk space evenly between both sides, but that requires relocating twice as many curbs, drains, lights, etc., and is the most expensive option. This approach may provide two still-inadequate sidewalks or it may provide one sunny sidewalk and one shady one.

Another approach, of course, is to widen the sidewalk on one side of the street only. This has the advantage of providing one sizeable sidewalk. For instance, removing one traffic lane would net about 10 feet which could be divided to give five feet of new sidewalk to each side or used on one side for a dramatic 10 foot addition. Even if the sidewalk were widened on one side only, the side could vary from block to block depending on the type of adjacent businesses. Shops, restaurants and high turnover activities should be favored while office buildings, churches, government buildings, retail outlets with large merchandise and car dealers should be avoided. As for layout, traffic engineers may argue to keep the alignment straight, but the drawing (below) shows how variations can be handled.

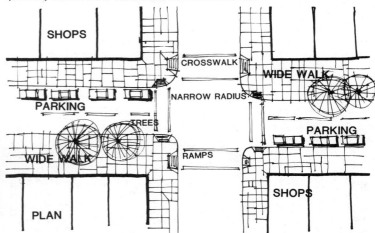

Construction of new driveways crossing the sidewalk should be discouraged. Driveways already crossing the sidewalk should be consolidated to expand on-street parking space and to improve the quality of the sidewalk. Driveways for drive-in businesses should *not* cross the sidewalk; they should be located instead on side or rear streets. Where drivers are necessary, they should be narrow: 10 feet for lots of ten or fewer cars and 16 feet for more cars than ten.

Trees help create pedestrian scale along a sidewalk and can be added with relative ease. While trees aren't necessary along the entire shopping street, one or two trees every block is often enough to relieve the harshness of the street. Trees should be planted in the ground, instead of in containers, and kept away from crowded areas. And, they should be two feet from the curb to maximize the sidewalk's width, even though many engineering standards recommend three feet. The three-foot distance, which compromises the pedestrian space, is unnecessary in most situations.

Merchants should be encouraged to improve their store fronts. A fresh coat of paint or awnings can unify and brighten up the street. The planner should select and suggest a color that merchant's use (for instance, earth tones, primary colors, etc.) in choosing paint colors so that the consistency of color will help visually tie the street together.

The author recommends the following capital improvements for small commercial districts:

Intersection Safe- Crosses	Street Trees
Mid-Block Crossings	Improvements to Store Fronts
Awnings	Shortcuts to Parking
Improved Parking	Benches

Walks can be wide—up to 35 feet if the shopping zone is varied and scaled down with street furniture (above). Widen sidewalks near restaurants that serve outside diners to encourage rest and breaks from the tiring aspects of walking. (Lower photo.)

Widen the sidewalk at bus stops where waiting passengers restrict normal flow of through pedestrians (above). Widen the walk at parking lots for extra buffer, rest area, and street furniture. Keep the driveway narrow, add fences and plant to maintain street continuity.

Don't widen sidewalks unnecessarily. Unpeopled places that lack activity, seating, bus stop, planting, sidewalk merchandising, etc., may be better left narrow (above). Avoid monotonous buildings next to the sidewalk. Long, uniform planters, bold, regularly spaces columns and single buildings a full block long decrease the joy of walking.

Widen to allow a clear walkway plus an area for benches, lights, traffic signals, trash cans, etc. Note the cantilevered awning for rain and sun protection, and the combined signal and street sign mounted at 7 feet so pedestrians can see them easily (above). Widen the walk at the busiest corner of a small downtown for image, comfort, and congregation. Note the ramps for wheelchairs and prams (below).

Widen walks to protect pedestrians at garage door openings. The narrow sidewalk, unprotected from exiting traffic, combined with an excessively long parking structure makes walking boring to many, and seem unsafe to others.

Vary the width to create areas of controlled congestion and areas of openness. Drop-off zones located in front of office buildings (instead of a retail business) work best.

New planting in the parking strip reduces traffic impact and makes the sidewalk seem wider. The brick paving adds visual diversity for the walker. The light is difficult to maintain as each light has to be individually changed. Note the drainage system under the planter with double curb bridged with plate steel. The water travels the length in the old gutter to catch basin at the intersection.

If the sidewalk can't be widened (as in alleys or narrow streets) add an internal arcade under the building. In this example, the brick piers are too massive, making the internal arcade dark and dangerous feeling. Note the metal bollards to keep cars off the sidewalk.

Should Main Street be a one- or two-way street? There are no easy answers. Converting to one-way allows the abandoned traffic lane to be used for sidewalk widening. One-way streets are easy to cross, but can cause difficulty for drivers trying to find their way from street to street. If traffic isn't policed, drivers tend to increase their speed,

making walking unpleasant. If the street is wide enough to accommodate sidewalk widening, the author prefers streets to be two-way.

Downtowns with four lane streets (two for through traffic and two for local traffic parking and turning) are unpleasant for pedestrians. These streets are too wide for easy crossing, and one side may seem detached from the other. Some shoppers will *not* freely cross the street, reducing shopping flexibility. Through traffic tends to assume a dominant role and travel too fast, creating noise and disharmony. What are the options?

A bypass on a parallel street would solve the problem for pedestrians but create one for residents of the street where traffic is being diverted. It may be better to eliminate two lanes of the four-lane main street so that through and shopping traffic could be mixed. Bottlenecks may cause some drivers to seek alternate routes to avoid delay. This approach was adopted by the city of Sausalito, California, where traffic flows slowly but without problems. To help the flow of traffic one of the lanes could be converted into a left-turn lane. The remaining lane could be used for widening of the sidewalk.

ALLEYWAY IMPROVEMENTS

If improving the main street is too difficult because of lack of cooperation or for physical reasons, an alternative is to improve alleyways behind the main street for pedestrian travel. This is possible if participating stores have a rear door and remodel so that the service entrance is attractive. Parking too might have to be upgraded. This approach could be carried out on a block-by-block basis where interest exists. It could be privately funded at relatively low cost and could lead to future improvement of the main street. If store entries are added to the alley, they must be obvious,

Business districts with busy Main Streets that cannot be made comfortable may have pedestrianized alleys or parking lots *behind* the shops. This alley is enhanced by small-scale merchants who sell specialty wares from the back of the stores, with doors leading to each major store.

barrier free, attractive and not go through storerooms; several shops might share an entry to increase its visual importance. A new sales counter might have to be added. Individual parking lots should be linked to allow shoppers more choice in parking and to reduce the need to drive from store to store.

Adding landscape elements to alleys—planters, trees, signs, special paving, makes them seem more than just a service space and improves the pedestrian usability. Temporary planters add pedestrian scale and may be cheaper and easier to install than permanent plantings in the ground.

Alleys and small roads leading to downtown should be coordinated for pedestrian access. Bollards reduce automobile use and make it comfortable for neighborhood residents to reach downtown on foot.

TRANSIT MALLS

Transit malls have become popular, probably because of the success of Minneapolis's Nicollett Mall and because the Department of Transportation has funded several transit mall projects. A transit mall is a street closed to normal traffic, but open to buses, taxis and, during set times, delivery trucks. Traffic lanes may be narrowed to eleven feet and parking eliminated, leaving room for wider sidewalks. Wider sidewalks are the principal benefit to pedestrians. Bus lanes may be flush with the sidewalk creating a unified pedestrian space, or lowered six inches with a curb to clearly distinguish the bus space from the sidewalk space.

Transit Malls. Transit malls are efficient for the bus system while the extra sidewalk width increases pedestrian comfort. Ideally buses using the street should be electric trolleys to minimize noise and fumes and planters might screen window shoppers and walkers from the large buses. The curving route makes walking pleasant as you are continually seeing new vistas. Crossing the street can be dangerous, so bollards with chains are used. The expanded sidewalk occurs at bus stops, with the extra room for thru walkers. (2 Photos)

Pedestrian problems in transit malls arise from the size of buses and frequency with which they travel. If buses are infrequent and pedestrians don't expect them, they may be lulled into a false sense of security. If there are many diesel buses, their noise, air pollution and size can offset the advantages of the mall. Moreover, transit malls reduce the opportunity to extend the pedestrian influence to side streets where buses might have stopped. A way to avoid this is to design the transit mall so that buses use a street parallel to the main street. This draws passengers past side street shops on their way to the main street which is free of buses.

Transit malls are typically located on main shopping streets. Merchants who have become used to transit on their street, value the bus traffic as it increases the visibility of their shops and allows direct service for transit users. This fact may be even more important in the future if transit use continues to increase, but it would make the possibility of shifting transit from main street to a parallel street marginal.

The planner should check out all the options. Is it attractive or possible to close the main street to private cars and trucks? If private vehicles can be rerouted to a parallel street, the possibility of converting the main street to a transit mall becomes more viable. The planner should also check the possibility of locating transit on parallel streets. If parallel streets are one-way or are not wide enough to handle transit, the only option may be a two-way cuplet. Unfortunately, two-way cuplets are confusing to many bus riders who find it difficult to get off at one place and on at a place two blocks removed. If parallel streets carry excessive traffic, the addition of buses may not work at all, making a main street transit mall the only option.

If the shopping street is normally not busy, buses may increase the activity of the area. Also transit service close to stores may be beneficial in area where climate is severe. If it seems that the running of buses on the main street will cause problems, a solution can be eased by operating a small-scale bus to run at relatively low speeds through the business district and connect outside the district to buses running to other areas of the community. In any event, running *all* of the community's buses through the transit mall should be avoided.

Portland, Oregon opted during the 1970's to withdraw its Interstate Freeway expansion funds, and substitute them for transit improvement including a downtown Transit Mall. The Transit Mall capitalizes on Portland's short blocks and extensive one-way street system. It occupies the two main streets, with each roadway narrowed to allow 25 to 35 feet side sidewalks. The entire length was extensively developed with special benches, trees, planters, fountains and large covered shelters to mitigate Portland's rainy weather. The Mall has a unique, one-way travel lane for taxis and private vehicles located every other block. The travel lane is used for pick-up and drop-off purposes, and creates a variation in the sidewalk width, with a wider "plaza" occurring every 2 to 3 blocks.

PORTLAND TRANSIT MALL

These large curbed planters separate pedestrians from transit vehicles on this mall. The treatment creates visual variety for the shopper, places to rest, and enhances safety from vehicular dangers. However, it does entrap pedestrians in a narrow corridor, which may create anxieties about mugging in some.

PLAZAS

Many plazas constructed in the recent past have been too large and uncomfortable for pedestrians, serving more to enhance the image for the building behind. Some of these are products of zoning laws which encouraged plaza construction in exchange for increased building height. However, bonus systems haven't ensured that the "public space" will actually be a public benefit. Decisions have been based on inches and feet, instead of on activity, use or orientation. The result has been a number of plazas with problems: some are windswept, others are on the shady side of buildings, while others break the continuity of shopping streets, or are inaccessible because of grade change. Most are without benches, planters, cover, shops or other pedestrian comforts. To be comfortable, large spaces should be divided into smaller ones. Landscaping, benches, wind and rain protection should be provided, and shopping and eating made accessible.

Examples of inappropriate plazas. Too large, too open and boring, nothing to do, poor orientation, few benches and poor accessibility are common problems.

It has been demonstrated *no* extra room should be provided. In fact, it is usually better to be a bit crowded than too open, and to provide many smaller spaces instead of a few large ones. It is better to have places to sit, planters and other conveniences for pedestrians than to have a clean, simple and "architectural" space. It is better to have windows for browsing and stores adjacent to the plaza space, with cross circulation between different uses than to have the plaza serve one use. It is better to have retailers rather than offices border the plaza. And, finally, it is better to have the plaza as part of the sidewalk instead of separated from the sidewalk with walls.

Many corporate entry plazas developed at the base of high rises are uncomfortable for pedestrians. They should be reduced in size with new shops, ground-oriented pedestrian services, benches, trees and other plaza amenities.

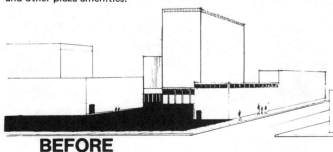

BEFORE

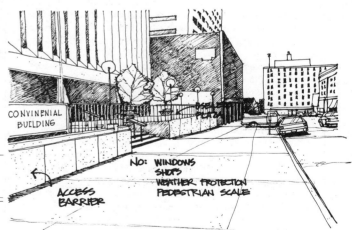

CONVINENIAL BUILDING

NO: WINDOWS
SHOPS
WEATHER PROTECTION
PEDESTRIAN SCALE

ACCESS BARRIER

Minimize building setbacks unless the space between is available for pedestrian use. This raised plaza is not easily accessible. It is isolated and useless. Access is restricted to one place because of the retaining wall, requiring longer walks for entry.

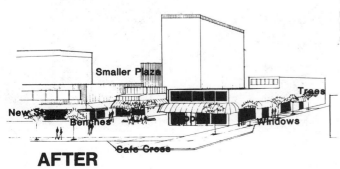

Smaller Plaza

Trees

New St

Benches

Windows

Safe Cross

AFTER

Where is the best place for a plaza? Plazas ideally should be located in places with good sun exposure and little wind exposure, in places that are protected from traffic noise and in those that are easily accessible from streets and to shops. A plaza should have a center as well as several subcenters.

The planner should inventory downtown for space that can be used for plazas, especially small ones. Appropriate spaces include: space where buildings may be demolished and new ones constructed, vacant land or streets that may be closed to traffic or may connect to parking. (See photo).

New stores can sometimes be set back 8 to 10 feet from the street to allow plaza space in exchange for increased density.

Avoid small plazas located below sidewalk grade. Avoid tall, sharp-faced planters that force people in and imply "through" movement, instead of a passive, meandering use (above). Avoid plaza separated from the street by tall walls which force entry through narrow locations. This concrete wall is harsh, boring and uncomfortable to walk alongside (below).

Avoid plazas and entries separated from the street by long flights of stairs (above).

Some suggestions for planners and developers of plazas include the following:

- Limit plaza size to create small, human-scaled spaces. A maximum size of 2,500 square feet is appropriate with several small plazas better than one large one.
- Enclose a plaza on one or two sides.
- Plan for at least 20 percent of the plaza to be planted.
- Provide seating in the sun and make it readily accessible to the public.
- Develop shops and stores along the plazas, excluding large banks, travel agents and offices that attract few pedestrians.
- Do not use large expanses of blank wall.
- Plan for prevailing sun angles and climatic conditions, using as a rule of thumb a minimum of 20 percent of daily sunshine hours on March 21.
- Encourage the use of bandstands, public display areas, outdoor dining space, skating rinks and other features which attract crowds. In cold or rainy areas, a covered galleria would benefit pedestrians more than an open plaza.
- Integrate indoor and outdoor space to make it more useful. Plan spaces to be small and informal in character and quality so as to be inviting, comfortable and non-oppressive.
- Avoid sunken plazas, since access is difficult and people feel uncomfortable in them. Keep them level or just sightly below sidewalk grade. For instance, at Rockefeller Center in New York City, the lower level originally had shops, which failed and were converted to the now famous ice skating rink. Most people view the rink from above while only users go below.
- Avoid architectural and geometrical bench arrangements. Instead consider where and how most people would prefer to sit. One reason so-called "undesirables" frequent many plazas is that benches are not usable by pedestrians. Movable chairs, heavy enough not to be stolen, but light enough to move, are recommended so that people can choose where they want to sit and what arrangement they prefer.

Older plazas can be redesigned to better serve pedestrians.

Three main tasks are necessary to convert an older plaza for increased pedestrian use:

- Integrate the plaza with the sidewalk to improve pedestrian access.
- Add structures and street furniture, such as planters, benches, fountains, arcades, to make the spaces smaller, more complex and more intimate.
- Add retail stores or connect the plaza to retail spaces in order to encourage shopping activity.

To integrate a plaza with the sidewalk, the planner should note where sidewalk and plaza are separated by walls or change in grade and figure out how to eliminate the barrier. Portions of depressed plazas might be raised near the sidewalk, making them more accessible. While some separation may have to remain, easy access should be available from two sides. Some stairways should be converted to ramps to meet barrier-free standards. Some walls might be constructed closer to the curb if protection from traffic is necessary.

Areas within the plaza itself could be divided into smaller units. There might be an entry space, a space with places for sitting and conversation, a play area for children, and perhaps an outside dining area adjacent to a cafe. The spaces should interconnect with easy circulation for everyone including those in wheelchairs.

Landscape elements to reduce the scale so a plaza is comfortable for pedestrians can be quite complex and varied. Architectural approaches, using geometric relationships and extreme simplification may not be comfortable for most people. Some desirable landscape elements are discussed below. Outdoor kiosk or pushcart type merchandising should be encouraged where there is enough pedestrian traffic to support it. Busy plazas can often support a

combination coffee, florist, and gift/candy shop. Benches or movable chairs should be added. Planters and retaining walls should be constructed 12 to 24 inches high so they can also be used for seating. They should have a level surface at least six inches wide.

Large, open plazas can be scaled to pedestrian comfort by adding tables, chairs, portable planters and kiosks selling food, beverage and other pedestrian merchandise. This town square in Central Europe is an active congregating area for town residents, and a favorite place to be in.

Ground-floor commercial spaces adjacent to a plaza should be converted to retail use. It may be possible to build a new facade of small shops in front of offices, decreasing the size of the plaza while creating new retail outlets and activity. Before suggesting that, the planner should be sure there is enough pedestrian traffic to justify the expense. Since plazas that are accessed by a number of doors instead of one monumental entrance are more comfortable for people, the planner should include them in plans for development. Their addition helps the cross-flow of pedestrians.

If it is possible for a plaza to be planned without exposure to weather, wind in particular, the planner should provide for cover and wind protection. Wind screens and covered walkways make being in a plaza more comfortable during inclement weather. Glass screens allow views into different areas while reducing wind penetration. And a solarium can provide a warm comfortable space in winter. To protect transit users, bus shelters should be integraded with a plaza. These stops don't necessarily have to resemble other bus stops but can be designed to fit the plaza.

If a park is desirable, build it so it can be expanded into an adjacent parking lot or alley for fairs and festivals. Many towns have built small parks adjacent to the main intersection. The intersection location is likely to be noisy and difficult to expand for fairs and festivals. A better solution may be at mid-block to allow expansion into the rear parking or into an internal alley system. When the business community schedules a festival, they can close the parking area, expanding the park for festival activities.

A half-up, half-down arrangement doubles sidewalk access to shop and adds streetscape open space. The lower courtyard and upper deck are more private and allow sales extensions. This isolation may also reduce the number of shoppers. Even with the ramp, handicapped access is difficult.

The massive wall insures protection for resting pedestrians who sit in what seems to be a precarious location. The wood benches with backs are comfortable though users find different ways to use them as shown by these two girls. Water splashing over rough-cut stones adds light, movement and patterns that are interesting to watch. Globe lamps cast low-level pedestrian light in a full circle illuminating the space rather than strictly the ground. (Note the center strip which simplifies crossings as shown by these J-walkers.)

Modular planters with seating increases user flexibility. Loose benches and chairs allow users to find the best location and groupings, and avoid stereotyped settings designers often provide.

DETAILS FOR IMPROVING DOWNTOWN STREETS

LOCATION

Where should a pedestrian street or precinct be located? How large should it be? What about disagreements? Creating an effective pedestrian precinct is more complex than closing a street, and depends on many actions by many different people. A large scale, comprehensive approach that may be appropriate for one town might be inappropriate for another town. Small-scale pedestrian improvements which won't disrupt traffic, can be implemented with fewer problems than would be expected in a full-blown effort. Individual opinions and disagreement may suggest piecemeal approaches, doing portions that merchants and residents want, and ignoring areas of disagreement.

Most downtowns are organized linearly with merchandising, commercial and office complexes strung out along several parallel streets. Side streets have lower rent and secondary services supporting the main street. One improvement alternative is a series of small malls, each centered around the busiest part of an identifiable district, for instance, a two-block long pedestrian street in the heart of downtown, serving the main department and clothing stores. The next few blocks might remain unimproved while a widened sidewalk might be constructed in the blocks that follow where stores selling gifts or boutiques are located or where a town park can be extended into the

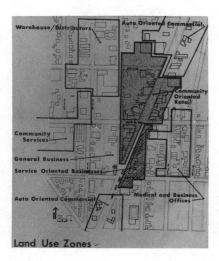

Land Use Zones

street. The pattern of sidewalk widening might be repeated wherever there is an attraction for pedestrians, such as restaurants, financial institutions or a medical complex. Traffic can usually be diverted around a few closed streets with few parking spaces lost and the downtown's image enhanced.

The plan must match the physical, economic and attitudinal values held by the landowners in town. The planner should study the town's land uses to identify areas that are condusive to pedestrians, travel and that have a positive image in people's mind. Places alive with interest for pedestrians include department stores, cultural facilities (churches, museums), corporation headquarters and fine shops. The planner should avoid areas without recognizable monuments or special activities, with secondary merchandising activities, lower rents, higher vacancies, transient tenancy and areas inundated with municipal or government offices.

Munich, Germany, is a good example of a downtown as described above. The downtown can be divided into quadrants formed by the principal pedestrian street which crosses the main street. Each quadrant had a definite use and character before the pedestrian street was constructed, which was either enhanced or diminished by the change. The center of activity is the old main street, where historic buildings provide a central focus with several department stores all located at each end. With the pedestrianizing of one street, Munich has developed a retailing and entertainment strength unparalleled in any other city. The quadrant between Odeons and Karlsplatz is an important and active place with the city's best hotel, its finest shops and headquarters of its corporate and religious organizations. This quadrant was integrated into the pedestrian precinct *but* several streets were left to serve nonshopping functions. Moreover, the quadrant between Karlsplatz and Sendlinger Tor has no recognizable monuments, historical character or special activities, and so was not developed further to serve pedestrians. It continues to accommodate secondary activities with lower rents, higher vacancies and transient tenancy. The area between Sendlinger Tor and Isator, with concentration of government offices, is devoid of shopping services and has little of interest to pedestrians. No

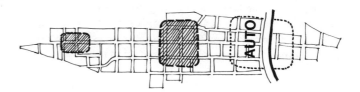

pedestrian improvements were added to either of these last two quadrants since they would have had little positive impact. Because the latter quadrant has theaters, the city's opera house and restaurants, and has matured into a successful evening entertainment area, some pedestrian improvements have been designed to provide congregating areas adjacent to each of these activities.

How large should a pedestrian street be? In theory it could cover the entire downtown. If there is enough business, major stores could be located every 500 to 600 yards, enabling pedestrians to shop at whichever location they could conveniently reach. In practice, pedestrian streets should be located around the most intense shopping area which should be at least two to three blocks long, a distance that allows store variety, creates identity and image and is walkable by most people. Development does not have to be linear, nor does it need to be limited to one grand effort. Several smaller pedestrian areas may be easier to implement, and work better in our car-oriented communities, than one large pedestrian area.

The exact size of the area to be closed to traffic is often much less than one might imagine. Merchants would prefer too many people using the streets than too few, since more people make the place look more festive and desirable. Spaces should be kept small and should be sited to accommodate the anticipated number of users. At 100 square feet per person, shopping movement is free and comfortable. At 1200 or more square feet per person, a place looks deserted. Allow at least 100 square feet per person for average days, assuming the space will be more crowded on weekends and special shopping days.

Most small downtowns or neighborhood business districts have active pedestrian shopping that extends one block on each side of the major cross street. Beyond that two-block length, the activity falls off drastically, and the shops become specialized, less convenience oriented, and attract fewer pedestrians. That doesn't mean development should be restricted to two blocks. Developing those portions beyond the main area to a lesser degree by widening the sidewalk on one side may be the right solution. Merchants outside a prime pedestrian area may not want to be part of a closed street scheme. They may sell merchandise to drive-in customers and need more exposure and parking.

LAYOUT

The classic pedestrian street layout should try to duplicate the layout of stores in suburban shopping malls with two anchor department stores, to draw customers, with smaller shops in between. Downtowns with only one department store might try to attract another. Suitable substitutions might be another large store, parking, a government or social services complex, a park, lake or river, or another attraction. Municipal funding may be necessary to develop a park or government services, and municipal cooperation with department store developers should aim at reducing red tape.

An existing department store might also decentralize, spreading several of its departments around town: clothing in one store, furniture in another, housewares in yet another. This would be a possibility if the character of the town is small scale and integrating a large store would be difficult. Decentralization could encourage customers to move around from store to store.

Napa, California, has developed a plan with a major downtown department store at one end of its main street and the government center at the other end. (See photo).

Shopping malls with interior development: benches, fountains, planters and push carts for children make them convenient for users. The same strategy might also be applied to downtown. Specialty kiosks added to the malls generate large sales, and could be included in downtown streets. (2 photos)

Nottingham, England, is somewhat special, in that it constructed two new shopping centers and then closed the streets between. One center has a distinctive middle-class feel with more expensive shops, while the other caters to working people and features lower prices. The stores between associate themselves with whichever center is closest. Activity between and at each center is extensive. The only stores that have not done well are those in the outskirts that were not part of the original plan. Most of these have been abandoned and their space rented by the local government to serve as offices for a library and welfare and social services agencies.

This large fountain at the beginning of a pedestrian mall masks automobile noise of the adjacent busy street. The stone stools protect people from cars straying into it, and are a place to rest.

TRIAL STREET CLOSURE

To see how a pedestrian street would work, the planner could suggest that the main street be closed during business hours, with a chain or swinging gate, on a trial basis. (See photo). The cost would be *low* since no construction would be necessary. Parking might be restricted from midnight, and morning hour traffic limited to delivery trucks. At 9 or 10:00 a.m., the gate might be closed, and pedestrians allowed to use the street until evening. It should be noted that the results may be somewhat disappointing since no benches, trees, special paving and other amenities would change the street's character. But people would be able to walk, shop, watch others, and enjoy themselves without the threat of cars.

Main street can be closed on a temporary basis with simple wood planters for resting and visual diversity. The upper photo street closing in a small English town suggests the freedom of crossing back and forth.

In the evening, the street would be returned to car use. Should the daytime closing prove successful, merchants might consider a permanent closing with pedestrian amenities. It is important to make sure the initial closing is well advertised. For best results, the closure should begin in summer or during nice weather, and the first few days should be made festive with balloons, restaurants serving outdoors and special sales. Christmas time should be avoided for the beginning of a street closure, as sales revenues may be lost in the confusion.

Assuring customer access. While merchants tend to press for assurances that their stores remain accessible, it has been proven that most shoppers will travel slightly out of their way to reach desirable shopping. If parallel streets remain open to cars, they can be used to reach the shopping precinct. Cross streets connecting distant neighborhoods should be kept open and should lead directly to customer parking. Through streets should be distinguished from those leading to parking with a safe-cross and signs.

Fire and emergency vehicles must have access along the length of any closed street. A clear zone, 12 feet wide and 14 feet high should satisfy most fire departments. The route can move around trees and street furniture, provided the centerline radius exceeds 50 feet. Fire department vehicles should not be allowed to drive through the pedestrian area at high speeds. If this is demanded, the planner should look for existing routes fire trucks can take to circumvent the area. The planner should question what pieces of equipment would be brought in and judge if they seem excessive (i.e., a hook-and-ladder when the tallest building is two stories). A test course using barricades or boxes for fountains, trees, and other street furniture should be set up for fire trucks to drive through.

The fire department may require that new fire hydrants be installed. That may be an acceptable trade for cooperation and approval. If there is sufficient room for fire trucks, then ambulances, police cars, garbage and service trucks will also have enough room.

This pedestrian main street has a 12 foot-wide fire lane that alternates from side to side the length of the street. It is defined by bollards and used by delivery trucks in the mornings and evenings. Since the street is not extensively used by pedestrians, the designers added trees, bollards, benches, planting, clocks, light fixtures, etc. to make it look active at all times. The seating is frequently used and the separation of through walking from window shopping serves those who want to move through quickly.

Cross traffic. A two-block-long pedestrian street on either side of the main cross street would likely be long enough for most small towns. Some cross-streets, which do not carry much traffic could be closed with little inconvenience. These could be made into cul-de-sac at the main street, providing pedestrian access, parking and delivery and emergency vehicle access. The several cross-streets with larger traffic volumes that lead to distant destinations could be left as through streets. At intersections, cross-streets should be narrowed and parking prohibited so as to shorten the crossing distance. A pick-up/drop-off lane incorporated on each side of a street crossing is a convenience. In Eugene, Oregon, a high roof was installed over an entire crossing to protect pedestrians wating for signals to change or for a bus. (See photo).

Grid pattern streets create a linear feeling that is uncomfortable for walking. This simple space frame connecting the four corners creates a downtown focal space that is more comfortable to walk through. It is useful on wide streets where it is difficult to make the street appear narrow.

Handling deliveries. Shops with rear access would not be affected by the closing of a main street since they could be serviced through their rear doors. Deliveries to stores without rear access could be done from the pedestrian street during certain hours, say from 8 to 10 in the morning and 6 to 8 in the evening. This is standard practice all over Europe and in most American cities that have pedestrian streets. Drivers making deliveries get used to the schedule and seldom have problems. Late arrivers could move merchandise by hand truck to small shops. Central delivery systems, though ideal in theory, are expensive and have not been implemented except at surburban shopping centers.

Truck deliveries to stores in pedestrianized areas are allowed during the early morning and late evening times. Between 10:00 and 6:00, deliveries are by hand-truck from vehicles parked on side streets.

Deliveries during times when vehicles are prohibited can occur with hand trucks from the nearest side street.

HANDLING HEAVY TRAFFIC

Towns wanting to decrease main street through traffic or to close streets to traffic face the problem of diverted traffic. The problem is potentially worsened *if* metropolitan traffic projections are believed. Many forecast continued increases in traffic for the next 10 to 15 years to as much as twice the number of cars as are now on the road. A considerable dollar investment and environmental toll will be necessary to accommodate this growth, while the closing of roads may be considered impossible.

Main street merchants even now face the dilemma of attracting passing drivers as shoppers. This author believes that roads bypassing the main street should be used as a last resort because they often lead potential shoppers past downtown to stores beyond. If merchants see this happening, they may relocate on the bypass, possibly in a strip development.

Environmental conditions on a bypass are likely to deteriorate with increased noise, exhaust fumes and access difficulties. The pedestrian quality of bypass streets is poor with slight chance for residential use, childrens' play, elderly walking and creation of a sense of community. Research has proved that along bypass roads, absent landlordships increases, that families move out, that neighborhood interaction decreases, and that old people stay indoors more and fear venturing outside. The cost of bypass construction is high, and the land may be better used to make improvements downtown.

Do Nothing

On small projects, a do-little approach usually works, that is, make no plans for rerouting main street traffic. Many drivers who formerly used a main street for through travel often find alternate routes if the street is narrowed or otherwise changed. The disappearing traffic phenomenon occurs because roads generate traffic, and if a road is changed to discourage traffic, drivers generally find another route or do not take the trip. "Disappearing" traffic can amount to up to 35 percent of the traffic volume along a given road. For instance, most pedestrianized German towns have closed their main streets without providing any traffic improvements and suffered *no* unreasonable traffic snarls. An attempt should be made to reduce the number of cars entering an area, hopefully to where no additional traffic reaches adjacent streets. This can be done by improving public transportation by providing parking outside the area of activity and by guiding unrelated traffic around the area.

This small business community had, as its main street, a state highway which could not be abandoned or rerouted. The pedestrian revitalization solution slowed traffic to 25 m.p.h., widened the sidewalks to 13 feet, defined parking spaces to protect the sidewalk, and constructed a 10 foot wide center planting strip. The development extends for one block on either side of the main cross street. The center planter separates traffic, makes street crossings relatively easy and scales down the former wide road. Widened sidewalks with parking, buffers passing vehicles and makes shopping and walking comfortable. Two mid-block crosswalks, marked with bold painted lines, make crossing the street easy and comfortable. The mid-block pedestrian refuge is flush with the pavement, but has a raised curb on each side to protect pedestrians from oncoming traffic. Sidewalk improvements include new street trees and a canopy to be constructed by each merchant to protect window shoppers from rain and sun.

Bypass

If a bypass is the only way to open up a main street for pedestrian traffic only, the planner should consider a plan to mitigate the problems created for those along the bypass and integrate the pedestrian with uses beyond it. Bypass traffic can be one-way couplets, using two parallel streets, or along one major through street. Most bypasses will, for financial reasons, need to be constructed within the existing right of ways. Streets should be selected on the basis of the least disturbance to residences; that is, those to receive more traffic should have as few residences as possible.

A typical plan would include a ring circulation pattern several blocks from the pedestrian zone with several one-way loops penetrating into the pedestrian area for service and pedestrian drop-off. A ring road is not appropriate for residences or for most shopping stores. Land adjacent to a ring is best used for commercial and government offices, warehousing, manufacturing parking, auto repair or auto-oriented stores. Even though ring roads are often used, as described above, this author feels their disadvantages far outweigh their advantages and that they should be avoided. Ring roads are always larger than necessary, and may be more destructive to a neighborhood than the initial problem that created them. It is unnecessary to send motorists *around* the center of downtown when bypassing can be done by one or two short roads.

Whatever bypass method is chosen, direction signs should be posted to let through traffic know to use the bypass and to tell shoppers where to go and how to park.

PARKING

Downtowns that do not provide easy access and parking will not survive the period of improvement. However, the other extreme of making parking as easy as in a shopping center should be avoided as well. Many towns have an adequate overall supply of parking, but the distribution is unbalanced with a deficit in the central core and a surplus in the fringe areas. The planner should figure out how many parking places would be lost by street alteration. The number of parking spaces needed is determined by checking the number of vacant parking places and the number of people seeking parking places.

Parking should be located so shoppers can park in one place and visit several stores. Cutting down driving between stores can reduce the total of spaces required.

Organizing employee parking is the cheapest way to gain extra parking space. Employees should park *outside* the shopping area on streets more than 500 feet from the main shopping precinct or on low cost lots provided by mer-

chants at the edge of the district. The extra distance would only take three to four minutes on foot and is the cheapest way to gain close-in customer parking space. Parking spaces for regular employees could be smaller or even tandem (bumper to bumper). Encouraging employees to car pool, use the bus or ride bicycles is even less costly and may be worth a monthly bonus. (The actual cost of a parking space is $30 per month and upwards.) Another measure to discourage employees from parking close to work is to have parking meters set for short parking time limits with strict enforcement of these limits. The planner should check the painted width of parking spaces. Cars are tending to be smaller and spaces should be restriped narrower. The remaining space could be used for adding new spaces. Parking dimensions can be reduced to 8½ to 9 feet and lengthened to 18 feet. Parking times should be kept short, two hours is usually long enough.

There are several ways to organize parking. The easiest (though not necessarily the most efficient) is to entice merchants to integrate adjoining parking areas. Customers should be able to drive between adjoining lots and walk to the shops they serve. This may mean moving fences, grading to match different levels, restriping and installing sidewalks to connect nearby stores.

Ideally parking should be located on the perimeter of the shopping district and distributed in several garages or lots. The pedestrian range of stores can be increased if shoppers choose parking carefully, walking to the most active area and beyond without moving their cars. Parking lots should be sited so people from different neighborhoods can reach them directly. Access drives should be on side streets and not across pedestrian streets. Walkways should be constructed and trees planted between parking lots and the shopping district.

Perpendicular or angle parking near shops can be attractive and unoffensive in small downtowns *if* the parking is organized and integrated into the streetscape. Define the beginning and end of the parking with curbed walks or planting areas. Widen the sidewalk to avoid vehicle overhangs crowding the pedestrian, plant trees and add wheelchair ramps.

New buildings should have all parking underground to decrease the ground space used for parking and to decrease the walking distances between stores. Relaxing some zoning or building codes in trade for garaged parking may be worthwhile.

Parking for handicapped people is essential. Local codes describe the exact requirements, but a good rule-of-thumb is 8 percent parking assigned for handicapped users. Parking spaces for the handicapped must be wider than normal, must be located in the space closest to the destination and must have ramps and protection. (See sketch). The parking spaces should be highly visible from passing cars and policed regularly to discourage illegal parking.

This short street off of the main shopping street was converted to angle parking to increase the sidewalk width and number of parking spaces. The plan weaves traffic to and fro the entire length with alternating sides joined by angled mid-block crossings.

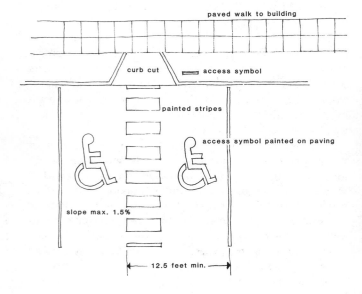

paved walk to building

curb cut — access symbol

painted stripes

access symbol painted on paving

slope max. 1.5%

12.5 feet min.

It is important to have uniform parking rates at meters and lots. Uniform fees discourage people from driving to find a cheaper meter or lot. The fewer cars looking for close-by parking, the better for pedestrians. It is possible to install parking meters that cancel the time that remains after a car leaves, making it also impossible for drivers in search for meters with free time.

Streets surrounding a downtown shopping area should be examined for possible conversion to parking. Little-used streets may be converted to angle or perpendicular parking, increasing the number of spaces two times. Conversion shouldn't cost much since the streets would already be owned by the municipality and may already be properly paved. The planner should make sure the pedestrian connection to the retail core is clear, safe and comfortable.

Kirkland, a small town in western Washington, converted part of its internal parking to a pleasant pedestrian area with new shop entrances. The other main street side is heavily trafficed and unpleasant. A newly constructed street extends the pedestrian realm further towards the housing area.

The interior of this business district was demolished and a new parking lot constructed with walkways leading to the main street. Note the wide wheelchair ramps, the marked crosswalks and the trees that in a few years will screen and soften the impact of the parking lots. The benches, surprisingly enough, are used as shown by the person in the righthand corner.

This parking lot is screened from pedestrian view by a sculptural precast intriguing concrete fence. The total space lost amounts to 3 feet.

Parking garages should have ground level shops for window shopping and to avoid the unpleasant views of park cars.

Replacing a store with a small park makes an attractive sitting area and pedestrian connection to parking. The space would be enhanced if the store on the right installed windows to diminish the isolated feeling inside the park.

Is parking on main street necessary? Or is parking the best way to use the main street's space? Parking requires 7 to 8 feet of width, equal to or wider than most sidewalks. The planner might question if there are as many people using the parking as might use the sidewalk if it were wider? To find out the planner should choose a representative block, time each parking stay and count the number of people who walk past the parked cars. A disproportionate ratio of pedestrians to parked cars may convince businesses that increasing pedestrian comfort by widening the sidewalk at the expense of parking is a valid trade.

Bicycle parking should be provided. One car parking space can serve 10 bicycles and may be a good investment if local conditions favor bicycling. If the area is crowded with pedestrians, bicycles should be parked in one of several centralized parking places so that bicyclists would walk for the rest of the shopping trip. If the area is not crowded and bicycles won't endanger walkers, they might be allowed to be ridden between stores with decentralized parking at each store. Bicycle racks should be clearly visible, easily reached, covered in a rainy climate, and provided with cables or chains. How many racks? The planner should estimate a number say 10 percent and monitor the results. If, after a year, they are mostly full, more may need to be added. If they are never used, the planner should try figure our why. Are they difficult to reach? Unsafe? Inconvenient? Nonuse is usually an indication of poor location.

EXPANDING THE PEDESTRIAN PRECINCT

Once the initial pedestrian precinct is operating, the planner should think of ways to increase the number of businesses and offices pedestrians can reach on foot. Increasing the length of the precinct only helps if it is not too long for walking. On the other hand, going up or down one floor can double the number of shops without measurably increasing walking distance. Then too, expanding horizontally with shops along routes leading to parking lots or to bus stops provides access and visibility for secondary shops. Moreover, moving bus routes one block off main street can move shoppers past side-street shops to reach buses and may make main street more pleasant for pedestrians.

Second-story expansion, intensifying pedestrian activity, can be used for businesses not dependent on impulse buying such as professional offices, medical services, real estate, insurance, cafes and travel agencies. Rents are lower than on the ground floor, while the business is still near the center of shopping activity. The second level can be extended with pedestrian bridges for easy street crossing. Eight bridges installed in a shopping complex in Minneapolis have doubled the number of people using the second floor. As a result, several new restaurants have been opened to serve them. The most difficult problem to overcome in second story extensions is to provide access for the handicapped. Since new laws require barrier-free access, that usually means an elevator. Skybridges help reduce the number of elevators needed. Elevator access can be designed to serve the maximum number of second-story spaces.

Upper story circulation could serve as a roof over the sidewalk below. Such an arcade would provide cover for pedestrians on the ground level and serve buildings above as well.

A word of caution. Skybridges can reduce on-street foot traffic which may decrease their quality. Skybridges should not be used if the street is not crowded, or if it is for the convenience of a small group of users. For instance, a skybridge connecting a hotel and parking garage, if *not* constructed would force the patrons to use the sidewalk, perhaps stopping to shop, eat, or drink, and adding activity to the street. Use them only where there is excessive demand, where they are open to the general public, and where it can be shown that there will be no detrimental effect to the pedestrian space beneath. Additionally, skybridges block pleasant views down the streets causing large cities like New York and San Francisco to discourage them.

Raising the pedestrian one level with sky bridges interconnecting blocks, places pedestrians safely above traffic. There are disadvantages—cost is high, and the ground level may be overpowered by cars since drivers don't have to worry about pedestrians. A deep arcade protects ground level pedestrians from fast-moving cars and San Francisco's rainy weather. Handicapped access is a problem, as is easy connection with the street level so users don't become disoriented. This particular development in San Francisco bridges eight square blocks, interconnecting residential, commercial and office buildings in the financial district.

Block to block arcades become short-cuts and increase the number of ground floor shops reachable on foot. The covered roof shelters shoppers during the wintertime, while the open portion allows daylight in. (2 photos)

Opening the interior of a shopping complex relieves the busy street and adds special character to the shops. The design can be nonlinear with benches, sculpture and other elements that often aren't located on the street.

IMPROVING PEDESTRIAN COMFORT

User comfort is increased by climate protection, parking close to shopping, good seating and ease of movement.

Orientation

When planning where to widen sidewalks or to add seating, the planner should select places that receive sun or wind protection. The sunniest side of grid streets is the north side, which receives sun from the south, of streets running east/west. These receive all-day sun except for early morning and late afternoon in summers. The shadiest is on the south side of streets that run east/west, because buildings block all but early morning and late afternoon summer sun. The west side of north/south-oriented streets receives morning sun, while the east side receives afternoon sun. Although sun may not be desirable in certain hot climates, shade can be easily provided with movable screens.

It is particularly important for the planner to ensure that in winter buildings don't cast a shadow on designated open spaces or on pedestrian streets. Sun is most important during mid-morning, mid-afternoon and lunch time when there is the most outdoor activity.

Shelter

As mentioned earlier, provision of protection against weather is important. Many shoppers like being outside and need only a little wind and rain protection to make a trip pleasant. Forms of protection include arcades, wind screens, waiting rooms (perhaps using a small wood burning stove), waiting areas in stores, shortcuts through stores, and covered sky bridges. The easiest way to add wind and rain protection is to have individual merchants install awnings. Towns can encourage awning installation by eliminating the need to obtain a permit for such installation. Even if several merchants decide not to add awnings, those that are installed offer protection and a festive appearance, as well. Variety in color, size or shape of awnings should be encouraged.

Tall buildings tend to generate wind currents and increase their speed. Wind then chills pedestrians and lowers their body temperatures, so they may feel discomfort. To avoid this, downtown bus shelters should have side walls that serve as wind barriers and even perhaps a radiant heater. New shelters should be sited near the curb to encourage people to move away from buildings. (See photo). Also, shelters should be transparent to let light through, strong enough to support the weight of people leaning against its walls, large enough to accommodate crowds, designed to allow maintenance to nearby stores, and conform to fire department access requirements. Covered areas are appropriate at intersections on cross-streets where they protect people waiting to cross a street. Cross-street shelters should have a 16-foot minimum clearance for through traffic.

Wind generated by tall buildings can hamper pedestrian activity downtown and on plazas. A study prepared for the National Science Foundation[1] confirmed that wind speeds on the ground around tall buildings were always higher and more gusty than wind speeds elsewhere in the area. Gusty wind is troublesome for pedestrians: it can blow off hats, break umbrellas, cause people to loose their balance and some to fall. Gusty wind is particularly hard on elderly, handicapped and shoppers carrying packages, and may cause many workers to remain indoors during their lunch hour.

In general terms, their study indicated that for average wind speeds over 6 to 8 m.p.h., with gusts of wind up to 20 to 30 m.p.h. pedestrians experience discomfort. For average wind speeds over 10 m.p.h. pedestrians experience considerable difficulty with carried objects, umbrellas and sometimes balance. Occasional gusts may be 30 to 40 m.p.h. around high rises, causing substantial difficulties for most people. Wind also chills and lowers body temperature; this may force workers to stay indoors during the winter. In the summer, wind gusts may be pleasing to those walking or standing in open sunshine.

Areas designed to encourage casual pedestrian activities should not be exposed to average winds greater than 6 to 8 m.p.h. High rise buildings designed with window shopping at their base may be unsuitable for this purpose because of unpleasant wind conditions. The most severe wind effects occur within 50 to 80 feet from a high-rise building. Crossing an area this size can take 15 to 20 seconds.

The report suggests several building configurations that can reduce wind exaggeration at ground level. It recommends mandatory wind tunnel tests for buildings over 250' where normal winds exceed 8 m.p.h., and for 200' tall buildings where winds exceed 12 m.p.h. Other options include orienting slab buildings *with* the wind direction (rather than perpendicular to it), using rounded corners or multisided buildings to reduce the harsh effect of a 90-degree corner, using a 30 to 40 foot tall building at the base of a taller building to absorb downdrafts, and installing canopies or roofed pedestrian walks at the base of the high rise. To improve pedestrian circulation, the planner should provide several entries allowing alternative routes, keep paths and doors away from corners, keep walks some distance from buildings and take special care in designing fountains and specifying plant material. On a windy plaza, water from a vertical fountain can blow quite a distance. Most plant material is susceptible to wind damage.

[1] *Pedestrian and Wind in the Urban Environment,* prepared by Institute for Man and Environment for National Science Foundation (1977).

	Cooling Power of Wind Expressed as "Equivalent Chill Temperature"								
	Temperature (°F)								
Calm	40	35	30	25	20	15	10	5	0
Wind Speed (MPH)	Equivalent Chill Temperature								
5	35	30	25	20	15	10	5	0	−5
10	30	20	15	10	5	0	−10	−15	−20
15	25	15	10	0	−5	−10	−20	−25	−30
20	20	10	5	0	−10	−15	−25	−30	−35
25	15	10	0	−5	−15	−20	−30	−35	−45
30	10	5	0	−10	−20	−25	−30	−40	−50

This handsome structure in downtown Boston provides rain protection and enclosures for window shoppers. The clear glazing lets sunlight in and gives a light feeling to the structure. Since the structure does not touch the building, there is occasional leakage. Lighting and drainage are built into the structure and stores can add signs along the lower edge. The post reduces the sidewalk width which is not a problem since the street is pedestrianized. The arcade was prefabricated and installed where they fit easily, bypassing difficult sections such as the store entries.

Roofed play area adds diversity for children and another reason for parents to shop downtown. Sunlight penetrates the clear cover, while keeping off the rain.

IMPROVING DOWNTOWN'S CLIMATE

• Locate permanent arcades on the shady side of the street, allowing the sun to shine through to the opposite side. Glass covered arcades are desirable in northern latitudes, while retractable awnings may help on the sunny side in warm climates.

• Face widened sidewalks to the south so they are in the sun. It is easy to temporarily shade a sunny spot, while it is impossible to make a shady spot sunny.

• Wide streets are favored in cool, temperate zones where sun angles are low. Conversely, narrow streets in hot, humid areas leave most of the street in shade and increase pedestrian comfort.

• North/south-oriented streets have some sun all day, with one side in the morning sun and the other in shade, and with the opposite happening in the afternoon. Morning and late afternoon sun is comfortable and sought by pedestrians.

• On east/west-oriented streets one side is in continual sun while the other is in continual shade. Typically the sunny side will attract the most interesting shops, while the shady side may have predominantly noncommercial activities.

• Diagonal streets (NE/SW and NW/SE) offer compromise conditions which should be carefully studied with morning, evening, winter and summer sun combinations.

• Cross-streets encourage air movement which is advantageous in hot/humid climates and disadvantageous in cold climates.

Cafes

Sidewalk cafes should be allowed and encouraged so that shoppers can rest and enjoy themselves out-of-doors. The sidewalk portion is easy to establish, if the restaurant's support services are housed inside the adjoining building. All that is needed is a sunny outdoor space for tables with umbrellas. Ideally, the space should be adjacent to the building where pedestrians pass on the street side. A small barrier or planter might enclose the table area, but isn't necessary. If a sidewalk isn't wide enough, the adjacent parking space would be rented and converted for cafe use. In this case, pedestrians would walk close to the building, with the cafe extending over the former parking space, which might be covered with permanent sidewalk material or temporary wood duckboards that can be stored during winter. Remuneration to the city for use of the street could be a monthly rent payment, provision of restrooms, or maintenance of a portion of the route. (see photos)

Outdoor dining enhances the restaurant business and vitalizes the downtown

Some European cafes even set tables and chairs across the street, proving the importance of such a service to their customers. Cafes can be as small as two tables with eight chairs, to as large as 50 tables and 200 chairs. Groceries, bakeries, liquor stores, and bars located along busy pedestrian ways should also be encouraged to provide a few tables and chairs and to sell coffee, beer, sandwiches, cake, etc. What's important is to provide reasons beside shopping for people to walk and rest spots to extend the walking time.

Trees

Trees are important elements in any pedestrian-oriented environment. Their quality of ever-changing light, sound, movement and pattern can serve as attractions to pedestrians while their structure can be used to define spaces. As structural elements, trees should be sited selectively to divide a long straight street into smaller spaces, to enclose a space, to provide shade, or to soften the harsh lines of a building.

The following are other planning considerations regarding trees:

• Try not to block important or interesting buildings, such as churches, historic or public buildings from view. Frame with one tree to improve the view, but avoid total blockage.

• Plant trees according to climate. In the hot south, plant where shade is desirable. In temperate climates, make sure that warm sun can get in.

• Treat street orientation carefully. On east/west streets the northern side is in almost continuous sunshine, while the southern side is in total shade (early summer morning and late afternoons don't provide enough sun to be considered important). In warm areas, plant trees on the north side of the street to increase shade, and against the southern side in moderate climates so as not to block the sun. That the street might appear "off balance" should not be a consideration.

• On north/south running streets the western side is in morning sun and eastern side in afternoon sun. Since afternoon sun is the warmest, trees which shade it are desirable in warm climates and vice versa in temperate climates. Deciduous trees should be used in moderate climates to allow maximum amounts of winter sun.

• One tree, strategically placed, can often create a feeling for the entire street. Don't overplant.

• Pruned limbs are not required on pedestrian streets as they are on streets with traffic. Thus, it may be desirable to let some branches come closer to the ground, creating a different feeling.

Clustering street furniture—a place to sit, combined newsstands, mailbox, and trees, in this widened sidewalk area reduces sidewalk congestion.

WINDOW SHOPPING
Lighting

A rule-of-thumb for planners is to provide for less light than engineering standards suggest. Most standards were developed by supply houses and are excessive. Overlighting not only wastes energy and costs more for extra fixtures, but it ignores the design opportunities of varying light and darkness. Overlighting eliminates shadows from buildings, pavement and other landscape elements which provide interest and dimension. Lower light levels needn't be considered unsafe if properly handled.

Typical road lighting directs all the light to the ground. This may make good engineering sense, but it does nothing to light the spaces or interesting buildings. Globe lights, round translucent light fixtures, light spaces including the ground and buildings. It may be necessary to shield the light from apartment buildings so as not to disturb residents. Most other uses can stand the normal light that globes provide.

Some suggestions to assure safety:

• Large areas need not be brightly lit, as it is possible to see a considerable distance and to walk safely in the middle. Lighting edges, intersections or places where people or cars might conflict is important.

• The planner should check to see how many store windows are lit at night, as well as the intensity and how late they stay lit. This amount of light can be subtracted from the total requirement. Electronic regulators should be used to adjust the brightness to predetermined levels and to complement other available light.

• The planner should consider using smaller fixtures mounted 12 to 20 feet off the ground to be in scale with pedestrians and to allow diversity of light level. However, the high cost of installation of additional fixtures plus the additional energy consumption may make their use limited to special areas.

• The recommended Barrier Free Access light level of 1-foot-candle at the ground surface is acceptable for pedestrians even though it is less than that recommended for vehicles. This light level will also reduce the number of fixtures required.

IMPROVING PEDESTRIAN SERVICES

- Encourage recreational facilities such as theaters, restaurants, cafes, movie houses, libraries with late night hours, hotels, meeting rooms, etc., to extend the pedestrian area to nighttime use.
- Add tourist attractions such as Munich's Glockenspiel or playing clock, Stockholm's whitewashed writing wall (with new whitewash everyday) fairs such as Octoberfest.
- Develop a farmers' market to attract people to town.
- Develop programs in which youngsters provide delivery services for shoppers downtown.
- Institute a merchant-sponsored *children's flea market* where children can sell and buy old toys, books, etc. (See photo).
- Develop a teen gathering place, such as the snack or games bar. The teenage "hangout" is an important contributor to individual self-realization, group cohesion and reality testing.
- Organize a supervised child care center in the downtown. This could be self-supporting or cooperative.
- Encourage package check areas at local stores to enable shoppers to buy and leave things until later. A posted, uniform sign at each cash register throughout downtown could announce the service.
- Provide package lockers for shoppers' ease.

Resting is an essential part of walking, particularly for older pedestrians. Streets converted to pedestrian use should include many places to sit and other landscape elements to visually break down the street's size.

Street merchants enhance the pedestrian experience. They provide visual diversity, a chance to talk to different people and to shop for unique merchandise. They should be allowed in business districts where sidewalks are wide enought to safely accomodate their displays and still allow a reasonable through access.

Scheduling shopper entertainment is important, in this case, a children's flea market where children age 12 and under can sell or exchange their toys. It's an attraction for both children and adults and reduces the cost of toys.

Protecting pedestrians from busy traffic with bollards, chains, regularly-spaced light poles and planters is important. The cantilevered arcade roof shelters shoppers from rain and defines the viewing space for window shoppers.

CROSSWALKS

Define and boldly mark crosswalks with 8" wide white stripes or pedestrian scaled material such as brick, concrete or stone. Add wheelchair ramps on all corners and refuges where traffic is confusing. Pedestrian refuges should extend beyond the crosswalk to provide additional protection. Ramps should ideally occupy the entire crosswalk width. The crosswalk should be minimum 12 feet wide, but can extend to 40 feet where a busy plaza or mall crosses the street.

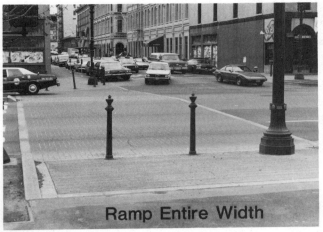

Ramp Entire Width

Pedestrian refuges are protected places in the center of wide streets for slow walkers to rest safely before crossing the other traffic lanes. Keep the crosswalk level with street grade, and raise a center divider on either end a minimum six inches for protection. Refuges should be at least four feet wide, and include a button to activate the traffic signal to avoid entrapment.

Extend the raised center divider beyond the pedestrian area as a barrier to eliminate cars cutting across the refuge. Adding a light pole, sign or tree helps identify the raised barrier.

IMPLEMENTATION

LAYING THE GROUNDWORK

Planning and constructing pedestrian improvements downtown is not a simple task. Before a project is begun, it is important to make sure that merchants are interested enough to unite and create an effective management unit to see a project through. Usually one person must be responsible for convincing others to follow.

The planner should check on the economic health of the area. How many stores, if any, have been abandoned? Are the department stores committed to staying downtown? How many other stores are likely to close because of retiring merchants or financial problems? This forecast may be largely a guess, for most merchants don't like to admit their problems. If many stores are likely to close, the planner should consider whether the time and investment will be worthwhile.

It is important that a spirit of belonging to downtown be encouraged in merchants and business people. Efforts might be made to interest merchants in cleaning, and fixing up their store fronts, policing and showing pride in their locations. Customers too should be encouraged to take an interest in improvements. Generally, people like to follow and be part of change. A column might be started in the local newspaper to focus on downtown, including information on what's happening, who is doing what, what new stores are opening, and what new products are being carried. Newspapers stand to gain if an area is vitalized and more advertisements are generated. Such a broadminded approach may divert attention from the narrow, self-centered view of merchants trying to gain financial advantage.

SUPPORT

All options should be examined. It may be that a large scale, comprehensive approach is inappropriate for a particular downtown. Individual opinions, bickering and disagreement may suggest piecemeal or eclectic approaches, implementing small improvements that some merchants and residents want and ignoring areas of disagreement.

Those interested in improving a downtown, might establish a Pedestrian Precinct covering the heart of downtown with extensions uniting adjacent neighborhoods. This district, similar to a Historic Preservation District, would establish a policy of favoring pedestrians over motor vehicles. It would set reduced speed limits, organize parking and drive-in business that compromise pedestrians, provide incentives for pedestrian improvements, etc.

Moreover, the planner should try to differentiate between changes and improvements that are useful to many people,

and those that aren't even though they would be desirable. The real challenge is for merchants and townspeople to understand that new environments can be created from old uses. For instance, who would imagine that from a noisy, smelly and overcrowded street, a pleasant, quiet and safe shopping precinct could be created. Understanding the possibilities is helped by planners and decision makers visiting or studying cities where pedestrian improvements have been made.

Listed below are types of pedestrian improvements that should be avoided:

- Projects that are difficult to stage.
- Projects requiring relocation.
- Projects with high acquisition costs.
- Schemes that cut into buildings for space to widen sidewalks.

Support for improvement projects can sometimes come from unexpected sources. Use improvements as a excuse to have deteriorated underground utilities replaced. The high costs of underground work should be charged to the appropriate agency and not included in expenses for pedestrian improvements. Sewer or water departments might help promote improvements if they too would be able to improve their physical plant. City engineers and traffic planners, those who usually work to accommodate the car, may not be quite as easy to convince about improvements for pedestrians. One approach is to convince them that pedestrians are good customers and that serving the pedestrian is just as important as creating clear ways for the car.

TIMING

Street projects are normally planned with abutting residents and merchants who participate in all design decisions. However, many stores and residents move on a regular basis, and it is important that everyone is kept abreast of the detailed design progress, and more importantly, that work be completed quickly. Several cities have had trouble when one group of merchants or residents approved a plan, the engineering department took several years to install it, and after it was installed, a new group objected strenuously and had the work removed. The lessons are:

1. Keep all interested parties abreast of design progress, changes in plans, and time schedules;
2. Make sure that whatever is decided is installed as quickly as possible.

FINANCING

Public improvements can be paid for privately or publicly. Private funding can be direct with each neighboring land-owner paying a percentage of total costs, or indirect as through a Local Improvement District allowing repayment over a longer period. Privately funded costs are added to the merchandise selling price, so customers actually pay for them. Public funding can be a combination of federal, state or local funds, with federal and state preferred since they won't directly raise property taxes. There are several twists to the public/private split that might look attractive.

The typical reasons for publicly funding pedestrian improvements are to stimulate new construction and to repay the costs through future taxes and new employment. The amount of affordable new construction is difficult to calculate, but can be approximated by prorating development costs over 10 (or 15) years to determine yearly costs, then dividing this yearly figure by the amount of the tax rate. While this figure doesn't account for fixed costs, a ballpark figure can be established. Conversely, *protecting* existing investments, taxes, and employment can also be used to justify public expenditure.

The municipality should pay for certain costs that are clearly public. Underground utility construction costs, which are high, might fall in this category. The municipality might pay for the resurfacing costs of widened sidewalks, improved lighting, traffic signals, curbs, parking, etc.

The Federal government has several programs, most notably Revenue Sharing, which might be tapped. Using State Highway or arterial funds to upgrade adjacent streets may be attractive. And DOT has granted funds for portions of transit malls, bus shelters, ramps for the handicapped and other public transport improvements.

Most small merchants can't pay large amounts at one time, so being able to defer payments over 10 to 15 years might be encouraging. Many states allow formation of a Local Improvement District (LID) for private funding of public improvements that benefit private parties. All improvements typically include sidewalks, benches, street trees and lights and all costs are tax deductible by the businesses.

A development corporation could be established and undertake planning and construction, charging corporate members for the costs over a set period of time. This corporation might manage, advertise, and handle maintenance and repairs for downtown.

Developers of new buildings might be convinced to provide public facilities in exchange for desirable development privileges. Provision of a small plaza, second-story walkway, or additional parking spaces may warrant permission to increase density, expand certain uses or develop an

A garage and several old shops remodeled into a town shopping mall patterned after an early 1900's Main Street. The shops are set back 20 feet, with its own shoppers' arcade, leaving the sidewalk for through walkers. The shops' specialty stores are contrived, but it is enjoyed by its users and has helped make the town a tourist destination. (2 photos)

arcaded sidewalk on public land. Since these improvements would otherwise be paid for by the public, there is no real disadvantage. A somewhat different approach in some states allows developers to be given a tax abatement for up to 20 years to cover the cost of constructing publicly owned improvements.

Part of the cost of converting auto streets to pedestrian usage might be borne by auto-generated taxes. For instance, many streets have been repeatedly paved to accommodate additional traffic. Consequently, increasingly thick pavement has shortened curb height and eliminated drainage in many places, making construction of pedestrian facilities expensive since the pavement often has to be replaced. Thus, it seems reasonable for taxes generated by auto use to be used to fix up streets for pedestrian use.

Funds for pedestrian improvements may be found by reevaluating the Street Improvement Program, and reprioritizing improvements that benefit automobile use. Many towns have 5-year Street Improvement Programs designating expenditures of relatively large amounts of money for arterial widening and other "improvements" that degrade the pedestrian environment while improving the speed and flow of vehicles. Reprioritizing by eliminating, cutting back, and reprogramming may allow enough to fund major pedestrian improvements.

HOW MUCH SHOULD MERCHANTS SPEND TO PEDESTRIANIZE A BUSINESS DISTRICT?

The principal reason to improve a business district is to attract new customers by making shopping more pleasant. New customers will eventually increase sales and profits. It is generally accepted that a "job well done," with attention to parking, beautification, creating image and identity, and solving pedestrian problems can increase overall sales by 15 percent. As a rule of thumb, 3 percent of that gross increase in sales over 10 years could be allocated to create improvements. As an example, an increase in total community sales of 1,000,000 would allow $30,000 construction (3 percent) or $300,000 for 10 years. The 15 percent gross sales increase is normally reduced because most business districts won't carry out all the necessary work. A 10 percent gross increase is more realistic to arrive at the 3 percent construction cost.

Implementation. Develop a Conflict Resolution Policy giving priority to "pedestrians and bicycle circulation" over automobile circulation. The policy would require that when a conflict arises between vehicles and pedestrians or bicyclists on any project or proposed funding, the solution will assure pedestrian and bicycle safety and comfort. The resolution can be used effectively to assign parking space to bicyclists, change signal timing to assure adequate crossing time, change speed limits to favor pedestrians. Most pedestrian and bicycle Capitol Improvement Projects could be given a higher priority than motor vehicle developments. Subsidize the bus system allowing free service on all downtown buses. Fares in cities offering the service are collected in the outlying areas—people going to downtown pay as they enter, while those going home pay as they leave the bus. People entering and leaving the bus downtown pay nothing. The free service speeds travel downtown, as no fares are collected, and discourages car use, since the bus is easier and free. Workers jump on the bus for short rides, and are able to extend their shopping or eat and shop in a different district on a lunch hour and still get back to work on time. Most cities feel the costs are reasonable as they can be a part of a city's plan to reduce air pollution.

Easy Improvements to Downtown Pedestrian Areas—*GOOD:*

- Reduce and enforce the speed of auto traffic
- Adjust signal timing to favor pedestrians
- Widen sidewalks at corners and mid-block with Safe-Crosses
- Landscape and install litter baskets, awnings, benches, etc.
- Add shuttle or transit service

A Bit More Adventurous Improvements—*BETTER:*

- Widen the sidewalk over its length
- Install arcades and covered areas
- Bisect long blocks with pedestrian passageways
- Add mini-parks, courtyards, and other open spaces
- Increase pedestrian elements: benches, fountains, bus, outdoor eating, shelters, sculpture, etc.

Spare No Expenses—*THE BEST:*

- Convert entire streets to pedestrian use
- Add special bus and shuttle service to and through the shopping area
- Enlarge covered walkway system
- Install selective escalators, moving sidewalks, underpasses, bridges
- Program activities such as concerts, displays, art shows, cafes, etc.

Some of these improvements will cause auto traffic delay and shift traffic to other streets—conditions must be dealt with by the planners.

ADAPTING SUBURBAN COMMUNITIES

ADAPTING SUBURBAN COMMUNITIES

Before the automobile became a part of most American households, many people who now live in suburbs were city dwellers who relied on walking for their transportation close to home and on streetcars, trolleys or trains for longer trips. The streetcar and railroad lines generally ran from cities to outlying neighborhoods where houses and businesses clustered near major stops. People usually walked from their homes to public transportation, much as they walked from home to the business district to do their shopping.

Once more and more people were able to afford their own cars, dependence on streetcars, trolleys and trains diminished as did the need to live near them. Since land farther away from city was less expensive, people from city neighborhoods began to see the fulfillment of their dream of owning a detached home with land around it. When developers of these homes learned that people would be willing to drive a little farther to buy even less expensive land, leap-frogging began. Leap-frogging is the practice of developing less expensive and farther from the city while leaving vacant more expensive land closer to the city. Developers of schools, businesses and parks too sought the least expensive land. Thus the result was scattered facilities and communities with no central focus. Because suburban building became so scattered, streetcar and rail transit was inappropriate, ending usually at the city's edge, and the car became the main means of transportation for suburban residents.

That suburban activities require the use of a car and generate large amounts of traffic is well known. In suburban commercial areas, heavy traffic starts early in the morning, and lasts for the entire day until the end of evening rush hour. Traffic is heavy because of the many trips from store to store made by shoppers who find driving between stores easier than walking or bicycling, even though distances may be short enough for these activities. Because of the active, internally generated traffic, walking and bicycling are not safe, or pleasurable or convenient. Consequently, before viable pedestrian improvements can be made, all-day peak traffic *must* be corrected.

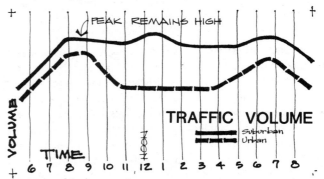

Comparison of urban and suburban traffic patterns throughout a typical weekday. Note that while urban traffic decreases between morning and afternoon peak commute periods, suburban traffic peaks and remains high all day long.

Major pedestrian improvements will come as land-use changes reduce the distances between daily activities. These land-use changes include increasing density and mixing land-uses, two actions residents of suburbs often believe are inappropriate for suburban lifestyles. That point may soon be moot, as increased density and mixed-uses in suburbs are on the upswing. Now apartments and commercial developments are being built along arterials and on land bypassed by leap-frogging. The pattern of development in many suburbs is infilling. This present pattern is now providing more opportunities for infill development to be designed to accommodate pedestrians and bicyclists as well as to take advantage of bus transportation. While converting to accommodate pedestrians and bicyclists is more difficult than downtown, low density development does allow improvements not possible in built-up neighborhoods.

Three typical pedestrian problems, those of safety, function, and pleasure, need to be addressed. *Safety* problems are real or perceived conflicts as people cross streets or walk where there are no sidewalks. Since suburban drivers cover longer distances, and drive faster, the dangers are magnified. The absence of pedestrians on suburban streets dulls drivers' awareness and further aggravates the problem of safety.

Wide intersections, lack of sidewalks and planting strips, large corner turning radii, and high vehicle speed make suburban walking unsafe or appear unsafe to many potential pedestrians.

Functional pedestrian problems are found wherever there is little or no walking space, lack of sidewalks, parked cars along the road's edge, wide driveways, few benches, and barriers. Beyond this another functional problem is the lack of destinations within a reasonable walking distance. Problems that create unpleasant environments for pedestrians and bicyclists are: walking next to noisy, fast moving cars, poor vistas; few rest stops; streetscapes with little of interest to someone who is not driving; vacant lots or large parking lots that are visually dull and potentially unsafe.

Lack of sidewalks, even on new roads, and parking lots located between the road and the shops or apartments, make walking uncomfortable and functionally difficult.

Abandoning the Street. Long driving distances necessary to serve low density increase the speed and volume of suburban traffic, making streets busy and uncomfortable places. To counter this, an "inside-out" development pattern—opposite from prevalent urban development patterns has evolved. While most urban communities focus on and utilize the street, suburban communities turn their backs to the street, and focus human activities on internal gardens, courtyards,

and open spaces. Typically, car parking separates front doors from the sidewalk, and makes using the car seem most natural. Unfortunately, the interior spaces are seldom interconnected, so walking or bicycling for long distances in them is not possible.

The shift was from the urban grid pattern to a suburban road "hierarchy." The grid, typical for many cities, allows free choice of routes, but doesn't necessarily distinguish between high or low volumes of traffic or between streets that are or aren't good to raise families on. The hierarchy changed that, with its system of roads from arterials carrying high traffic volumes, to cul-de-sacs with virtually no vehicular traffic. The secret lies in *not* interconnecting streets, which positively directed through traffic to arterials. Cul-de-sacs soon became the favored street to live on.

Grid patterns developed when travel by foot was important. As the grid was infinitely divisible, it created a fine-grain network that benefitted foot traffic. The hierarchy developed to accommodate the automobile, recognizing that cars can easily travel extra distance, and that as traffic disperses, certain roads should carry more or less traffic than others. Pedestrians unfortunately cannot easily travel longer distances, and are the losers.

The hierarchy, in its conceptual form, includes a separate pedestrian system "internal" to the road system that proportedly assures pedestrian access to different parts of the community. Unfortunately, the internal system was not provided in most cases, and when it was, it didn't lead to the places people wanted to reach because they were located on the roads. Internal circulation spaces were often unsafe because there was so little foot traffic and the varied ownership made access dependent on private property rights. A strategy of: (1) linking internal spaces where possible, and (2) making *the street* usable for pedestrians and bicyclists will enhance suburban living for many people.

Most apartment complexes have ignored foot access to the main entries, treating it mearly as a portion of the driveway. An unattractive entry is not conducive to walking and does not tell residents that walking is desirable or possible. The right photos show two pedestrian-oriented apartment entries extended out to the parking, making it comfortable, safe and pleasant to walk on.

USERS

To begin, the planner should determine where people want or need to travel, the routes they might travel and who these people, the users of improved facilities, are. The most likely users of improved sidewalks and bicycle routes are:

• Children who must be driven to school, play and other activities. Their lives would be improved with safe walks and bikeways leading to schools, and across busy arterials, to shops and recreation facilities.

• Parents who have to drive children would appreciate safe sidewalks and bikeways so their children can move around the community by themselves. Parents too could benefit from walking and bicycling along improved routes. A fully developed bicycle system might eliminate the need for families to own the second or third cars.

• Older people, who may not drive but have time to walk or bicycle, may be able to carry out some of their daily chores, enjoy the out-of-doors, and exercise all on the same trip. Even though an older suburban population is emerging, this age group has all but been ignored in planning. Improved bicycle and walking facilities coupled with smaller, affordable houses may help older residents continue to live in their communities.

• Commuters who live within four to five miles of work may be able to bicycle the distance, saving money while benefitting from physical exercise. Those living further may be able to walk or bike to bus or carpool stops.

• Recreationists, particularly those who regularly walk, jog, or bicycle, would benefit from improved routes and separation from fast-moving traffic.

Slowing down traffic in pedestrian areas is essential to improve the pedestrian's perception of the area's safety, as well as to give a feeling that it is a comfortable place. Motorists driving at 25 m.p.h. or faster have difficulty perceiving that a pedestrian is ready to cross a street, deciding to slow down, and actually doing so. The normal driver usually decides to speed up, assuming that another car will stop. Older pedestrians know this and seldom exert their right. Traffic in pedestrian precincts should be slowed to 20 m.p.h. and policed to achieve a balanced measure of pedestrian safety.

A STRATEGY

Eventually entire suburban communities should be accessible, safe and comfortable for all pedestrians and bicyclists. While that will take time and will require changes in land use, it is possible to prioritize improvements to be made in the foreseeable future. These improvements might include the following:

• facilities that serve the largest group of existing pedestrians;
• facilities that correct the most dangerous, frequently-used places;
• facilities at the busiest locations;
• facilities designed to attract new users, and;
• bicycle facilities.

PRESENT SUBURBAN LAND USES

Suburban land uses affecting pedestrians can be divided into three categories. (Sketch) First, there are *individual tract subdivisions,* planned as units, with a sense of order derived from the in road systems. Access is limited to one or two points. Most are single-family residential though some warehousing, shopping and medical developments exhibit the same characteristics. The distinguishing characteristics are that each subdivision is a recognizable unit, planned as a whole, and can be replanned to better serve the pedestrian.

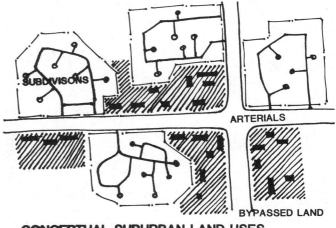

CONCEPTUAL SUBURBAN LAND USES

The second type of land use is *linear arterials* which unite the community through cars. While the roadway portion of arterials most likely was engineered, land-use planning was never done for the apartments, warehouses, offices and business that line arterials. However, arterials with these activities form the backbone of most suburban communities, serving both long distance driving and local business transactions. Arterial strips often convey a sense of the community's image or identity. While this image is presently seldom distinguishing or pleasant, it could be improved with pedestrian-bicycle-related amenities.

Arterials are obvious locations for bicycle and pedestrian improvements since these roads pass most community facilities and are the only direct and relatively long through-roads in the suburban community. However, most arterials have pedestrian safety and environmental problems that must be overcome. If these problems are too great, it may be possible to improve a route parallel to the arterial but one block removed.

The third general type of suburban land use is *bypassed land,* forgotten during initial development, as entrepreneurs leap-frogged out to find cheaper land. These lands infill slower and more haphazardly than planned subdivisions, are likely to have many owners and a variety of land uses, though perhaps not as many as along arterials. Bypassed lands may be the easiest to adapt to pedestrians and bicycle-related improvements, as they have the highest densities, mixed land uses, and are close to a variety of services.

Arterials would be improved by: 1) adding a sidewalk; 2) separating the sidewalk from the roadway with a planter strip; 3) limiting and reducing the width of driveway crossings; 4) narrowing the roadway with center island planting; 5) adding parking to reduce vehicle travel speed, and 6) shifting parking lots to locations behind the building (above). Verify the condition and projected use of all arterials. Many suburban planning agencies expect traffic volumes to increase by up to twice the current volumes. Such an increase would have a dramatic and negative effect on pedestrian and bicycle use of the roadways, unless careful attention is paid to all details (below).

Bypassed land, though almost urban in its density and land use mixture, is primarily auto-oriented. Though streets are regularly widened, traffic speed and volume increase, businesses spread further apart, and parking lots abound, mixed use and higher density make them targets for pedestrianization.

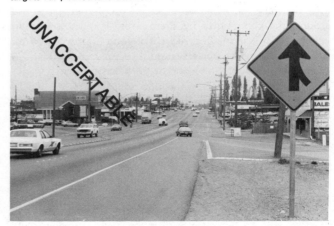

Identify all areas where the sidewalks are too narrow for 2 people to walk abreast of each other, or where the sidewalks are not separated from busy traffic by a planter strip with trees or shrubbery.

AVERAGE DAILY TRAFFIC (ADT)	YEAR	ADT
	1974	1600
	1977	14000
	1990	38000

SAFETY PROBLEMS

The most dangerous places for pedestrians are along suburban roads without sidewalks and intersection treatment.

Minimal safety and comfort can be achieved by narrowing the roadway to reduce travel speed and adding curbs to protect pedestrians and bicycles. Road lanes should be narrowed to 12 feet and the walks should be at least 6 feet wide. Paint the curb white and slow traffic to 25 m.p.h. (above). Improved safety and comfort is achieved by raising the walk and protecting it from cars with a planter strip (above).

Bypass Walkway

Separate the walk from street where there is not enough room to construct it adjacent to the street. Note that even with the separate walk, people have walked in the dirt along the road.

These roads are usually arterials located near schools, bus stops, businesses, or parks. Intersections of residential streets and arterials that have no sidewalks or signals also contribute to risk. Moreover, bus stops have often been located where there are no sidewalks, contributing further to pedestrian hazards.

Because safety problems related to pedestrians are so many in the suburbs, improvements to make bicycling safe may, on balance, prove a better *initial* investment than improvements for pedestrians. Bicycles can travel 5 to 6 miles with relative ease, serving kids going to school, commute trips and many shopping activities. Initial bicycle improvements are inexpensive if striping, shoulder widening and curb cuts are done. Striping and lane alteration could provide space for bicyclists on existing roads, giving them the same access as motorists, and might cost only 5 to 10,000 dollars per mile.

Widen and Stripe for Bicycles

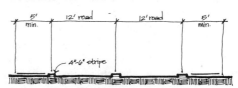

RESTRIPE BUSY ROADS FOR BICYCLES

Develop safe route maps to improve school access safety. As noted, a majority of pedestrian accidents occur to young people, many of them traveling to and from school. To reduce accidents, develop a school trip map, combining the expertise and resources of the Police, Engineering and School Department and local parents. The safe route maps should be developed by walking each access street to identify the safest walking routes and dangerous intersections. The program should develop and distribute handout maps, correct dangerous situations, and continue an ongoing evaluation of the selected routes.

PLANNING WITH THE CAR IN MIND

It is necessary to extend walking and bicycling potential in the suburbs *without* eliminating the car. Suburbs were organized around automobile travel and in many instances won't function well without it. Yet, the car needn't always be dominant and uncontrolled.

Increased car usage has constrained its own flexibility because roads have become more crowded and fuel costs have risen. Extending pedestrian and bicycle access with a community may eliminate some need for the car, allowing increased flexibility for those who have to drive. Walkways should be planned for physical and psychological safety from the auto, yet allow direct and easy access to all types of activities. Most walkways should be planned *in conjunction with* roads, so pedestrians can reach all developments that are located along the road.

PLANNING FOR PEDESTRIAN ROUTES

Conceptual planning is relatively simple. It consists of determining the general direction that walkways should take. These satisfy conditions discussed earlier: focus on shops, schools, cultural attractions and work and play places. Designing the exact route is the complex part. While many people might articulate the desirability of pedestrian routes, few will agree to have their street changed, reduce parking or pay for a widened pedestrian area. Design, then, should be based first on routes that exist, before establishing new ones. Privacy, views, access and local character must be understood and incorporated in the design.

Suburban areas typically consist of many small residential developments, each abutting a major road. These major roads lead to services such as shopping, schools and parks. Pedestrian and bicycle safety problems usually do *not* exist inside individual suburban developments (unless they are large), but they increase on the major roads. The first consideration is: Should these major arterial streets be organized and developed for nonmotorized traffic or do they have unsurmountable auto-related problems that suggest finding an alternative route?

Origin/Destination information is necessary in the suburbs not so much because of the crush of users, but to see where users come from and where they go. Simple pedestrian volume count seldom yields enough information about where people are going or come from, the reason for the trip, and any special pedestrian needs that should be met. This kind of data may be best obtained through observation of by an origin/destination survey that should include the following information:

1. The location of major pedestrian generators such as parking facilities, transit stations, and major residential developments; that is, *where people are coming from.*
2. The location of main pedestrian attractions such as shopping centers, office and public buildings, schools, theaters, colleges, hospitals, sports stadiums; that is, *where people are going.*
3. Existing and potential pedestrian routes between major destinations.
4. Time periods in which major pedestrian flow occurs.

Some new questions to consider:

• Do existing pedestrian routes satisfy the heaviest travel demand? Can a need for new routes be clearly identified?
• Do existing pedestrian routes require improvement to resolve pedestrian circulation problems?
• Which areas seem to be preferred locations for development of new activities to generate pedestrian movement. Note: each activity stimulates more pedestrian movement.
• If new commercial developments are proposed, where will pedestrians travel from to reach them? Will this require adjustments to the existing pedestrian network?

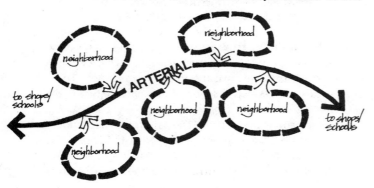

SIDEWALKS

Since destination points were scattered and sidewalks were expensive to construct, early suburban communities had no sidewalks. Later, some communities required developers to install sidewalks. In most suburbs there is a patchwork of sidewalks that stop and start but often aren't linked. In some developments where sidewalks were required, developers constructed them adjacent to the curb, which visually enlarges the roadway, and places pedestrians next to traffic or parked cars. Separation from the street however, by planting strips with trees, lawn or shrubs protects pedestrians from cars, reduces the apparent road width and is essential in new construction. While landscape development increases the short term cost, it makes walking safer and more pleasant for years to come.

The lack of sidewalk, continuous driveways and ground level parking makes this impassible for pedestrians or bicyclists. Introduction of sidewalk with a single auto access leading to internalized auto circulation, is surely appropriate at this housing density. Trees, fences and other landscape development would improve the realm. It may not be possible to serve all of these parking spaces with an internal driveway unless the street is narrowed or used differently. (see sketch).

All sidewalks need not be wide. If traffic is light, and the road narrow, a 3-foot-wide paved strip along the curb allows movement between houses, to and from the car and to places beyond.

This townhouse development is totally oriented to the automobile, with no place to walk except in the street. There are no sidewalks or connections between the internal pedestrian space and the streetscape. Guests must also (shown below) walk in the street to reach their friend's house. Lack of places to walk discourages walking for pleasure and is hazardous for older user groups. Reconstruction providing street trees and sidewalk by narrowing the road would help. It may also be possible to pave between each driveway and provide a safe walk location. Street connections to the internal pedestrian walk should be marked by trellises, fences, street trees or lighting.

Single-loaded roads that twist and turn and carry few cars are acceptable for walking in the street. In this case, a sidewalk may detract from the visual quality of the place and would create an unnecessary air of formality. It may be attractive long-term to provide more trees on the right side of the road, increasing visual diversity and further slowing the speed of traffic. The walk is made safe by its twisting and turning character that slows drivers and increases their alertness.

Add Planting Strip

Separate sidewalks from busy traffic with a planting strip or concrete rail. Close proximity to fast moving traffic is frightening to many people (above). Make sure sidewalks aren't used to widen streets. Some suburban communities require developers to install sidewalks when they develop their property, which makes good economic sense but may make poor pedestrian sense. The walk is forever "disappearing," leaving no protection from cars, and if set back an extra 20 feet, a defacto widening has occurred. Wide streets allow fast moving and increased volumes of traffic, which only worsens the pedestrian environment (below).

Sidewalk width should vary to adjust to physical conditions and pedestrian volume. Sidewalks near schools and stores need more width to accommodate more people. Anyplace where there is a view the sidewalk should be widened and a bench and landscaping added. Should a tree be in the way of the walk, it could be made to curve around the tree. A walk may in places be as narrow as three feet although that serves only one person. Four feet of width barely allows two people to pass while five feet is more comfortable and is considered a standard sidewalk width by many communities. Moreover, a sidewalk along one side is sufficient for most low-density communities.

The City of Bellevue, a suburban community near Seattle, Washington, recommends that the minimum sidewalk widths on residential streets be five feet; on arterial streets, six feet; and on business district streets, eight feet. Five feet is recommended as the width for one-way bicycle routes and eight feet for two-way routes.

Intersections should have larger sidewalk areas to provide waiting room. Curb-cuts should be used on all new sidewalks not exceeding 8% slope. (See Sketch.) Unfortunately, many towns have installed curb-cuts to the side of the sidewalk, but this clutters the intersection, endangers wheelchair users by placing them out of the crosswalk and forces an awkward turn for bicyclists using the sidewalk. The planner should make sure the curb-cut is protected from cars turning the corner. The curb-cut should drain to prevent puddling, and a new drain outlet should be added to the uphill side. In suburbs where a rolled curb is typical, it should be replaced with a curb-cut ramp to accommodate wheelchairs.

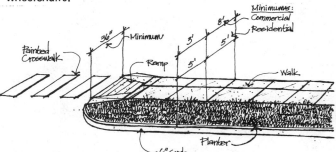

MINIMUM SIDEWALK STANDARDS

Curb cuts imply curbs which, to many suburban residents, are unnecessary and undesirable. The curb, they say, is an *urban* device that takes away from the rural atmosphere. However, curbs are one of the most efficient ways to define where cars can't travel, and when carefully used, improve pedestrian safety and comfort.

Curb Radii. Minimize intersection curb radii to reduce traffic speed and to enlarge the corner pedestrian waiting area. Most curb radii were originally between 2 and 5 feet, but they have been widened to serve faster-moving and larger vehicles. Shorter cars and trucks and increased environmental awareness now allow smaller turning radii at places including:

- The NO-TURN corner of one-way streets can be reduced to a 2 foot radius, as vehicles will never turn in that direction;
- Streets with curbside parking can utilize a 5 foot radius. Parked cars force vehicles to turn from the travel lane, creating its own "artificial" radius of at least 15 feet. This new "artificial" radius is outside the 5 foot curb radius, and therefore, creates no turning problem;

- Intersections with stop signs can have a 5 foot radius as the stop sign forces vehicles to turn slowly, enabling them to negotiate the smaller radius;
- Residential neighborhoods, with slow vehicular speeds should restrict curb radius to 5 feet. Emergency and service vehicles can turn using the other lanes, as few cars are normally present.

Sidewalks are appropriate on suburban roads without curbs but should be separated from the road to avoid their being used for parking. These walks may be constructed of asphalt and may bend around trees or other obstacles in their way. These walks also should ramp to match road grade at intersections so bicyclists and wheelchair users can ride directly into the road. Although constructing temporary sidewalks by widening the road's shoulder often results only in more parking space, there is no pedestrian gain. If a proper sidewalk can't be afforded, a widened shoulder sidewalk should be protected by raising it 6 inches, or by constructing a rolled curb between it and the road.

In order to identify where sidewalks are needed, the planner should mark on a map the type of traffic (little, much, slow, fast) on all residential streets. Streets should be noted that have sidewalks on at least *one* side. From a planning standpoint a sidewalk on *one* side of each residential suburban street is a reasonable goal. Any sidewalks at all may elicit complaints from people who believe that sidewalks are for cities, not suburbs. However, well designed sidewalks need not conform to grid patterns, need not be constructed in straight lines, or uniform in width and are usually not paralleled by curbs. In other words, suburban sidewalks should not necessarily be linear and geometric but should flow with the landscape.

For instance, a sidewalk may wander to and fro, it may lack a curb and it may be separated from the road by a planted swale that serves as a gutter. The walk may be surfaced with asphalt or gravel. It may be landscaped with trees planted in random patterns, in clumps, or densely as in a forest. And it may be very narrow in some places, say three feet, or very wide, say six feet, in other places.

The planner should note the location of schools, and busy streets which children must cross to get there. Special notice should be given to known short cuts and off-road routes used by children. The location should be recorded of convenience shopping complexes used on a regular basis, with such stores as grocery, department, drug, clothing, liquor, stationery, hardware, bank, etc. However, the planner should *ignore* specialty outlets such as car repair, furniture stores, lumber yards, etc. It is important to pinpoint access routes of pedestrians and bicyclists who follow busy roads. Then the planner should locate pedestrian and bicycle safety problems such as street crossings, wide driveways and large parking lots on each access road and propose solutions to correct these problems.

Planting trees in an irregular arrangement within the parking lane reduces the linearity and openness of many streets and adds pedestrian scale to the space.

Locate all convenience shopping stores that are relatively close to nearby neighborhoods. Add sidewalks, reduce drive entry widths and narrow streets to improve the pedestrian realm.

The location of commuter bus stops, particularly "flyer" park-and-ride stops, should be marked as well as any difficult pedestrian/bicycle access problems, such as busy streets to cross or walk along. Opportunities such as short cuts that make access easier should be noted as well. The planner should try to envision how pedestrian/bicycle routes could connect bus stops to residential developments in the community. Since the success of suburban transit depends partly on the adequacy of sidewalks and the ease with which people can walk to bus stops, it is essential that safe sidewalks, separated from traffic, lead to each bus stop from nearby developments.

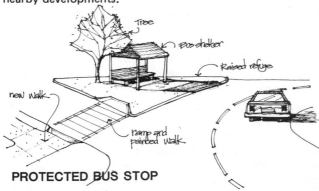

PROTECTED BUS STOP

Sidewalks should be incorporated into parking lots to separate buildings from roads and to enhance each entry. Separating roads from buildings makes living inside quieter and more private. Building entries connected to the public sidewalks can enhance transit use and stimulate walking.

Avoid roads and parking spaces that block building entries. The road passing this close to a doorway is a danger both for people entering or leaving the apartments and should be separated from the door with a walk space and planter. In the photo below, the building entry is completely blocked by a parking space, which should be removed and converted to a raised sidewalk with pedestrian scale and detail—perhaps mail boxes, landscaping, a bench, special paving, etc.

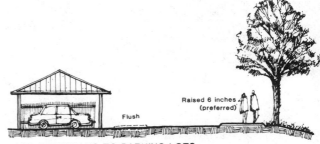

ADD WALKWAYS TO PARKING LOTS

The sidewalk can be flush with the roadway if there isn't enough room, or it can be raised providing additional protection for the walker. Where possible, plant trees to provide visual variety and some weather protection for the walker.

SUMMARY OF SIDEWALK REQUIREMENTS

Walkways which are to be sufficiently safe, convenient, secure, and cause the least nuisance to residents must:

1. Traverse the shortest routes possible between homes and community facilities;
2. Be segregated from arterial roads and busy residential streets by a wide planter or parking lane;
3. Have gradients below eight percent, and ideally below five percent (particularly where elderly and disabled people live and walk);
4. Be busy, well-lit, and overlooked by dwellings, and passing traffic;
5. Have curbs or other barriers to prevent vehicles from using the sidewalk or planting strips;
6. Offer some protection from rain, wind, or snow; and
7. Be sufficiently wide to allow easy flow of pedestrian and bicycle traffic.

Enlarge traffic islands to provide protected space for waiting to cross. The minimum perpendicular dimensions for a raised refuge should be 12 feet. Smaller refuges should be curbed at the apex for protection with a flush walk to facilitate smooth through movement. (See sketch.)

Parking lots used for pedestrian circulation need not be totally paved. Concrete strips for cars to park on, with the space between left and grass is attractive for walkers as well as for upper story residents who look at the parking lot.

The private street is a suburban phenomena used to develop substandard streets to service medium-density housing. These streets are unlike public streets in many ways: they generally have no sidewalks; the houses are detached and separated from them; few units overview the street; they are seldom used for anything but driving; and, they are not congenial for pedestrians. Most could be corrected or enhanced for pedestrian use.

STREET CLOSINGS

There is little need to close *most* suburban streets, because at low densities, traffic volumes are usually light and most residents are not willing to give up their streets. However, there are some places where street closings would enhance a neighborhood or community. Although most homes have gardens, the extent of suburban growth makes drives to scenic or recreational areas long and often unpleasant, thus excluding people who have little free time. The need to find recreation and scenery close at hand is growing, and can be partly met by converting little used streets into common greens. Even though the concept of a common green in many cities is of a manicured lawn surrounded with an iron fence, the suburban counterpart may take on a very different form, perhaps meadow grass and informal tree plantings with a walk along one side or a forest of trees. A common green could be a play area for neighborhood children with a basketball hoop, tennis court or grass for active sports. Or it could be used as a neighborhod pea patch for raising produce. The following are several situations where closing suburban streets makes good sense.

• Any community without curbs, gutters and proper street paving should consider closing some streets instead of having them improved. The cost savings to the community may be enough reason for closing streets. It may be possible to serve a community with several one-way streets, and several closed streets converted to community open space. (See example.)

• Suburban apartment communities can benefit from street closings because there are large numbers of people to use the new space. Often noise and safety problems can be corrected by closing certain streets. Efforts should begin with construction of safe-crosses at key corners, to ease crossing problems and define legal parking spaces. Some parking lots could be used as local streets, allowing more flexibility for closing other streets. Some examples of street closings are shown.

• Many suburban streets belong to property owners rather than municipalities. For such streets, problems of approval for conversion are somewaht reduced, though municipalities will require fire and police access after conversion. Residents seeking to make their communities more distinctive and useful may find that converting streets to pedestrian or other recreational uses does just that. It isn't necessary to close many streets, just enough to create a special feeling and to provide some community focus with a pedestrian trail or small park. For example, Greenwood Commons, a community in Berkeley, California, created from an unbuilt street has enormous charm and attraction for residents and others who use it.

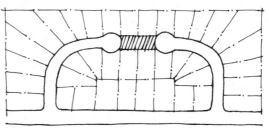

CLOSE LOOP WITH CUL-DE-SACS

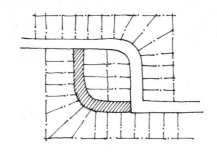

ADD TRAFFIC ISLAND IN CUL-DE-SACS

NARROW STREET IN PLACES

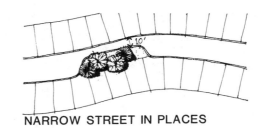

Existing streets can be removed, regarded and planted at a reasonable cost *if* treatment is kept simple. Where there are no utilities, old pavement can be buried with a mount. Trees should be planted so as to avoid underground utilities. Grass could be a rough meadow type, such as to withstand heavy use. Neighboring residents could change their front yards by fencing to gain more privacy.

• There is no physical reason why certain municipally owned streets in suburban developments could not be closed. This would require overall community agreement which might be difficult to obtain. However, if the decision were left to smaller units within the community, such as residents who want to close a street in front of their homes, the decision may be easier.

Not every street can be closed. Main streets that serve cul-de-sac and loop roads must remain open, though they may be narrowed with a bicycle path and sidewalk. Since most cul-de-sacs are already quiet, there would be no reason to close them. However, their turn-arounds could be re-landscaped to be more distinctive. Another suggestion is for loop roads to be cut in half, forming two culs-de-sac, and the area between them to be closed. A summary of streets that could be closed is shown.

Closing streets will, most likely, not be accomplished without opposition because of upkeep and vandalism problems, as well as problems of assuring driveway access and privacy. However, each can be solved with proper planning. Maintenance is easier if the landscaping is a simple forest or meadow where grasses are left in their natural state, which is green in winter and brown in summer. Costs can be lower if a proper street has never been constructed than if one has, though removal of an existing street and replacement with a simple landscape is not too expensive if neighborhood labor is organized. Vandalism of the new space can be minimized if there are enough users, and the place is overviewed by nearby residents.

Some streets have all the characteristics necessary for closure except that some garages need access. Leaving a narrow roadway to garages generally won't meet municipalities' road standards and won't allow enough room for pedestrian improvements. It is, however, permissible for residents whose access is lost to drive slowly on a wide pedestrian walk to get to their garages. Policing by residents to prevent parking on pedestrian walks would be necessary, and motorists would have to drive carefully to get to their garages. (See sketch.) Alternately new garages could be constructed outside the street closing area.

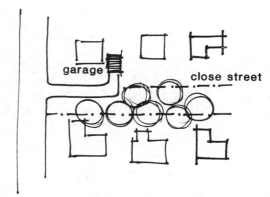

Sidewalks immediately adjacent to roadways have become almost standard in suburban residential neighborhoods. Unfortunately they widen the street visually causing increased traffic speed and decreased pedestrian safety.* Vary the treatment—adding planters to narrow the street on occasions and to instill a sense of care in drivers while enhancing the walking space.

Narrowing a road to 12 feet allows access without the noise and safety problems of fast-moving traffic. The surplus land was added to each garden, though it could have used side of the road for a widened walk or bikeway.

IMPROVEMENTS IN ARTERIALS

The entire arterial length need *not* be improved for pedestrians and bicyclists. Since arterials change in character over distance, for instance, being commercial development, then perhaps warehouses, apartments, developed parks, etc., pedestrian treatment should change along the way to relate to each land use. However, the *entire* arterial should be made safe and pleasant for bicyclists. Using arterials as commuter bicycle routes may be the most efficient way to increase nonmotorized circulation. Arterials lead to places where people work, shop and recreate and tend to serve bicyclists living within a 5 to 6 mile radius.

Rolled curbs provide minimal but necessary protection to encourage active use. Pedestrian areas immediately adjacent to arterials (i.e. not separated by parked cars) should be minimum 8 feet wide and protected with a curb. To improve this condition, either move the curb toward the street (a possibility here, as the curb lane is 14 feet wide) or add a paved walk on the property side. Adding sidewalks may necessitate obtaining an easement or purchasing private property. Raising the sidewalk 6-8 inches above the street, and separating it with a planter strip further improves safety. (Upper photo.) Arterials with wide shoulders are easily converted for bicycle use. Simply pave an 8 foot wide raised path on one side of the road, leaving room for arterial expansion on the other side and drainage swales.

CHANGING THE HIERARCHICAL ROAD SYSTEM

The traffic planning system organizes streets hierarchically according to the amount of traffic carried and the speed at which it flows. The hierarchy includes three or four levels, from major freeways, to arterials and finally, local roads. The current pedestrian interest lies in protecting local roads from traffic problems, with little effort concentrated on improving arterials. Drivers use arterials for access and inner-city travel. Arterials are also the only access for bicyclists and pedestrians to reach work, shopping or school. Most arterials are restricted from being adjusted to better serve pedestrians by regulations embodied in our hierarchical traffic planning approach.

The question put forth is: Should we modify that system, and allow *all roads* to be adjusted as necessary to contain traffic and make the place attractive for pedestrians and bicyclists? Restraining traffic on arterials would reduce the numbers of cars and speed of travel, making room for increased pedestrian and bicycle activity. It would also make it more pleasant for those living, working or shopping on the arterial. Presently, a large number of people work or live on arterials—that is, the density of apartments and commercial activity is high on arterials. This is an anomaly as arterials are typically the worst environments to live on.

It may be impossible to use extreme traffic control devices on arterials, for instance, cul-de-sacs and diverters. However, narrowing the street, using safe-crosses at intersections, adding stop signs and rumble strips, raising the crosswalk, and adding parking (particularly angled parking) help reduce the speed of travel.

What would happen to the traffic? Some of it would probably disappear—the "phenomenon of disappearing traffic"—that is, some drivers would convert to foot, bicycle, bus, or postpone the trip. Some may be transferred to nearby local residential streets, and that might cause an uproar. However, this author believes that pressures from local residents protecting their street would control that traffic.

Eliminating the hierarchy has other theoretical planning ties. For instance, there is continual discussion of the need to increase density and mix land-uses to benefit pedestrian circulation. The hierarchy in traffic planning was directly linked to early attempts to separate land uses. Separate, single-purpose land uses and separate road types went hand in hand. Mixed land-uses and higher densities and separate, single-purpose road types seem less appropriate. Must we revise our thinking about roads to fit our current thinking about land use?

Some planners suggest a two-category road hierarchy; one category for through travel, and the other for local use. This would eliminate many arterials and concentrate traffic on freeways, highways or major boulevards with all other roads for local or less active use. This would also be a major change in road planning, and would require sufficient funding to make sure that through roads were carefully designed and planned to insure the quality of the abutting environment.

AREAS TO CONSIDER

The first areas to consider for pedestrian improvements are those along arterials that have neighborhood convenience shopping or those on cross streets leading to nearby neighborhoods. Pedestrian improvements should begin at these busy intersections and continue along the arterial in both directions for the length of the business district. Presently, arterial traffic problems in business districts are largely conflicts between through and shopping traffic. If each store is able to be reached only by car, the cars traveling between stores conflict with through traffic, making walking between stores nearly impossible. Conflicts are made worse by the disorganized arrangement of stores, by large and overused intersections, by lack of consolidated parking, and by an undefined relationship between cars, pedestrians and bicyclists. On the plus side, some through traffic can be rerouted and some internally generated traffic eased as well.

INFORMATION GATHERING

In order to start the planning effort for arterials, it is necessary to develop an analysis of each arterial and locate convenience shopping nodes, apartments, obvious beginnings and ends of each strip development, natural amenities, and well-known landmarks such as signs and stores that are visible from the road. The planner should also make note of:

- auto-dominated intersections;
- conflict between through and commercial traffic;
- excessive driveway and cross street interruptions along the arterial;
- all bus stops;
- stretches of road with no sidewalks;
- sidewalks that directly abut streets;
- schools and parks;
- major commercial nodes; and
- interesting topography.

CHECK OFFICIAL PLANS TO DETERMINE WHAT IMPROVEMENTS ARE PLANNED:

- What is the Engineering and Transportation Planning Section missing? If they are responsible for planning and carrying out a "balanced transportation plan," catering to pedestrians, as well as cars, they could be forced to follow their ordinance mandate.
- Check the Arterial Plan to learn the official traffic position. Many towns anticipate traffic doubling during the next ten years and have scheduled road improvements to handle that traffic. Enlarging present capacity is likely to be too complex to reasonably handle without serious consequences to the overall pedestrian quality. Question the projected growth, and raise the issue politically. The environmental and dollar expense to meet large increased traffic volumes is high, and funds may be better used to enhance non-motorized circulation.
- Compare the Bicycle Plan (if there is any) with the Arterial Plan and mark overlapping areas as needing extra study and development.

ARTERIAL CIRCULATION						
STREET TYPE	TRAFFIC LANES		SIDEWALKS		BIKEWAYS	
	EXISTING	ULTIMATE	EXISTING	ULTIMATE	EXISTING	ULTIMATE
FREEWAY/EXPWAY						
PRINCIPAL ARTERIALS						
MINOR ARTERIALS						
COLLECTORS						

BARELY ACCEPTABLE

Stripe for bicycles

The first low cost step may be to stripe inside the pavement edge, creating minimal recognition of bicycle safety. Allow 5 feet of pavement on each side for two direction flows (above). Organize parking lots to minimize curb-cut entries and begin to define a safer walking area. Restrict parking to assure through walking space and slow traffic speed (below).

Better

Avoid bicycle barriers

Construct raised walks separated from the road by either adjacent parking or planting strips. Encourage retail businesses to relocate adjacent to the road, with parking in the rear. Plant heavily.

Convert wide arterials to two streets—a through road and an adjacent service road. Encourage pedestrian and bicycle use of the service road with wide walks, wheelchair ramps, trees, and shops with windows. A one-way road serving parallel parking on 2 sides need be only 24 feet wide. Add 6 feet of walk on the road side, and 8' on the shop side. (See photos and plan below.)

UNACCEPTABLE
No Pedestrian Safety or Pleasure

Walk with shops

Ramps

Wide outside lane

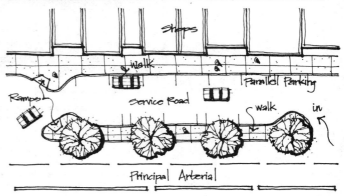

A COMPLETE PEDESTRIAN SYSTEM

FACTORS TO CONSIDER

To establish complete pedestrian and bicycle circulation, the planner should consider several factors simultaneously: What land is available? What origins/destinations exist? What funding is possible? What conceptual ideas are valid? And, what design opportunities can be created? A complete pedestrian/bicycle network must be varied, complex, intertwining, and literally connect everybody to everything. Much of the network will probably be standard sidewalks, perhaps landscaped and made to appear more than "just standard". Shortcuts are extremely important because they increase the number of possible destinations without increasing distances. In designing a network, it is important to consider the types of people who would use a pedestrian-bicycle route.

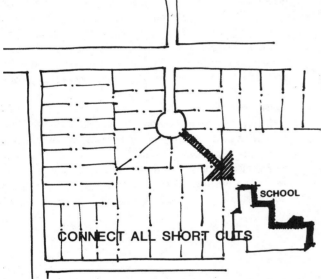

Open pedestrian ways connecting cul-de-sacs to schools, parks or public services. A network of access routes that avoid arterials increases walking pleasure and safety. These routes could be connected along the property lines—by obtaining an easement or allowing a tax abatement to one or both properties.

- *Recreationists* who are enjoying leisure time. These users are concerned with experience and amenity. Getting somewhere in a hurry isn't important. Long, continuous walkways with pleasant views, rest areas, refreshments and safety from car dangers are needed. Recreational elements such as parks, lakes, natural areas, recreation centers, refreshment stands and community cultural facilities could be linked. Pedestrian and bicycle routes could be combined.
- *Commuters* who are interested in getting somewhere. They need origin/destination routes that connect neighborhoods with downtown, other employment/activity centers and transit. Efficiency is most important, but not at the expense of safety and some experience. These routes

should be associated with existing roads and should link to natural, architectural and historical features and convenience shopping, as well.

- *Neighborhood* users are interested in getting everywhere within the community. Special circulation routes in neighborhoods are difficult to justify due to lack of volume or definable destination. The best solution is to plan for sidewalks with planter strips, corner curbcuts, street trees, lighting and necessary safety features along major neighborhood streets.

There are several attractive parts of this suburban streetscape: the garage doors make it difficult for a pedestrian to accidentally be run over and they tidy up the streetscape; second-floor balconies provide views of the street making it safer and offering the potential to say "hello" to neighbors as they walk through the neighborhood; and the small planters plus sidewalk make it attractive to walk. However, the sidewalk's location—immediately abutting the roadway with depressions for driveways make walking somewhat difficult as the sidewalk is continually rising and falling and one can trip over the undulations. A narrow planting strip or a rolled curb would increase pedestrian comfort.

A pedestrian route along an arterial has an important function; that is to:

- *Link All Social Services:* Schools, parks, libraries, churches, playgrounds, cultural facilities, all public services likely to attract pedestrians. The linkages will most likely be along existing roads but could be routed through vacant land, around natural features, along abandoned roads and through parking lots or underused areas.
- *Link All Community Services.* Beside social services, these include shopping, medical-professional offices and entertainment.
- *Link All Amenities:* View areas, forests, streams, rivers, shorelines wherever possible. Diversity and activity, whether commercial or recreational should be included on all walking routes.

Enhancing pedestrian circulation is a matter of several interrelated improvements:

1. *Determining Pedestrian Precincts.* Locate areas where walking distances are reasonably short (or can be made short) and concentrate on improving function and convenience of walking within each area. Link these PRECINCTS with important work and housing places by means other than the car to reduce the number of cars within the pedestrian precinct. Reducing the number of cars eases the suburban traffic buildup that makes it difficult (maybe impossible) to move from location to location. What ares can be Pedestrian Precincts? Places of employment, downtowns, campuses, shopping complexes, recreation areas, apartment complexes, etc. Some pedestrian precincts may need only one function eased—for instance, if most workers commute by foot, bicycle or bus, there may be sufficient road capacity to allow shoppers to drive to the pedestrian shopping precinct, but carry out their shopping on foot, returning occasionally to the car with packages. However, they would not move the car between shops as that distance could be covered easier on foot.

Each pedestrian precinct would be divided into zones roughly a quarter of a mile in diameter and originating from some central focus. A quarter mile is a reasonable distance to walk between daytime activities and can be covered in travel in five minutes. The need for a bicycle, car or a bus is minimal to nonexistent. A neighborhood, community center or campus may have four or five different pedestrian zones, each with a central focus that could be identified as having users and activities that are used frequently or an amenity that is attractive.

In addition to these pedestrian zones would be two other zones used for organizing commute trips. There should be a one-mile walk zone within which people could walk to work easily and return again in the evening. A one-mile walk requires about 20 minutes for an average walker and is within the realm of reasonable commuting. There may be several walk zones that focus around each quarter-mile pedestrian zone. It's assumed that no motorized assist would be necessary within a one-mile walk zone and that buses, cars or other motorized assists would not generally be used. On top of that would be a five-mile bicycle commute zone where easy access to and from work, to and from shopping and other daily activities could be accomplished easily on the bicycle. These zones would help establish priority for improving pedestrian bicycle circulation. Conflict resolutions and capitol improve-

ment and maintenance funds should favor pedestrians within the quarter-mile zones where walking occurs continually during the day and would decrease as it moved out toward the five-mile bicycle zone.

Develop a Pedestrian Precinct zoning district for each type of use and designate each area. This could be like a historic district in organization. In these precincts, traffic would travel slower, through traffic would be discouraged, certain streets would be converted to predominantly pedestrian uses, noise and pollution levels would be reduced, and walkers' safety would be increased. Building design and landscaping would be pedestrian-scaled with increased visual detail, resting and eating places and protection from the elements. Mixed and higher-density land uses should be encouraged throughout the precinct.

2. *Improving Access.* Improved access to pedestrian and bicycle attractions—schools, shops, work and play places, and cultural and public buildings. Determine rationally where most people will come from—close by neighborhoods, neighborhoods with many children or elderly people, residential communities near factories, a neighborhood with low-car ownership, close to parks, schools or shops or places well-served by public transit.

Make sure pedestrians can safely reach all neighborhood stores. Increasing the number of stores at one location achieves a community focus and may encourage people to walk. Zoning relief to encourage new pedestrian businesses and down zoning along strips outside the business district to centralize new shopping may be necessary. Allocating parking is always a dilem-

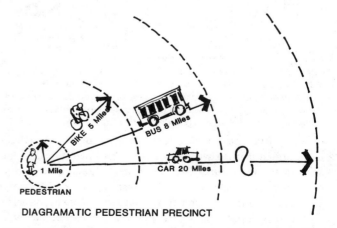

DIAGRAMATIC PEDESTRIAN PRECINCT

Open a pedestrian way connecting cul-de-sacs to schools, parks or public services. A network of access routes that avoids arterials increases walking pleasure and safety. These routes could be connected along the property lines—by obtaining an easement or allowing a tax abatement to one or both properties.

ma and some interim compromise between foot and car access must be reached. Providing safe, clear pedestrian access even at the expense of additional parking encourages walking.

Devise a long-term street improvement approach, even if it is eclectic. Two conceptual options exist: Make *all* streets attractive and safe for walking—a vast net which afforts many different ways to each destination: or the opposite—several organized, special pedestrian routes which focus on known pedestrian destinations. The first is appropriate if the neighborhood is large and no primary routes are evident, while the second may function well near known destinations and as the volume of walkers increases. The special route can be separate from the streets, but pedestrians walks that don't follow the street can be disorienting to users. People are used to the streets, are familiar and orient easily to them, and have learned how to get around on them. Take the streets away and some people may become lost or disoriented, uncomfortable or confused over their right to be there, their safety and possible escape routes.

Should all streets be pedestrianized? Pedestrians and cars are compatible in many instances, but there are times when one gets in the other's way and should be eliminated, or when one is more appropriate and should prevail. Most streets fit into one of five categories of pedestrian-auto compatibility. At the extremes are roads that serve only the car or only the pedestrians. These two, the *freeway* and the pedestrian mall or *Foot Streets* occur only in limited parts of the total town or city. One notch down are two opposites: *Main Streets* and *Arterials,* each serving both users but favoring one. Business district main streets are destinations serving pedestrians but still needing some auto access. They should cater to both, but favor the PEDESTRIAN. Cars should drive slowly, pedestrian areas should be enlarged, driveways and drive-ins should be eliminated, parking organized, defined and landscaped, and the general flavor scales to pedestrians. Arterials are through-ways and though they connect some places that pedestrians (more likely bicyclists) need to reach, auto circulation should be emphasized with bicyclists and pedestrians allocated as safe travel place. A sidewalk with curb cuts for handicapped and bicycles is a good start, with minimal landscaping and safe access to abutting business districts. Reaching strip-type businesses is often difficult to implement, for it will cut into the car's domain. However, the fact that businesses have added special handicapped parking and facilities suggests that they may also be able to find

space for walkers and bicyclists. Restriping parking lots to accommodate smaller cars may free up enough space for pedestrian needs.

The fifth category, is a shared street, where both the traffic and pedestrian usage is light and there is no need to assign priority. Residential streets that do not serve as travel ways to neighborhoods beyond are examples. Cars, pedestrians and bicyclists can safely share this space with no disadvantage to the other.

The planner should study all possibilities and then prepare a list of places where the best pedestrian route should go regardless of ownership or political considerations. Sometimes knowing the optimum possibility regardless of feasibility or cost can lead to a solution previously considered impossible. Areas to include on a wish list are:

- *Vacant Lands.* Open space, unbuilt land, underused land such as industrial areas, parking lots, gas stations, corporation yards and cemeteries are potentially "soft" land which may be purchased or used at minimum cost. Planting and development could be done over time. The most important step is acquiring fee ownership or right-of-way.

- *River or Drainage Channel.* Many neighborhoods have drainage systems which are almost level, flow long distances and offer the potential for a pedestrian route with the addition of some landscaping. Walkways can be increased in apparent length by varying the landscape treatment and decreasing the scale. One section of a walk can even be laid out parallel to another part, provided plantings and grade changes are carefully handled. Subtle design devices used in oriental gardens should be studied.

Link suburban neighborhoods through ravines, along creeks and streams, through forests and any other places with relief from the streetscape. This informal walk along a drainage ditch offers change from the normal street pattern and is used for recreation as well as short-cuts by commuters.

Requiring public access along drainage easements, particularly in apartment areas allows safe, pleasant and continuous foot access for many people. Preserve a minimum 20 foot strip extending occasionally with benches, play equipment, landscape development, etc.

Walkway route size and completeness depend on the intensity of use and extent of automobile conflict. The walkway can be compared to road system with feeder roads leading to local roads, which lead to highways, each increasing in size and requiring increased amounts of pedestrian separation. In single-family areas with light pedestrian use and limited auto traffic, standard sidewalks are fine. Bicyclists can use either the street or the sidewalk. As the route approaches more intense activity, it may include intersection safe-crosses or wider walkway areas where many pedestrians can congregate.

The planner should explore the possibility of developing shortcuts linking tract developments so pedestrian/bicyclists don't have to use the main arterials. Shortcuts may go through school yards, parks, along easements and along property lines of lots that have sufficient width so owners might sell or donate a small strip. (See sketch.) Fences will be necessary along shortcuts where the walkway should be paved and some planting provided. Five feet is suggested width for such a shortcut, although 8 to 10 feet would allow room for path and planting. The planner should look

for possible linkages between parcels of unbuilt land. As the land is developed, the municipality may bargain to have walkways constructed through the land or along an edge in exchange for favorable zoning treatment.

Planning for the future. Some pedestrian shortcuts won't be appreciated for a number of years. However, this narrow walk connecting a cul-de-sac with adjacent street should enjoy increased use over time. The closely spaced bollards and incomplete paving decrease present usage (above).

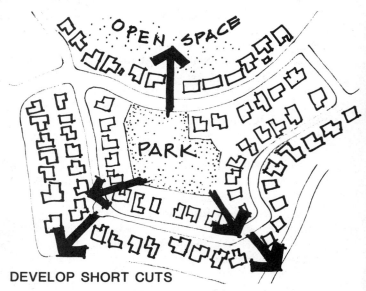

DEVELOP SHORT CUTS

The planner should urge the municipality to adopt P.U.D. requirements for all subdivision and lot splits. Under a P.U.D. a developer is required to construct walkways through a development in exchange for relaxation of setback restrictions and more flexible planning. Subdivision developers are now asked to install streets and utilities but could also construct bicycle and pedestrian routes through their property. Walks could be located between or behind dwelling units, along the street, or street and interior paths could be combined. The least costly method is to narrow the suburban streets' width, using the recaptured space for sidewalks and bicycle paths. Roads could be narrowed to a 26 foot width with parking on only one side. A single pedestrian walk could then be 10 to 15 feet wide including space for trees and landscaping and further widened in places to take advantage of views or natural amenities.

Pedestrian ways, whether separate or alongside the road, may thread through a community to:

- Link parks, school yards and other public lands;
- Connect and go through shopping and commercial centers;
- Pass through higher density portions of a community. These routes might be parklike to compensate for high density.
- Replace underused streets, converting a two-way street to one-way, and using the remaining land for pedestrians and bicyclists;
- Parallel streams or rivers. Pedestrian walks and "conservation uses" are often compatible if this land is not developed intensively;
- Serve as buffer space, between different land uses, around the perimeter of a development or along a highway. With a little extra effort, buffers can become useful open space.

Make sure that all separate pedestrian routes have provisions for handling the bicycle.

THE DUTCH WOONERF

Several years ago, the Dutch city of Delft converted several small residential streets from traffic roads to "living places" shared by both cars and pedestrians. They are called Woonerf—which means "living courtyards" or "residential courtyards." The Woonerf is created by narrowing the entry to the street at each end and placing other obstacles in the way of the drivers throughout the course of the street. The street is posted for a maximum emergency vehicle speed of about 15 miles per hour, and a maximum car speed of 8 miles per hour. Parking is allowed in marked areas and play and walking can occur any place within the street. Drivers know that they must be aware of children, pedestrians, and the peace and quiet demanded by residents living alongside the road.

Woonerfs work in Holland for several reasons. First, they are used *only* on short isolated residential streets and do not force through traffic onto other streets. Secondly, they are placed randomly, rather than as an organized system, which further restricts buildup of excessive traffic. Thirdly, because of poor Dutch soil, the Public Works Department must rebuild streets every ten years. Consequent-

ly, the Government has a relatively high budget for street work and a need to do it on a periodic basis. It is just as easy to build raised areas to decrease speed as to build normal streets.

There have been comments as to their walkability as they can become so filled with contraptions to slow traffic that they are not truly walkable. The objective of slowing traffic can be taken too seriously, with more landscape elements added than is necessary.

In America, the need for extensive development may not exist in most suburban communities. Wide residential streets are easier to make safe than narrow Dutch streets. It could be attractive in urban neighborhoods in larger cities, and has been tried in Boston and New York. However, the fact that some cities have developed this type of street pattern, that residents enjoy it, that relatively large amounts of money are spent to create them and that they work is useful information. It may be that simpler developments would satisfy the same needs—close down the street with safe crosses and a raised crosswalk, add extra street trees instead of bollards in the street, etc.

Convert some residential street to a European type "Play Street." Many European communities have reconstructed suburban streets to force traffic to drive slowly. The streets are narrow, irregular, bend frequently, and are treated to enhance walking. Cars and pedestrians share the street, with no special sidewalks. This street *almost* succeeds. It is narrow, varied, parking is in small, contained spaces, garage doors are used, and the street is landscaped.

Some new suburban communities are installing large-diameter metal drainage culverts for pedestrian and bicycle underpasses. The culvert is depressed slightly while the road is raised slightly to balance cut and fill and to minimize the length of ramps. (See photo.) A relatively inexpensive underpass can be graded to blend with the overall topography during initial site preparation provided that the road is not over 30 feet wide, that drainage is adequate and that careful landscape and lighting treatment are included. It may be possible to select a valley or drainage swale and construct a car bridge overhead with pedestrians crossing beneath. Ideally the bridge should be open construction rather than earth fill to assure light and protection for pedestrians and bicyclists.

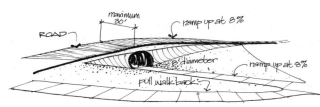

INEXPENSIVE UNDERPASS

Criteria for evaluating sidewalk and bicycle locations would include:

1. Coordination with local plans
2. Access to population
3. Access to recreational sources
4. Access to urban activities
5. Linkages with different systems
6. Aesthetic and visual interest
7. Multiple use of the corridor
8. Prior activities
9. Feasibility
10. Urgency of acquisition

WAYS TO IMPROVE

Reduced Speeds. Reducing the speed of travel, say to 25 m.p.h., on arterials may be the easiest step to improve the roadway for pedestrians and bicyclists. Twenty-five miles per hour is enforceable. Furthermore, a reduced speed increases the road's traffic capacity, which may be beneficial for roads that are narrowed to accommodate bicycles and pedestrians.

Separation. Separation of pedestrians and motorized traffic is essential along arterials. Many suburban arterials have no sidewalks or a narrow sidewalk that directly abuts the street. Problems caused by no or inadequate sidewalks are:

• The lack of a sidewalk prevents walking or forces pedestrians onto the shoulder in good weather, and in the street when it rains and the shoulder becomes muddy and wet.

• Pedestrians walking on dark pavement are not visible at night, thus endangering themselves. A sidewalk separated from the street by a planting strip is necessary where pedestrians are likely to walk. It has been shown that sidewalks decrease pedestrian accidents by as much as 25 percent. Unfortunately, when many arterials have been widened to fill the entire road right-of-way, the only way to separate pedestrians from traffic is to narrow the road.

Elimination of Parking Lanes. Roads with parking one or both parking lanes can be eliminated to provide space for a sidewalk. The space gained could be used on both sides of the road or allocated to one side if there are more destination points on that side. Elimination of parking can improve traffic flow, since the interruption of car parking is eliminated. Parking spaces at intersections should be eliminated in favor of safe-cross sidewalk extensions to define the parking and ease pedestrian street crossings.

Five-Lane Roads. On five-lane arterials with a common road section of two lanes in each direction and a left-turn lane, three lanes could be maintained for traffic and the other two lanes converted to pedestrian use. The three lanes should be divided into a wide lane for each direction and a narrower turning lane shared by both. Each traffic lane should accommodate between 1200 and 1800 vehicles per hour, depending on the number of driveways and intersections that interrupt it. The two outside lanes could be converted to pedestrian and bicycle use with new curbs and gutters, and signs, or each could be striped for bicycle use. Only on the roadway with a sidewalk on the building side. The bicycle lane would keep fast-moving cars separated from pedestrians.

Slowing down traffic speed by narrowing wide arterials is essential if pedestrians and bicyclists are to use the road. Narrow and consolidate driveway entries to reduce sidewalk interruptions.

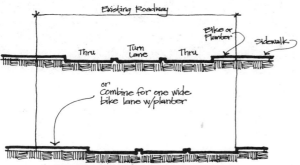

4 LANE CONVERSIONS

Four-Lane Roads. Four-lane arterials can be converted into roadways with three traffic lanes, one left-turn and two through lanes. The turning lane can aid free movement, while each single, wide traffic lane with no adjacent parking can handle high traffic volumes. The remaining lane can be added to one or both sides of the street for pedestrian and bicycle use.

Bicycling. Safe bicycling should be a prime consideration on arterials. Though experienced bicyclists are sometimes willing to ride in the street with the traffic, a separate lane will be necessary to make conditions safer for them as well as to attract new bicyclists. The bicycle lane could be integrated with the sidewalk to help make the pedestrian area feel more substantial. (See photos, and also page 00.) One-way bicycle lanes, no less than four feet wide, on each side of an arterial are preferable, although a two-way single bicycle lane could work if intersections and intervening traffic is not heavy. A two-way route should be a minimum of eight feet but preferably ten feet wide.

Improvements for bicycle riding safety and pleasure also benefits pedestrians and abutting houses. Locate parking on one side and divide the remaining space for a minimum 4 foot wide trail on each side. Stripe the trail initially, then over time as ridership and funds allow, raise it to match the sidewalk level. This wide travel lane makes it ideal for accomplished riders, however beginners are forced to remain on the sidewalk (note the children on left).

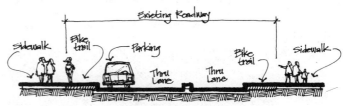

ADDING BICYCLE LANES TO ARTERIALS

Rural roads without curbing can be made safe for walking and bicycling by separating a pedestrian and bicycle route from the road by the shoulder. Try to leave at least six feet of shoulder for emergency pull-offs and barrier and pave the walk eight feet wide if possible, six-foot minimum.

SIDEWALKS.

Development of sidewalks throughout the suburban community may be the most important physical pedestrian improvement. Sidewalks can vary in width to match user demands, with 3 feet being the minimum. All sidewalks, except those on very narrow roads should be separated from the road by a planter strip or drainage swale.

Install sidewalk or curbed pedestrian protection at community mailboxes. The curb may be rolled to allow mail delivery vehicles and bicycles to roll to the boxes, and should extend at least 50 feet in both directions.

Perpendicular parking should have a walkway in front of the car to prevent accidents as cars enter and leave. Note the end of the parking lot is an ideal location for landscaped development and extra trees.

Sidewalks and Noncommercial Development. Sidewalks passing noncommercial areas should be five feet wide, and separated from the street by a five-foot wide planter strip. There is little advantage to paving right up to the curb, even if parking is allowed since, for noncommercial activities, parking turnover will be infrequent. Trees and the planter strips can be added and parked cars screened. If there is a setback, extra trees could be added on the setback side.

Rural roads that have been widened, but not yet infilled with commercial or residential uses, serve few pedestrians and should initially be made safe and comfortable only for bicycling. As commercial development occurs, sidewalks and other pedestrian amenities could be added if needed.

Sidewalks and Open Land. Sidewalks at the edge of parks and vacant land could be widened and curbed gently. Within a park, bicycle paths and walkways could be separated and widened to allow freer movement.

Sidewalks and Bus Stops. The planner should make sure a safe sidewalk, separated from the traffic, leads from each bus stop along an arterial into the nearby communities. The walk should continue until traffic problems diminish and walking along the road is safe. Suburban transit success depends partially on the adequacy of the sidewalk and the ease with which people can reach bus stops.

A bus shelter adjacent to each development will be an amenity in the future. Though this is handsome architecturally and blends with the buildings, it would be improved functionally with the addition of a bench inside the shelter, paved area connecting the shelter to the street or bus pull-out lane, and a sky light to light the inside.

Boulevard Conversion. Stretches of arterials with apartments could be converted into boulevards to enhance the housing and improve walking comfort. The road edges should include a combination bicycle and pedestrian path and planter strips planted heavily with street trees. Parking on the street might be eliminated on one side to provide the needed room, even though this probably would not be popular with residents. If there is room, the planner could include a center divider to visually reduce the road's width, and a pedestrian refuge in the center island to ease street crossing. Ramps should be constructed on the refuge for wheeled access. Planted center strips add a distinctive touch and create an identity that adds to the quality of the residential community. The planter should be raised to protect it from traffic.

Parking at Businesses. Many businesses along arterials have perpendicular parking in front of their buildings. If there is room for a single driveway with parking along it, the long parking strip should be eliminated and a sidewalk added. If parking is on municipal property or violates a setback ordinance, legal means may be necessary to ensure compliance. Elimination of the continuous driveway adds one on-street parking space for two off-street spaces removed, so the parking loss is not total. In some cases, perpendicular parking might be reorganized to serve four cars off a single driveway, plus two on the street where previously six parking spaces existed. This arrangement would reduce a driveway width from 60 feet to 20 feet and improve pedestrian circulation. (See sketch.) A reduced driveway width can increase pedestrian safety and pleasure while improving business or a store's appearance, and allow for a better flow of traffic since backing into the street is no longer necessary.

Parking lots entered off the street should be screened from the sidewalk with planting or a fence, and have a narrow driveway. The narrow driveway reduces the speed of entering and exiting autos, and reduces the apparent size of the parking lot for passers-by. A small lot like this can operate with a 12-foot-wide driveway.

Traffic Signals. Traffic signals should be set to allow safe pedestrian street crossings on wide arterials. Arterials' width makes crossing them difficult. Signals should be timed to allow street crossers to safely reach the other side and not become trapped partway across. Using an average walking speed of 3.5 feet per second allows enough time for most people to cross a street including those in wheelchairs. This speed would require 14 seconds of green light for a person to cross a 50 foot-wide four-lane road. The planner should suggest that a few extra seconds be added to allow for delays. Expanding the sidewalk with the safe-cross reduces the crossing time since pedestrians do not have to walk so far. On long blocks, mid-block crossings with a signal to stop heavy traffic may be needed. The signal at mid-block can cause problems if drivers don't notice it, so the planner should make sure it is well marked and visible for about 250 feet. Competing visual clutter may have to be removed to ensure good visibility.

Avoid large scale traffic signals in pedestrian areas. Many new signal installations include mast arms, gigantic support poles, and heavy hardware designed for 40-50 m.p.h. speeds. These are oversized and out of scale to the pedestrian. Their high visibility tends to increase traffic speed. Keep them smaller in all dimensions, use 6" or 8" lights instead of 12", mount them on 12 foot poles, and use corner mounted fixtures instead of overhead mast arms. Reduce travel speed, and reset them to benefit pedestrians. The cost of installing smaller fixtures will go way down. Set signals to minimize pedestrian wait time. A delay of longer than 20 seconds[*] causes most people to become slightly nervous and think about an illegal crossing. To counter this tendency consider allowing pedestrians to cross *against* the red light when conditions are clear. Prohibiting free right turns should be instituted to insure crossing safety.

When assigning traffic light priorities, integrate pedestrian needs into the evaluation system and treat them as an *equal* component. Delay, wait and go times should be calculated at at least equivalent, and in inclement weather conditions, should favor pedestrians. It may be more efficient to allocate excess pedestrian time to the WALK mode rather than the DON'T WALK mode. Shifting could be beneficial from both a reduced delay and compliance standpoint as it would decrease pedestrian delay time significantly, which outweighs the increase vehicle delay if the *total* intersection delay is reduced. Pedestrian compliance to the WALK mode is increased with more available time, while the compliance to the DON'T WALK mode should not be affected.

Pedestrian Refuge. To ease crossing, the arterial might be divided with a center strip at a major commercial node. The center strip, preferably planted with trees, might serve as a pedestrian refuge. (See p. 36.)

• The refuge should be raised to discourage driving on it but it should be ramped to accommodate wheelchairs and bicycles. Furthermore, a pedestrian-activated signal button is needed so that pedestrians don't become trapped on the refuge. Ten feet is the recommended width for a safe, planted refuge although one could be as narrow as four feet wide.

• On streets that have been designated for pedestrian use, driveways and drive-in businesses should be relocated to cross-streets or alleys. The development of alleys in suburban communities may channel service and parking vehicles away from the street, allowing pedestrians to utilize the street's sidewalk. Drive-in businesses (cleaners, banks, and fast-food outlets) should be discouraged from streets that are pedestrian-designated because these activities take up too much linear street frontage and destroy the continuity of the sidewalk. Ideally, the drive-in aspect of businesses could be eliminated entirely, then drivers could park their cars behind the stores and walk to different destinations using only one parking space. Energy use would then be reduced since cars would not have to idle while the drivers wait in line.

• Driveway widths have increased over the years, partly to account for increases in travel speed and to allow greater driver flexibility. Reducing driveway widths forces drivers to travel slower when turning and, in turn, makes the sidewalk more pleasant. One-way driveway widths can be reduced to ten feet. Two-way drives that serve permanent parking lots of ten or fewer cars can also be reduced to ten-foot width. At ten feet of driveway width, two cars can't pass simultaneously, and occasionally one car may have to wait for another to enter or exit. Entries to lots for short-term parking should be **16-feet-wide** allowing free, simultaneous access and egress.

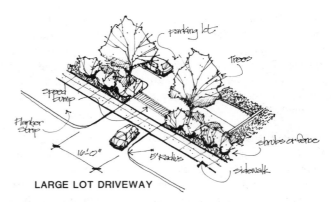

LARGE LOT DRIVEWAY

Parallel Route. Where no additional room to accommodate bicycles and pedestrians exists, an alternate parallel route should be found. The parallel route might be along another street, might move through parking lots or be located in the center of shopping blocks. The latter would take re-organization to allow a continuous route, but would put pedestrians and bicyclists in the middle of the business community.

In order to adapt commercial areas along arterials to use by pedestrians and bicyclists, the planner should try to achieve the following:

• Infill parking lots and vacant property around the core of the pedestrian area to increase the range of choice for shoppers.
• Eliminate driveways from the core area and relocate to side streets. Attempt to relocate drive-ins (banks, cleaners, eateries) to side streets and other areas outside the core.
• Shift the center of activity away from the busy arterial by developing pedestrian ways that are perpendicular to the strip.
• Organize parking around the perimeter of the core, in small lots that lead to the core, and provide pedestrian access to all streets.
• Provide landscaping, benches and other pedestrian amenities.
• Encourage opening of restaurants, outdoors if possible.
• Develop walkways and bike routes that lead to the nearby developments.
• Encourage all buses in the area to stop in the most advantageous place, preferably near the center of the core.

Prioritizing and tailoring are needed to match each individual situation. Most improvements will happen only when the merchants organize and start working with local authorities. Improvements like parking and sidewalk improvements are generally the businessmen's responsibility and may be fundable through a Local Improvement District. Street work and signals may be the municipality's responsibility. Cooperation is the key to success to improvements from integrating parking to adding awnings to advertising.

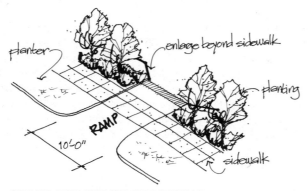

STANDARD WIDTH DRIVEWAY

ADAPTING APARTMENT COMPLEXES

Many suburban communities have 2 to 3 story apartment complexes interspersed with smaller developments creating a substantial block of apartments. Many line arterials, separated from it by parking lots. Accommodating bicyclists and pedestrians may be possible by linking parking lots and open spaces, improving public transport and introducing some commercial mixed used. The higher density and the large number of people may warrant such improvements. Apartment complexes located near shopping can be connected by paths, allowing some residents to shop without driving. (See p. 36.)

A one-story shopping complex can replace the streetside parking lots of many apartment buildings, with roof gardens for the apartments behind, a new place to shop, and an improved streetscape for people walking in the neighborhood.

Planning and design are relatively simple, while the difficult part is convincing landlords that the benefits outweigh the problems. Two options for incorporating a route into an apartment complex are: 1) through parking lots, or 2) through open space. Using parking lots lessens privacy and access problems and may be the best solution. However,

interior open spaces may make a more pleasant route if privacy problems can be worked out. A route incorporating both may prove the most flexible.

Create a safe pedestrian trail system by constructing through routes in either parking lots or informal open spaces. Separate and identify the route with low fences, signs, a special walk type, etc.

On an aerial photo, the planner should mark the entires and exits of each apartment complex that connect to shopping, bus stops, parks, schools, offices or public buildings. Both pedestrian and auto entries should be noted. The planner should then try to interconnect these through parking lots and interior open spaces. Any drainage channel or stream offers creative possibilities and should be explored. Older parking lots can be restriped to a 54-foot width for smaller cars with the excess land used for a path or walkway. The routes should be raised 6 inches above the parking lot and planted with trees. If there is room, the walk can be widened and benches added.

Parking lots between arterial and building could be converted into new units or shops with new parking constructed underneath. Shops help pedestrianize the street, form another focus for internal walkways and allow residents to shop without using their cars. Shops buffer the apartment from the road and eliminate unsightly parking. Underground parking should be affordable in exchange for the right to build new commercial buildings. Some on-grade customer parking may be necessary, unless the new space is used for offices instead of shops. (See photo.)

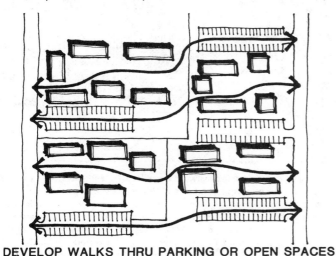

DEVELOP WALKS THRU PARKING OR OPEN SPACES

Finding room for a public walk in an existing residential community is difficult as it should not unnecessarily invade the privacy of the existing residents. This walkway placed next to an end elevation, and separated by both distance and berms from the residents on the left, bothers few people, and should not cause problems. The additional fences as shown in the other photo protects the privacy of adjacent residents.

Alterations of parking lot to through-ways for pedestrian/bicycle use interconnecting developments is enhanced if the parking lot is detailed for pedestrian viewing. This concrete grid adds texture and presence of nature when the lot is empty, while the trees shade walkers, and add shadow patterns.

Converting apartment driveways to pedestrian walkways. Many mid-60's apartment complexes use a peripheral parking road with all the housing units located on an island internal to that road. Because everybody was presumed to arrive by car, no sidewalks or street-scape amenities were provided. Times have changed, and more people walk on the street to reach a bus or car pool. With the reduction in size of most cars, it may now be possible to add a sidewalk to many of these streets and still have room for automobile maneuvering.

IMPROVING PARKING LOTS

Parking lots in most suburban apartment developments are laid out with little respect for pedestrian circulation between the lot and the units. When this lot is full, access between the parking in a unit will be difficult and involve unpleasant and dangerous movement between parked cars and there are no direction signs indicating how visitors would walk to their friends house. The other photo shows a more rational approach, with parking abutting a sidewalk leading directly to the different apartments. Getting out of your car, walking to the front of it to the sidewalk and then on the sidewalk to different apartments is both safe, pleasant and clear. The addition of planting islands with omittrees, shades the cars and reduces the visual impact of the parking lot on pedestrians.

These three photos illustrate an attractive relationship between the parking and unit entries in medium-density housing. Each has a raised walkway for safety and to prevent cars from parking on it. Placing the walk in front of the car prevents the walker from returning to the street and reduces danger.

Separating parking from buildings by 20 feet allows for a sidewalk with planting and room for residents to walk and possibly meet neighbors, or to reach a main street via the sidewalk.

Reduce the size of parking lots, add garage doors, trellis, small scale pedestrian paving, and planting to convert a parking lot to a pedestrian/parking courtyard. The place is comfortable to walk or work in, or to look at from adjacent units.

A covered walkway connecting decentralized parking with a number of units allows the parking to be removed from the houses and provides a pleasant walking experience for residents moving from car to house. It also allows neighbors to get to know one another, meet and exchange comments about their community and other things.

201

Converting an open parking lot to garages with doors improves the pedestrian experience. The door is visually more pleasant to walk past and its opening warns pedestrians that a car may appear. Or, a large parking space could be converted to small lots with one entry serving four cars. This would eliminate some sidewalk crossings, which would be replaced with plantings or other landscape treatment. This arrangement nets the same number of parking spaces with two now located on the street, where previously it was impossible to park because of overlap with driveways. (See photo and sketch.)

IMPORTANT OTHER CHANGES

Public works road standards may have to be revised in order for improvements to pedestrian circulation to be made. Since suburban communities are organized so that cars can travel at relatively high speeds, reducing the spacious road widths would slow down cars, making pedestrians more comfortable, and driving less desirable. Reducing road widths would also help lower construction costs somewhat.

The following are some easily implemented changes that could benefit pedestrians:

• Change standard driveway widths to *maximum* 8 feet for a single-car garage and to *maximum* 12 feet for a two-car garage and for parking lots serving less than 10 cars. (Driveways could expand for 14 or 16 feet once across the sidewalk.) Driveway width for parking lots of 11 to 50 cars should be a maximum of 16 feet wide. These narrower widths reduce the speed of entry and exit, thus enhancing the pedestrian domain.

Minimize the number of entry and exit driveways. Many two-driveway developments could work with only one, and most are wider than is needed. The change would improve the street's visual quality by minimizing disruption of planters, trees, etc., and improve the walking environment, as it reduces the number of crosswalk interruptions.

• Determine which streets should have *no* driveway access across them. Existing driveways should be removed over a five-year period, enough time for the costs to be amortized.

• Institute new intersection corner treatment to include a safe-cross and narrower radius where traffic is slow moving or turns prohibited. Corner radius *without* a safe-cross can be narrowed to 5 feet if there is a parking lane, since turning cars have space to avoid the corner. The narrow radius adds pedestrian space, eases street crossing and reduces the visual impact of streets and car speeds, as well. Streets intersecting a one-way street can use a 5 foot radius on the no-turn direction. (See sketch.)

• Institute the safe-cross on all streets where parking occurs (except those used for "clear zone" rush hour traffic). The safe-cross defines the legal parking spaces (eliminating need for signs) and enlarges the pedestrian space, while it diminishes the visual impact of the street. If designed properly, there need be no impediment to traffic flow.

• Develop a parking lot ordinance that would require a set number of trees per car (as three trees per car) for all parking lots constructed in the jurisdiction.

• Develop a standard requiring curb cuts and ramps to be constructed with all new or remodeled sidewalks. The curb cut would ideally be depressed over the width of the radius to facilitate elderly, wheelchairs, and wheeled vehicles such as bicycles, grocery carts, etc. Also develop a minimum standard describing the proper way to construct them. Most existing ramps are too narrow, or improperly located and don't really work.

• Locate buildings close to the street to increase pedestrian activity, reduce resident isolation, and foster pedestrian services such as retail outlets that could locate along pedestrian streets connecting higher-density units. Fill in open areas with row housing and develop new "pedestrian ways" perpendicular to existing streets to connect isolated units.

• To avoid noisy streets, most apartments are arranged with compact buildings set back from the street and surrounded by large parking lots. Separation from the street limits pedestrian activity, increases a chance of street crime and curtails street-oriented retail outlets and activities that could attract pedestrians. Large open spaces reduce the frequency of contacts and of meeting people, making it difficult to develop friends or to get to know people living in your complex.

• Eliminate drive-in services—banks, cleaners, restaurants, etc.—to improve pedestrian circulation. Once drivers are out of their cars, they can walk to other destinations and carry out several errands with one parking spot. Energy demand is reduced and air pollution lessened as cars don't have to idle while the drivers wait in line.

• Devise a sidewalk and bike lane plan, and require each new developer to construct the portion in front of his building, even if there are no other connecting walks. Eventually the total route will be completed. The presence of partial walks may encourage neighboring landowners to have their walks constructed. (Neighbors can work with one contractor, adding the construction of their portion of the sidewalk to the existing job at little extra cost.)

Each sidewalk should include planter strips separating the walk from the road and from parking on the inside. New sidewalks should be sited to establish as narrow a road as is possible. (Contrary to standard practice of siting walks close to the property in anticipation of road widening.)

• Encourage low-cost Local Improvement Districts (LID) by easing construction standards and limiting administrative expense padding. Administrative costs added to LID's are often so padded due to engineering department inefficiencies that these costs can double the actual construction costs. Additionally, many contractors add an extra percentage to city work because experience indicates that many unnecessary steps will probably be required. Work in the private sector can often be accomplished for less if the town is willing to let the LID planning be done by a private designer (and paid for by the owners), and then to allow the private sector to let bids and pay directly for the work. This should be done for simple improvements such as sidewalks and alleys.

The planner should encourage apartment complex owners to extend the complex's entrancewalk so it connects with the street. Most recently-built apartments have poor pedestrian street connections, making access difficult for those using the bus or walking. The walk should be free of auto intrusion, lighted for night use, planted and covered where possible. If the complex is large, an expanded and covered drop-off area is recommended.

Around apartment complexes traffic should be slowed to improve the pedestrian's perception of the area's safety and comfort. Traffic moving faster than 20 m.p.h. is usually unable or unwilling to give the right-of-way to a pedestrian wanting to cross the street. Thus, traffic in areas around apartments should be slowed to 20 m.p.h. and policed as well.

• Require all service stations and drive-ins with drives wider than 10 feet to narrow them to 10 feet over the next five years, again enough time for the costs to be amortized.

• Develop a parking lot ordinance that would require a set number of trees per car (as three trees per car) for all parking lots constructed in the jurisdiction.

• Develop a standard requiring curb cuts and ramps to be constructed with all new or remodeled sidewalks. The curb cut would ideally be depressed over the width of the radius to facilitate elderly, wheelchairs, and wheeled vehicles such as bicycles, grocery carts, etc. Develop, also minimum standard describing the proper way to construct them. Most existing ramps are too narrow, or improperly located and don't really work.

• Locate buildings close to the street to increase pedestrian activity, reduce resident isolation, and foster pedestrian services such as retail outlets that could locate along pedestrian streets connecting higher-density units. In-fill open areas with row housing and develop new "pedestrian ways" perpendicular to existing streets to connect isolated units.

To avoid noisy streets, most apartments are arranged with compact buildings set back from the street and surrounded by large, parking lots. Separation from the street limits pedestrian activity, increases a chance of street crime and curtails street-oriented retail outlets and activities that could attract pedestrians. Large open spaces reduce the frequency of contacts and of meeting people, making it difficult to develop friends or to get to know people living in your complex.

• Eliminate drive-in services—banks, cleaners, restaurants, etc., to improve pedestrian circulation. Once drivers are out of their cars, they can walk to other destinations and carry out several errands with one parking spot. Energy demand is reduced and air pollution lessened as cars don't have to idle while the drivers wait in line.

Analyze service stations to anticipate which might go out of business, and could be replaced with a pedestrian-oriented shop or service. Service stations located at intersections could be prime pedestrian places since people wait, pass, and congregate there. Reorient proposed buildings to adjacent to the road with parking behind, minimize drivers, add bus shelter with benches, sidewalks, curb cuts, trees, etc.

ADAPTING SUBURBAN BUSINESS AREAS

Shopping in suburban shopping centers has become part of the lifestyle of most suburban residents. Besides shopping, the centers are now used for social and recreational purposes. A mix of uses can be found, particularly in regional shopping malls, but is being sought in smaller shopping centers, as well. Though shopping malls are, at present, the most developed pedestrian environments in the suburbs, they have the potential to serve more people in more ways. This chapter, then, focuses on the potential for adapting malls and smaller shopping centers to offer more opportunities for and to better serve the pedestrian, the bicyclist and the transit user.

Suburban stores constructed since 1950 have been planned around the automobile. Because places in the suburbs are spread out and motorists expect to drive from one place to another, stores naturally have been designed to be reached by car and to provide parking for the car. Consequently, facilities to accommodate people other than motorists, that is, pedestrians, bicyclists and transit riders, have not been included in planning.

IMPACT OF AUTOMOBILE

Let's examine for a moment the impact of the automobile on suburban shopping areas. Traffic volumes tend to be high throughout the entire day, because people are driving from place to place within a relatively small area. Motorists expect free parking spaces adjacent to each store. It is not unusual for a shopper to drive, rather than walk, several hundred feet from one store to another. Walking wouldn't be easy, anyway, since there probably are no safe sidewalks between stores. "Customer only" parking lots with individual entrances and exits and separated from adjacent lots by fences, barricades or abrupt grade changes, force drivers to use the street to move from one business to another. Furthermore, numerous entrances and exits create excessive left-turn and right-turn conflicts in the street, increasing congestion even more.

Increased costs and limited supplies of gasoline will ultimately change car use and shopping habits, as well. One-stop shopping centers will be needed to offer a full range of goods and services. Shopping trips may then occur less often, be more organized and less spontaneous, and be shared with neighbors. Moreover, the need for large parking areas may decrease, allowing room for development of new shopping or commercial facilities. Smaller cars will even further reduce the size of parking lots.

The potential of shopping centers becoming mixed-use facilities, integrating retail, entertainment, medical, educational, recreational and housing uses, is just beginning to become a reality. When the variety of uses is increased, the pedestrian experience is enhanced. For instance, shoppers enjoy variety, humor, change, color and excitement, all generally missing from predominately retail shopping areas. By mixing uses in shopping centers, people will be drawn there for more than one activity and the place will be more vibrant for everyone. With more reasons for people to visit a shopping center, there is the potential of an increased need for parking. However, if bus service is improved, car pooling (especially for those who work there) and bicycling encouraged, and parking rearranged in garages, parking demand might be reduced. Space gained from changing parking could then be used for more development.

> Suburban land near shopping centers is becoming valuable enough for some centers to construct decked parking garages, and to intensify retail development on the previous parking lot.

A PLANNING OVERVIEW

Adapting shopping centers for nonmotorized use utilizes many of the interrelated techniques discussed earlier: reducing the car's impact on pedestrians, mixing land uses and increasing density so pedestrians can accomplish many tasks on foot, and providing an environment that is comfortable for walking.

Reducing Traffic

Reducing traffic is essential if pedestrians are to be safe and comfortable. With less traffic, roads can be narrowed, sidewalks can be added, and people can walk more safely. But accomplishing this is no easy task, since people are used to driving to shopping centers. As a start, bicycle and bus access should be improved so that people will have alternative means of transportation to reach shopping centers. Encouraging shoppers, other visitors, and shopping center employees to carpool would also help reduce traffic. Longer term solutions would require changes in streets and the way land is used.

In a typical suburban business community, parking spaces are used about 65% of the business time, leaving 35% vacant or for anticipated use. This 35% vacancy adds to the visual blight of suburban communities, and increases the walking distance to shops and offices.

INCREASING DENSITY AND CHANGING LAND USES

Increasing density and allowing more uses that attract people in and around shopping centers would mean that more people would live closer to and presumably be able to walk to shopping centers, which would offer a wider variety of activities and services. Moreover, people driving to the center could accomplish several tasks without moving their cars. And, too, as activities are diversified and more people are attracted to a shopping center, there may be justification for increased bus service from nearby neighborhoods.

Permitting the development of apartments and condominiums with direct walking access near shopping centers would increase pedestrian use of its facilities. Commercial offices near the center would generate pedestrian traffic as workers would use the center on lunch hours and after work.

The rear or service side of many shopping centers are undeveloped, blank, and unattractive for pedestrians. Add a new retail wing to the blank face with walks connecting nearby apartments to reduce the blight and better integrate the center with the surrounding community.

Pedestrian Comfort

Although reducing the speed of traffic and the number of cars is a big step toward making pedestrians feel more comfortable, it is also necessary to provide safe street intersections, benches to rest on, bus stops, waiting areas with protection from weather, and a pedestrian scale that makes walking visually comfortable. Sidewalks should lead to all destinations. Sidewalks or walks that end abruptly make walking unpleasant and unsafe. Furthermore, sidewalk pavement details and activities along a sidewalk must be varied so pedestrians won't become bored. Finally, package checking at stores helps those on foot.

The balance of this chapter examines four types of suburban shopping areas: regional shopping mall, neighborhood shopping center, disbursed development and commercial strip development. Each section examines the characteristics of each that make walking difficult and proposes solutions to these problems. Some solutions would be easily implementable and would cause little inconvenience, while others would require major changes.

Lack of safe, defined pedestrian walks between stores and from the street to shops leads to many unnecessary short driving trips (above). Leaving barriers in assigned walkways suggests that walking is not really desirable. The striped walk connecting two buildings should be raised for safety and identity with a long, shallow speed bump. On the positive side, the covered walk is safe, attractive, and comfortable (below).

Covered walks allow walking between distant shops or to adjacent residential and office communities.

REGIONAL SHOPPING MALL

Regional shopping mall is a huge shopping complex, perhaps up to a million square feet of space for the stores alone. It is generally sited in the center of a great field of parking and is accessible mostly by car only. Once shoppers have found their way from the parking lot to the mall, they find themselves in a world designed for the pedestrian. Covered walks and enclosed interior spaces, plants, benches, a festive feeling and comparative shopping all help attract serious and recreational shoppers.

Adapting a regional mall for pedestrians can be accomplished by the following four interrelated activities:

- Improving non-auto access to the mall from surrounding communities;
- Reducing the impact of parking and the distance between buildings;
- Increasing the range of activities and services, and;
- Connecting the mall with businesses, homes, and services in the neighborhood.

Retail shops and offices are islands in an auto-oriented landscape.

Regional malls have the potential of becoming the central focus for suburban communities. The malls of the future are likely to have more buildings with less parking and more service-oriented facilities such as libraries and health centers. They may provide day-and-night shopping and entertainment, with theaters, cinemas, restaurants as well as retail stores. Malls could even incorporate or relate to hotels and convention centers to provide additional shops, meeting rooms, restaurants, theaters and to extend nighttime activities. Their development may be the catalyst for development of new, high-density housing located nearby and connected by sidewalks or pedestrian bridges. They can become a hub for transportation with bus service to and from other neighborhoods and communities.

ACCESS

The planner's first step would be to define potential pedestrian centers that would connect the mall and surrounding land uses. The mall itself might be considered the pedestrian center of the community, surrounded by several unrelated centers with attractions for pedestrians. Each of these centers would be identifiable, and would be comfortable for walking. (See sketch.) Each of these centers, also, would be connected to the others by safe, comfortable walkways making the entire complex accessible to pedestrians. These sub-centers could be in residential, commercial, or office uses. Each sub-center might have a diameter of 1,000 feet. If the sub-centers were separated by more than 1,000 feet, bicycle or bus routes could be used to connect them.

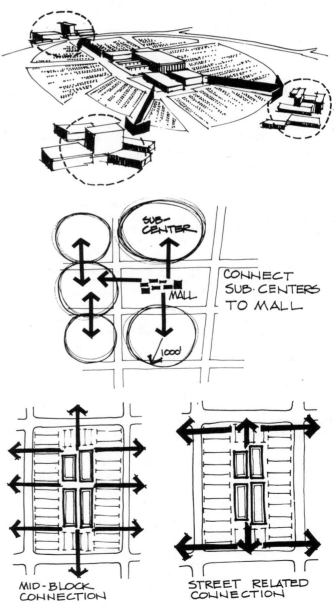

CONNECT SUB-CENTERS TO MALL

MID-BLOCK CONNECTION

STREET RELATED CONNECTION

To identify these pedestrian centers, the planner would need to prepare comprehensive circulation and land use plans. The circulation plan would include all arterials, neighborhood streets, bus routes, bicycle routes, parking lots, as well as the internal circulation system of the mall itself. A similar analysis should be prepared of land uses around the mall. It would include vacant land, underused land, residences (high and low densities) parking areas, the mall itself, and commercial complexes that surround the mall. The two plans could be compared to see where potential pedestrian activity might occur. The planner should look for places where new facilities such as housing, commercial, convention center, offices, or parking garages might logically be developed. The planner should then try to connect the external road circulation system of the community to the internal circulation system of the mall, to determine conversely where pedestrian and bicycle routes would be appropriate. Existing pedestrian and bicycle routes connecting the mall to surrounding neighborhoods and roads need to be augmented and reinforced. The goal is to make the pedestrian area of the mall part of the general structure of the community, with shopping arcades and sidewalks extending beyond the private mall toward the bordering retail and residential properties. It should be possible to relate existing sidewalks and streets with extensions of streets to the shopping mall.

Shopping centers, unlike downtown areas, provide only one activity—SHOPPING. "Downtown" caters to a variety of activities—shopping, offices, light manufacturing, business services, and government and public services such as libraries, health care and transit. This diversity of activity attracts many different users and allows the place to be more interesting and serviceable for people who are there. The variety offers people a chance to meet somebody they know (or don't know), the chance to see somebody who doesn't look like you or who is there for a different purpose. One complaint from many shopping center shoppers is the lack of this variety and the abundance of similar people doing the same thing. Increasing the density and mixing uses with offices, housing, public and government services, maybe craft or light manufacturing, would overlay different groups of people and places and create a more interesting street scene. The worry of attracting bums or undesirables is probably minimal as the need for auto access, combined with relatively low use intensity and restrictive programming would effectively thwart their invasion.

Pedestrian bridges could be used for crossing busy arterials that, of necessity, must carry heavy traffic around the mall. The addition of second and third-floor shopping to the part of the mall would provide a logical connection to a pedestrian bridge. A second-story could be accessed by ramps instead of stairs, thus keeping the bridge within the mainstream of pedestrian traffic. Shopping could be located on either side of the bridge as had been done with old bridges of Venice.

A wide pedestrian bridge can be park like, with trees, benches, and special paving. This bridge is one of four that cross busy streets in a San Francisco shopping center. The center combines shopping with offices, with the offices accounting for the large number of shoppers and people in the photo.

Getting to a mall may be a problem for people who have no car and no other means of transportation. Bus service then might help those people, particularly senior citizens who have free time and now make up an important group of daytime shoppers. Senior citizens tend to stay longer at malls with other activities (organized card games, social security clearinghouse, makeup demonstrations, classes, dances, etc.). Improving pedestrian, bicycle and bus access to a mall from nearby neighborhoods can often be accomplished with little difficulty. Since about 50 percent of the people visiting a mall travel less than five miles to get there, use of bicycles for those short distances should be encouraged. A combined two-way bicycle route related to pedestrian routes between sub-centers should provide adequate access to a mall. The planner should analyze the road system to see if some roads could be reduced in size and converted to predominantly pedestrian or bicycle use while others would maintain a dominant auto-traffic role.

Each mall entrance should be pedestrianized. Most malls have a wide road with drop-off area near the entry. Although these entries are used extensively by pedestrians, they are usually auto-oriented. The grade of the entry/drop-off area should be raised to the level of the entrance to the building.

Too Wide

An unacceptable mall entrance. The sidewalk does not extend to neighboring streets, restricting neighbors from walking safely to the center. The road is too wide for safe crossing, as it encourages fast-moving traffic. To correct it, narrow or twist the road, raise the main crosswalk with a gentle speed bump, and add special paving.

Windows

Bike Storage

Planting

Indirect entry

Traffic should be separated by bollards defining the pedestrian realm, and speed limits reduced. Then the entry area should be repaved with a rich-textured, pedestrian-scaled paving material such as brick, exposed aggregate concrete, or concrete blocks. The pedestrian area should be ramped up from the parking lot and connected to it by a narrow roadway. This design should signal drivers that they need to be careful of pedestrians in this entry area. In addition a large covered and protected waiting area should be provided near the mall's entrances. (See sketches.)

PARKING

For Cars

Improving parking efficiency is the key to intensifying land use and adapting for pedestrian travel since parking is the principal land consumer and deterrent to walking. Reorganization of employee parking, as well as encouraging the use of car pools, buses and bicycles to reduce the need for parking may be the first step.

Parking should be concentrated so that it is organized into major blocks that relate to different sections of the mall. Dividing the mall into four quadrants, similar to the environmental areas proposed by Colin Buchanan, is one method of conceptual organization that should work for shopping mall planning.[1] Each quadrant would have its related parking block. The linear area between parking blocks could provide connections between local neighborhoods and the mall itself.

Replacing on-grade parking with garaged parking may be necessary to increase density. Internalize parking structures to create continuous pedestrian plazas and circulation routes and reduce the "backsideness" of most shopping centers. Take advantage of any grade change, consolidating parking at lower elevations, with pedestrian space running on the level above it. Parking may shift from single use to joint use, serving shops, offices and a variety of owners.

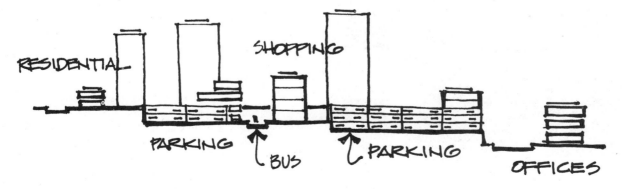

RESIDENTIAL   SHOPPING

PARKING   BUS   PARKING   OFFICES

Restriping lots to reduce the size of parking spaces to serve smaller cars can reduce parking area considerably. (See sketch.) For larger shopping centers, four parking spaces per 1,000 square feet of gross leaseable space may replace the traditional 5.5 figure, assuming changes in employee parking. New construction should have decked

or multistory parking in trade for approval to expand shopping facilities. As an example, Chicago's Brickyard Regional Shopping Center can accommodate 1,000 cars on the roof allowing for more stores below.

Some parking lots have separate pedestrian walks from each parking space to the destination points. While a separate walkway improves safety and pleasure for users, it is land consumptive and increases the size of parking lots. The question is: should walking in the parking lot be made pleasant, or should the parking area be compact without the walkway connections? Though not as pleasant or safe as walking on a separate way, walking across a parking lot is acceptable if traffic is light and if shoppers do not drive from store to store to store.

To enhance neighborhood pedestrian use of a regional mall, invert the traditional parking model, placing some shops on the street, with parking in the interior. The street front, like a main street of a small town would allow nearby neighbors to walk easily and comfortably to it, then to the mall beyond. Though this conceptual redevelopment diagram may better serve the local neighborhood, it obviously won't fulfill the drive-in functions of the regional market as we now know them. Walking distances would be somewhat increased, and available parking decreased. Fronting the community on only one side, along one or two intersections may serve local neighborhood needs without compromising the regional market. Increasing density and pedestrian access from adjacent neighborhoods would be important.

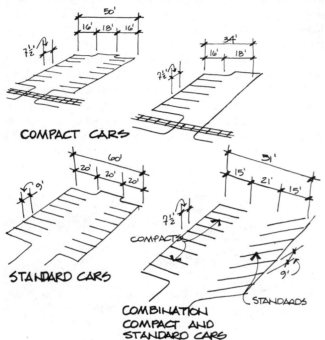

SQUARE FOOT COMPARISON OF REQUIRED PARKING AREA FOR COMPACT AND REGULAR SIZE CARS

STALL WIDTH	STALL DEPTH	AISLE WIDTH	STALL DEPTH	SQUARE FOOT/CAR
10'	20'	25'	20'	325
7½'	16'	18'	16'	188
7½' & 9'	16'	21'	15'	225
9'	20'	20'	20'	252

Trees and shrubs should be planted on slopes to visually reduce the parking lot size and aid micro-climate. Extensive asphalt paving offers no visual diversity and is boring and uncomfortable for pedestrians.

Multi-story garage parking decreases walking distance and tightens the entire mall. Covered pedestrian bridges can be aligned to lead through the garage to surrounding residential community, allowing neighbors to walk to the center. Note the extensive planting, narrow driveway entries, and sidewalks.

DENSITY

Density could be increased at the mall as well as the sub-centers mentioned earlier. It is feasible for second and third stories with a mall to feature shopping or commercial, medical and office activity. Since multistoried malls have been successful in many urban communities in the country and Europe, there is no reason why they should not work in suburban communities as well. Construction of high-density housing should be encouraged near the mall with direct access to the mall over pedestrian bridges or on walkways. Although high-density could mean low or high-rise buildings, the point is to house as many people as close to the community's center as is possible. A large population base nearby means that the center would be accessible to many people, that nighttime entertainment could be more feasible, and that the mall might attract a variety of activities. Parking to serve new high-density housing developments should be multistory garages or garages under the buildings.

For Bicycles

At malls where bicycle traffic is light, the entrances of major shopping stores should be enlarged and covered so that bicycles can be parked under them. Cover is important, to protect riders and their bicycles from the elements. Roofed protection near the front door serves as a deterent to theft, since it is highly visible from inside the building. (Photo)

As the use of bicycles increases, parking them near store entrances may have to be discontinued. Large numbers of bicycles entering and leaving the front door area are likely to be confusing and dangerous to pedestrians using the same door. When this point is reached, a new bicycle parking area should be developed some distance away from but directly connected with the entry. It should be connected directly to the front entrances of stores by a clear and landscaped walkway. Furthermore, it should be well-lit, visible from several adjacent areas, covered and provided with lockable racks for easy use.

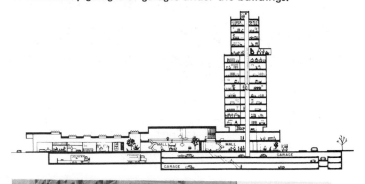

The density of retail stores and offices on pedestrian streets near the mall should be increased by the addition of second and third floors. If traffic volume is not too high, housing might even use some of this space. Office buildings could even be high-rise with parking organized in multilevel garages or in garages under the buildings. The effort in all cases should be to avoid perpetuating spread-out pattern of suburban development by increasing building heights, using multilevel parking, and minimizing on-grade parking lots.

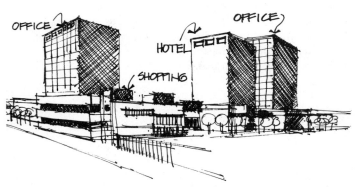

The Galleria in suburban Houston combines offices, garaged parking, hotels, and shopping to mix uses and increase density.

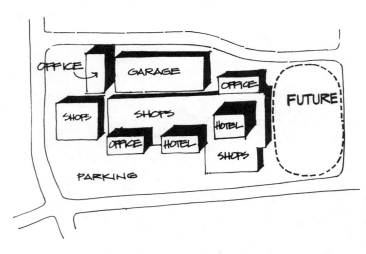

CONNECTIONS

One way to connect a mall with the neighborhood and adjoining businesses might be a combination pedestrian and transit mall. A transit mall would separate buses from cars. Elimination of auto traffic from the street would allow sidewalk widening, providing a defined pedestrian space. The pedestrian walk should be lined with stores and covered for weather protection over most of the route. The best length for such a walk would be no longer than about 1,000 feet. If it needs to be longer, several areas with shopping and other uses, could be interconnected to provide more of interest to pedestrians. In addition, buses might be scheduled to take pedestrians from one area to another.

Some regional malls may be the right scale for raised pedestrian walkway systems which would leave the ground floor for automobile circulation. Since there are so many cars at suburban shopping centers, it might be argued that they should occupy the ground level while pedestrians should be graciously lifted up one floor. Whether or not this would work would depend, to some extent, on topography, and on the variations that would allow the bridge system to connect with stores and parking. If all is favorable, the bridge could form the connection between a mall and the surrounding community. The bridge could be made strong enough to support a small electric or gas-powered bus to transport pedestrians over long distances. Uses abutting the bridge would vary, depending on the length of the mall where rows of shops should extend no farther than 1,000 linear feet. If the distance is longer, uses could shift to residences or offices between the shopping nodes. The sketches described a proposal for development of a large suburban shopping precinct in Bellevue, Washington, utilizing a bridge to connect the various elements.

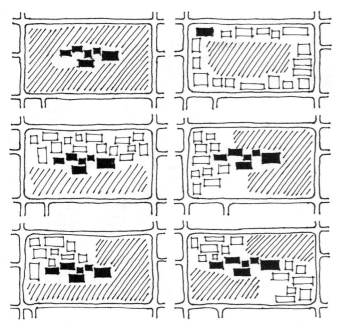

Existing malls could expand in the direction of neighboring shopping or residential areas, thereby providing pedestrian access to the original mall. In this series, the original mall, shown in dark and surrounded by parking, is adapted for expansion in the direction of adjacent nearby concentrations of businesses or residences.

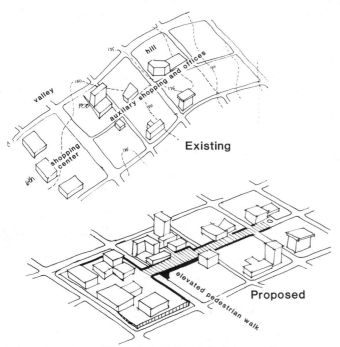

Concept of an Elevated Mall for Bellevue, Wa.

Credit: Dennis Ryan
         Jack Seidner

One problem with the enclosed places of many shopping centers is that they are sterile, antiseptic and unimaginative in design. Pedestrians need stimulation and become bored with the sameness of repeated patterns and activity. Extending shopping activities to outdoor spaces by using kiosks is one solution. Kiosks, open-sided temporary structures used as stands for sales of newspapers, food and other convenience items, could also be used for sales of fast-turnover wares in heavily trafficked areas outside the mall. Such kiosks generate higher sales per square foot than retail and permanent shops, primarily because of the narrow range of merchandise and high exposure. Since kiosks, as small stores, attract as many onlookers as purchasers, they can be considered to provide entertainment. In addition, kiosks can be used for the sale of food.

Stanford Center, one of the most successful shopping centers in the United States, was recently remodeled. Because the weather is good most of the year and people like the openness, a decision was made *not* to enclose the center. To provide some protection, some of the walks have glass sidewalk enclosures. The remodeling included new outdoor eating areas and central courtyards, and 3,000 trees and shrubs in the parking lots to break up the expanse of asphalt.

NEIGHBORHOOD SHOPPING CENTERS

Neighborhood shopping centers, constructed during the early days of suburban development and now surrounded by residential development, may have the greatest potential for pedestrian improvements. Since they are normally close to housing, they may become a neighborhood focus similar to that of a small town's center. Short-term changes such as improving access, enhancing shopper comfort and providing more entertainment and restaurants are easy to implement. While enclosing centers isn't usually necessary, covered walks, plantings, benches, outdoor shopping, and perhaps a garden can give a center a unique atmosphere of its own.

Typical of many neighborhood shopping centers, this is separated from the street and neighborhood by a large parking lot, with no clear place to walk, no focus, and little landscape development.

A small informal garden courtyard with covered walks, benches, cafe, planting, etc. enhances the neighborhood shopping center.

Neighborhood or community shopping centers operated under one management often consist of single shops with parking located between them and the roads. Several variations include two buildings placed at 90-degree angles to each other or one building placed behind another. These small shopping centers typically have four pedestrian-related problems:

1. They are small, offering an incomplete range of shopping services, and one often bypassed by neighboring residents who could walk to them but favor driving to larger centers nearby.
2. They are linear in shape with no pedestrian focus or amenity, and little protection or separation from the automobile.
3. Foot access between the parking lots and stores and between the stores themselves is often difficult, unpleasant, and unsafe.
4. Reaching them on foot, bicycle, or bus from nearby neighborhoods is generally difficult, uncomfortable and unsafe.

The approach, as discussed in earlier chapters, of concentrating stores, developing congregating spaces for pedestrians, creating pedestrian streets with narrow-fronted shops and window displays, and increasing density by adding new shops and additional floors will help correct the first and second problems. (See sketch.) Problems 3 and 4 can be reduced by modifying parking lots to include some pedestrian and automobile separation, particularly where they intersect cross-streets with rapidly moving cars, and by developing pedestrian access routes that serve parking lots and then connect to bus stops and neighborhoods beyond. A pedestrian access route might resemble a main street with a raised sidewalk and trees with a bus stop, and with

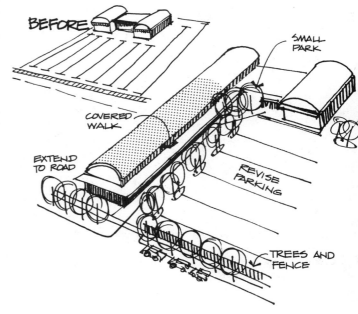

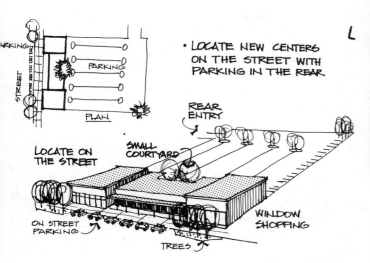

• LOCATE NEW CENTERS ON THE STREET WITH PARKING IN THE REAR

PARKING

STREET

PLAN

LOCATE ON THE STREET

SMALL COURTYARD

REAR ENTRY

ON STREET PARKING

TREES

WINDOW SHOPPING

a safe place to cross the street to reach the nearby neighborhood. On this route new buildings might be developed with shops extending the existing stores to the street (see sketch.)

A study of a shopping center's parking lots may reveal opportunities for reducing parking space for expansion of the center itself. Parking spaces could be restriped for smaller car sizes, and employees could be encouraged not to drive to work. Any new construction should include parking beneath or should provide for decked parking over the existing lot so as not to increase the amount of on-grade parking.

Most shopping centers serve the pedestrian better if the density of shopping is increased and commercial and medical/dental activities are available to users. All new buildings should have their parking underground or in multistory garages. Buildings should be expanded with additional floors for commercial and business offices, or specialized shopping that can survive in less-accessible locations. New buildings should be sited to internalize pedestrian space as a focus for the center. (See sketch.) Other buildings should be sited as linkages to the community, perhaps along the entrance route. Shopping centers could be expanded with public spaces such as library, senior or day care center, or organized play facilities to serve community needs. Others might include a mini-city hall, or other functions to draw more users, allowing them to engage in several activities on one trip. And, too, an increased permanent work force and nonshopping activity would make a center more interesting.

Adding a small, protected pedestrian space at the main entrance makes shoppers feel welcome. Four parking spaces were replaced with a protective planter, bench and several trees. Note the wheelchair ramp, and covered walks beyond (above). Extend the walk to the street to increase safety to customers walking to their car or to the street beyond. Raise it 6 inches with a shallow vehicle ramp before and after to improve safety and visibility (below).

Construct a new row of buildings to connect the shopping center to the street. Angle parking with a walk, adjacent to the shop fronts duplicates a traditional small downtown. The approach is convenient and acceptable *if* the walk is sufficiently wide for pedestrians to move freely betwe... stores. This 3 foot wide walk is *not* adequate, and should be increased to a minimum of 6 feet. The covered portion is important in rainy climates.

The best new tenant for a neighborhood shopping center may be a restaurant. Since studies suggest that shoppers spent about twice as much time in a large mall per visit as in a small shopping center, the latter should try to provide some of the same attractions as a mall, in particular, restaurants. The availability of food is important to shoppers who can rest and break up the shopping time by enjoying a snack or lunch. Restaurants, in particular, draw those for whom shopping is a form of recreation, since eating is associated with relaxing.

Employees of commercial and business offices who can reach work on transit, foot, bicycles or in a carpool, comprise a group of shoppers who won't need to park for work, or lunch break or shopping. Likewise, if other shoppers would consciously arrange their shopping trips so they could share rides with others and try to accomplish more activities per trip on foot, the need for extra parking would be diminished.

CONVERTING A SHOPPING CENTER TO A TOWN CENTER

Many suburban communities have no traditional main street or town center, but have a nearby shopping center that could be converted to duplicate the traditional main street with a small-town feeling. The following drawings illustrate conceptually how this may happen.

In converting a neighborhood shopping center, the main street image sought would be similar to that of older, small American towns that have a variety of shopping and commercial offices along streets, interspersed with small parking areas and open spaces. The main street would be surrounded by close-in living, which combines existing single-family

housing with new higher-density units. Existing stores would remain but would be updated to blend with newer buildings constructed in former parking lots and areas between buildings. While this model is idealized, it does have potential for implementation. Such a model is admittedly short on parking and optimistic about the potential for people walking, bicycling, carpooling and busriding. Neighborhood cooperation would of course be needed in order for parking to change and housing density to increase.

Typical of most auto-oriented shopping centers, it contrasts the wooded and residential community surrounding it (above and left). A vision of what a town center could be—compact rather than sprawling and for the pedestrian rather than automobile. There could be a mixture or retail, commercial, residential, service functions, and parking (below).

Credit: Ken Thiem
          Musheer Siddiqi

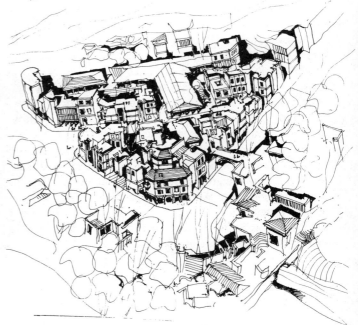

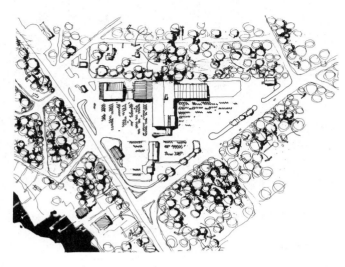

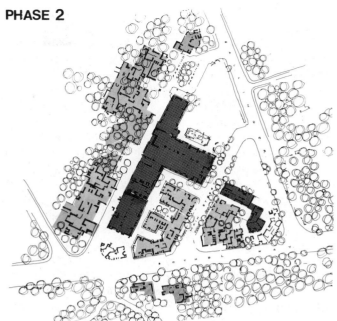

PHASE 2

PHASE 3

The center is marked by large parking areas, an absence of vegetation and lack of diversity in the architecture, spatial character and shop selection. Reconstruction of the town center would be a complex process, with many phasing variables to promote pedestrian activity, reduce auto dependence, and not compromise long term viability. The first step could be construction of medium density housing in or near the town center to help create a true pedestrian environment and improve the center's economic condition.

PHASE 1

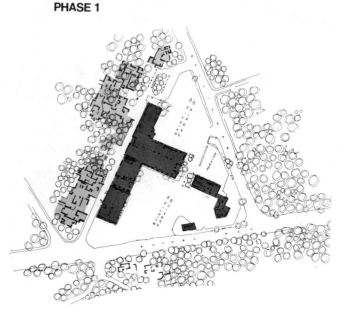

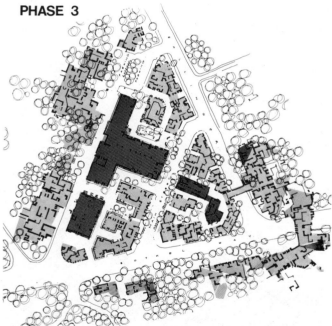

Construction of office space could be the next step. This should increase revenue and stimulate local trade without generating much additional traffic. Architects, engineers, lawyers and other professional people should be encouraged to rent, lease or buy space (above). The next step is the construction of a Main Street. Additional retail businesses could develop as community need for goods and services increases. Pedestrian and bicycle trails linking residential areas, and the town center should be constructed to increase access to businesses and encourage people to use non-polluting transportation.

For a shopping center to present an image of a friendly main street, everything must be scaled down. The back side of all buildings should be planned so there aren't visually-displeasing service and garbage areas. (photo) The perimeter of the street should be fenced and planted heavily. Then, too, parking and service areas should be broken into smaller lots and landscaped carefully. To provide a pleasant gathering place, a landscaped courtyard might be planned with fountain, benches, sculpture, places for children to play, and protection from the automobile. If there are many teenagers in the neighborhood, a meeting place might be provided for them, perhaps a coffee/cola shop with entertainment or a space that can be rented by them and run like a business selling the same. Of course, such a place would need to be supervised, perhaps by an older person, a big brother enterprise, the YMCA, fire or police department. The object is to break down the inward focus of these shopping centers, to relate them to members of the community, to unite indoors with outdoors, and to add new building faces to the street. When there is continuity within the center, it will have increased vitality.

Treat the streetscape with wide walks, narrow auto entries, defined pedestrian entries to store, and extensive tree planting. Add bus shelters with benches and wide crosswalks with ramps (above). Summary action to enhance pedestrian use of neighborhood shopping centers—narrow entry roads, widen sidewalks, interconnect all stores, add housing and offices to the second floor and shops connecting to the street.

Connect outlining stores and offices with a defined pedestrian way. Stripe first, add planters, and eventually replace with covered walks or a new row of shops. Install curb cuts and ramps at each change in elevation.

Adding second-floor offices or residences extends the pedestrian realm. Note the covered walks and lawn area for pedestrian use.

DISPERSED SHOPPING DISTRICTS

The dispersed shopping district, the third type of suburban shopping district, is composed of individual shops often isolated on relatively small parcels of land. Though the small parcel size might seem to suggest a district is pedestrian-scaled, the large number of property owners may make it difficult to achieve the unity required for pedestrian improvements. These shopping precincts generally are developed around larger shopping centers, along arterial roads, or on bypassed land. Each store is isolated by its own small "customer only" parking lot, and may be completely different in looks and services from its neighbor. Store diversity minimizes comparative shopping on foot, and window shopping is all but impossible. Surrounding streets are often overcrowded with traffic, and on-street parking may not be allowed. In addition, since sidewalks may not exist, walking between stores is impossible or, at best, difficult. Driving between stores is safer, but not necessarily pleasant or easy.

Typical dispersed shopping district—linear and set too far back from the road (above). Orient a new row of shops perpendicular to the street allows street users a safe walk to shops beyond. Note the generous walk width, seating areas, small parking bays, covered window shopping and lighting (below).

Adapting such areas to pedestrian and bicycle use is possible, but slow. Any solution will have a rather loose patchwork of possibilities rather than a highly structured solution such as is possible at a regional shopping mall under one ownership. One solution is to unify individual shops and to connect adjoining parking lots. This reduces the need for motorists to drive between shops because they can shop in several stores at one stop, and it minimizes the number of driveways. For this to work, cooperation and monitoring will be necessary to protect individual merchants' rights. The stores could be connected with curbed walks so customers could move between them once out of their cars. Further enhancement would involve the planting of trees as well as the addition of awnings and wheelchair ramps. (See sketches.)

The planner should first analyze the district's circulation system for streets that might be converted to pedestrian uses. It is possible that all streets in the vicinity are arterial-like, which suggests that the real need may be for greater variety of street types and street character. Arterials that lead to a freeway, and those that lead to large neighborhoods beyond, may be best left as arterials. However, if a street is lined with retail shops, there may be advantages to diverting traffic and narrowing it by constructing sidewalks. Analyzing traffic pattern and buildup, the planner can see if reducing cars would allow reduction in the widths of certain road. The planner might then examine options based on increased carpooling, public transit access, bicycle and pedestrian access, and diversified uses that allow users to accomplish more activities in one visit. And, finally, the planner might study the possibility of reducing opportunities to drive between stores, assuming that pedestrian improvements would be made and that shoppers are able to reach more shops on foot. (Photo)

Duplicating a small town streetscape may be a long-term goal. As buildings are replaced, construct them adjacent to the street, with parking lots in the rear. Add a sidewalk and other pedestrian amenities. Limit parking lot access to side streets to ensure pedestrian safety and comfort.

Streets that can be narrowed with sidewalks and pedestrian areas offer several design options. Ideally, shops would directly abut the sidewalk so that pedestrians could window shop and participate in the activities such as those offered of an urban shopping street. However, some stores may be set back a distance, others may have parking in front, and the uniformity may vary considerably. Three alignment possibilities include:

1. A traditional street is easiest or organize and implement, since it can be accomplished on public property, using LID and other organized implementation techniques. Stores that sit back from a sidewalk would have to remodel to accommodate pedestrian traffic. Some might rebuild closer to the street, while others might reorganize their parking lots to integrate pedestrians. In a number of years, improvements would provide a pleasant balance along the street. In the interim, a new sidewalk, street trees, reduced driveway widths, and landscaped parking lots would enhance the district for pedestrians.

2. A pedestrian walkway could be developed at the store fronts to connect the different stores. Presumably, there would be parking between this walk and the street. If not, the street could be narrowed, and a sidewalk installed, though every effort should be made for the walk to be sited adjacent to stores. This walk should be at least eight feet wide, have window shopping potential, and be continuous along its length. Moreover, the walk should be raised by a curb from the parking lot so cars won't park on it, and ramps should be added to aid handicapped users.

3. A walkway system would be developed on the back sides of the shops. If the street is busy with traffic, the interior side would provide a quieter way to unify streets and shops. This was done in Kirkland, Washington, (see photos) where a new pedestrian entrance was established behind stores accessed from a new parking lot. Sidewalks with plantings and benches make the area pleasant for pedestrians, as well as the walkway's connection to a waterfront park.

Add planters and organize traffic to make alleys an attractive alternative to the main street. Note the road is not straight, causing traffic to slow down.

Stores developed on the four corners of busy arterials are difficult to pedestrianize. Most function as four independent stores and customers drive from one to the other. There are several possibilities for uniting such corners, ranging from simple street improvements to allow easier crossing, to complex solutions involving bypasses. The easiest solution is to channelize the intersection by eliminating nearby driveways and installing curbs and sidewalks with safe crosses to shorten the street crossing distance. If the street is wide, a pedestrian refuge might be added in the center; this is particularly important in communities where many elderly people live. In addition "yield to pedestrians" signs can be added and signals retimed to encourage walking. Lastly, the intersection could be linked to the stores with a safe landscaped walkway.

The other possibilities for handling the four-corner intersection, shown in conceptual diagrams, require using portions of the street. First, if either cross street is not heavily used, it might be closed to traffic, allowing pedestrian access between stores on either side of the closed

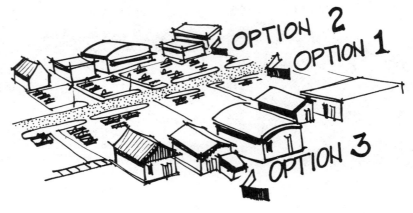

street. Secondly, constructing a diagonal street diverter could connect stores located catercorner from each other. A diverter, a good choice for lightly travelled roads, forces cars to turn left or right. A landscaped walkway should cross the diverter to connect the two corners.

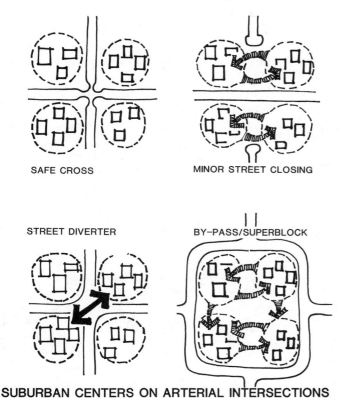

SAFE CROSS

MINOR STREET CLOSING

STREET DIVERTER

BY–PASS/SUPERBLOCK

SUBURBAN CENTERS ON ARTERIAL INTERSECTIONS

Lastly, the cross-streets could be closed and traffic routed around the intersection in a bypass arrangement. Presumably, the road would be diverted through parking lots, behind the stores, on land traded to the municipality. Then the stores fronts could be united by the two streets converted to pedestrian use. (See sketches.) The principal disadvantage of a bypass is that it isolates the pedestrian zone from the surrounding areas if traffic on the bypass travels at high speeds. The ring road in Bracknell, a British new town, is nearly impossible to walk or bicycle across to reach downtown from outlying areas. (See p. 40).

In its favor, a bypass eliminates traffic which formerly bisected a shopping area, creating a large superblock. This superblock can be divided into quadrants with loops penetrating into but not through the center. Loop roads do not generate much traffic and can be easily crossed on foot, while allowing easy auto access to nearly all businesses. Old roads in the center could be closed for pedestrian and transit use, or carry only one-way traffic or be converted into space for a parking garage. (See sketch.)

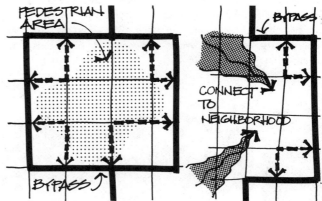

Ring roads don't have to encircle an entire superblock. A road system bypassing one side of the superblock may serve all traffic needs and still leave one or more portions of the center connected to other parts of the neighborhood. Most drivers need only to bypass, not go around, the entire center.

Superblocks internalize pedestrian traffic and suggest improved intersection and mid-block crossings. Mid-block crossings are sometimes confusing to drivers who expect to stop for pedestrians only at intersections. Signals and clear views to make pedestrians visible and encourage drivers to stop are necessary. A safe-cross expansion into the parking lane allows pedestrians to move farther into traffic safely and reduces street crossing distances. The addition of trees, traffic lights, "yield to pedestrian" signs, and a pedestrian-activated signal would make crossing safer and more convenient. Measures to enhance the superblock space for pedestrians might include raising and widening sidewalks, placing sidewalks next to store windows, encouraging merchants to extend businesses to the sidewalks, and adding new buildings to create courtyards. Conversion of a small parking lot to several shops surrounding a courtyard could make an attractive shopping environment. Different sections of a district with dispersed stores might be interconnected with several courtyards serving as attractions to pedestrians and as protected environments separate from the street. Each court could vary in size, shape and finish details.

COMMERCIAL STRIP DEVELOPMENTS

Commercial strips offer instant access for people with cars. Parking is bountiful, the merchandising pace is fast, people service themselves, and large inventories of specialty items are maintained. Strips draw customers from a large community, but offer little for the pedestrian or bicyclist. Yet the disorganization, visual clutter, traffic conflicts, repetitive services and awkward intersections may actually be a disservice to auto-oriented shoppers. Because land and energy were cheap when strip development began, the spread-out pattern was desirable. But now as land and energy are becoming more expensive, a need exists for organizing greater efficiency.

Strip commercial developments restrict safe flow of pedestrians and bicycles from store to store. Combining several stores into a loosely organized complex with connecting walks is the first improvement.

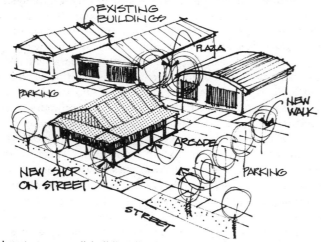

Locate new retail buildings in the parking lot between the street and existing buildings located to the rear. The building could have a covered arcade leading from the street to the buildings behind. A small plaza could be developed between the new and old buildings. Add trees, sidewalks and windows for viewing.

Converting strip developments to pedestrian use is not always easy but may be possible within limits. The basic structure of strip developments, that is, long, linear, punctuated with driveways and parking lots, with setbacks from the road and buildings spaces some distance apart, is antithetical to walking. Pedestrians need concentrations of activities and a concentric, rather than linear, pattern to provide more shopping opportunities per walking distance. Pedestrian problems along strips are compounded by through traffic. This conflict in street purposes is difficult to overcome and may limit the chance of successfully improving the strip for pedestrians.

Pedestrianizing a strip requires infilling parcels of land until the walking distances are reasonable for the average person. This may mean changes in merchandising practices to provide a mix of stores more approximating those in convenience shopping districts. Adjacent parking lots should be consolidated, pedestrian paths linking stores and parking developed, and bicycle circulation improved. New infill construction should be encouraged adjacent to buildings with underground parking to compress walking distances and the visual clutter of on-grade parking.

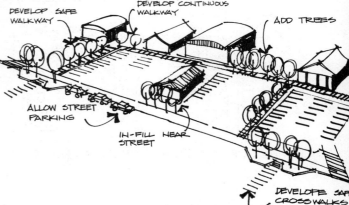

Selecting portions of a strip for pedestrian improvements that are likely to succeed is the crucial step. Not every place will work and unnecessary investment may be saved by careful evaluation. Some characteristics that may help a project be successful are:

- Proximity to an existing residential neighborhood.
- Proximity to a grocery store, drug store or other business that people frequent *every day.* Focusing on daily activities increases chances of a project's survival.
- Lack of competition within a reasonable driving distance.
- Availability of land for expansion *away* from the arterial.

Eliminate continuous left-turn lanes to improve sidewalk safety. Consolidate driveways to reduce the continuity of parking lot access. Move buildings closer to the street to allow window shopping. Though this walk space is wide, the stripe does *not* offer real security, and it should be replaced with a raised walk (upper photo). Sidewalks along wide arterials should be separated from the roadway with a planter strip or row of parked cars. This walk, immediately adjacent to fast-moving traffic is not used, as pedestrians perceive it as unsafe (lower photo).

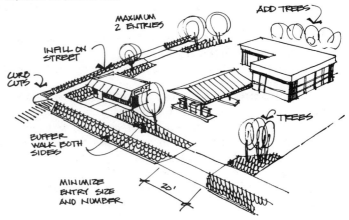

Reduce the openness of gas stations by limiting driveway openings, adding planters on *both* sides of the walk and reducing the size of the paved area with the station. Combine gas stations with pedestrian services such as grocery, cafe, drug, etc., to make it more acceptable for pedestrians.

Remove continuous angle or perpendicular parking that crosses the walkway (above). This won't be easy but is necessary for the comfort and safety of pedestrians. Combine drives for access to rear parking and replace angle parking with sidewalks as shown above right.

Safe-crosses should be added at intersections where parking is allowed and where there is no rush hour clear zone. The safe-cross delineates the parking, eliminating the need for "No Parking" signs. It allows those crossing the street to move safely farther into the street to see if cars are coming and reduces crossing distances. The safe-cross should be depressed for easy access by those in wheelchairs, with prams and shopping carts and on bicycles. The maximum slope for the ramp should be 8 percent.

Sidewalks along arterials that pass large parking lots might be moved next to stores. The walk might be widened by stores, and awnings, trees and benches added. (See sketch.) They could rejoin the street on the other side of the shopping area, thus putting pedestrians closer to shopping and areas of interest. The planner should determine the shortest link and try to combine it with walkways that those parking might also use.

Divide wide arterials into 2 roads—a through road for traffic and a retail frontage lane for pedestrians. This small lane could be better buffered from the busy street, but does have several convenient parking spaces and a sidewalk linking the shops.

Other Considerations

A few other options for the planner to consider are given below.

- Eliminate continuous left-turn lanes;
- Consolidate to reduce the number of driveways;
- Eliminate angle parking that crosses the sidewalk space;
- Place buildings close to the road, with parking in the rear;
- Add raised sidewalks;
- Separate sidewalks from fast-moving traffic with planting strips;
- Develop pedestrian walks from the street through parking lots to retail building;
- Screen and improve pedestrian safety around gas stations.

Diagonal street intersections should be realigned so they meet at right angles. The remaining space could be used for landscaping. Be sure zoning is not changed to a higher zone that may shift uses from small shops to warehousing or auto-oriented commercial. Try to encourage quality multifamily or townhouse development adjacent to these strip business districts. Devise regulations for new development to include:

- consolidated parking and access;
- pedestrian access and circulation;
- landscaping and signage; and
- frontage road use and alignment.

Add low bench walls to protect pedestrians from fast-moving vehicles; particularly at intersections. The wall can be designed to serve other functions such as planter, bike racks, benches, street signs, etc.

Reduce and concentrate land zoned for Commercial use. Many communities have less retail demand than the amount of land available for commercial development. When too much land is zoned commercial, new development tends to sprawl instead of infilling in established commercial centers. To counter this, rezone autooriented commercial uses that are outside established pedestrian centers to residential, residential/office, or Planned Unit Development.

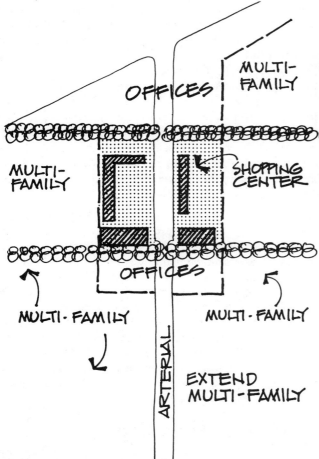

SUBURBAN OFFICE PARKS

Suburban office parks, drive-to buildings isolated from other buildings by roads, parking lots and landscaping, have become popular in suburban communities. They serve the suburban lifestyle; they are auto-oriented, isolated and utilize improved technologies to communicate with the outside world. Workers and visitors arrive by car, and activities such as lunch or shopping require a trip by car.

Suburban office parks that separate buildings from roads by parking, and don't interconnect buildings with sidewalks should be discouraged and remodeled. Add sidewalks, infill new buildings to minimize walk distances, narrow roads, and add covered walks to encourage walking.

Pedestrian improvements should minimize but not eliminate car use. For new developments a superblock pattern can be superimposed over the existing land, leaving the car on the periphery and freeing the interior for pedestrian use. Three actions are necessary:

1. Minimize the setbacks, and build close to the road so people walking on the sidewalk will feel some relationship to businesses and buildings instead of to parking lots;

2. Create internal walks and paths to allow shortcutting between offices, and nearby shopping and housing; and

3. Encourage mixed land uses, such as cafes and convenience shopping, to locate nearby serving both the internal walks and the street.

If the land is platted but not developed, the easiest way may be to convert some of the unbuilt streets to walkways. (See sketch.) Buildings should be located with minimum street setbacks and internal parking in landscaped lots or under buildings. A ten-foot-wide interior walkway, connecting all buildings could be constructed by the developer and then landscaped by each abutting property. Parking should be screened and a walk should connect to each building where necessary. Seating, athletic facilities, tables, benches, lawns, are just a few elements that could be added for employee use. Pedestrians should have access and a safe, pleasant way on both internal and street walks.

Setbacks are needed only to create usable open areas, and should be increased on the *internal* walk side and decreased on the auto side. While this is not typical for the suburbs, it would provide space that pedestrians and noon-time recreationists might enjoy. Parking could be included in the setback if it were landscaped with trees to soften its overall impact. (See diagrams.)

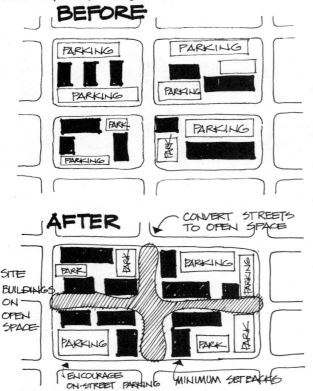

MORE ON PARKING LOTS

Parking lots have become the dominant visual element of most suburban streetscapes, replacing buildings or landscape as the main form givers. Americans now expect automobile storage everywhere. The closer to one's destination, the better. Parking lot paving often runs right up to the sidewalk, causing visual intrusion and safety hazards. For most Americans the journey is over when their car is parked, even though they still must walk from the parking lot to work, school, play or shopping, and generally the walk is not pleasant, because sidewalk construction has been based on municipal codes that provide little or no space for pedestrian protection and enjoyment.

Reducing the amount of parking can improve the pedestrian realm and may allow room for new buildings, as well. It can be accomplished without much loss of convenience if a comprehensive approach is used. The place to start is with organization of employee parking. Employees

should be encouraged to carpool or use transit or bicycles, and possibly might be given a small pay raise to exchange for the parking spaces they would have used. (The cost of one parking space including land is approximately $3,000 or about $30 investment per month.) No one, except someone who is handicapped, should park immediately adjacent to his or her place of work. Instead special "employee" parking areas, with smaller parking spaces, should be designated on the periphery of a shopping center. Some assigned tandem spaces (one car blocking another) would be acceptable if most employees leave work at approximately the same time. A shuttle bus could be used between places of business and parking lots.

Pedestrianizing parking lots includes visual buffers between the sidewalk and parking lot, overall tree planting to soften visual impact of the lot from a distance, auto access and circulation that doesn't compromise pedestrian activity, and an adequate maintenance program. Solving these problems may increase parking costs, but this author feels that motorists should pay for the privilege of parking and that charging for parking in suburban shopping centers may reduce parking demand.

From car to destination. All parking lots for more than ten cars should have a safe pedestrian walk from car to destination. This requires identification of destinations and development of a sensible pathway. Parking areas should be sited perpendicular to the final destination and sidewalks installed between every two parking bays. The walk should be raised six inches, paved differently than the road, and planted with trees. (See photo.) One planted walkway may serve as a collector for up to four bays of parked cars. The walk should be seven-feet-wide, allowing for a 24 inches auto-overhang on each side. If cars back into the parking space, the sidewalk width must be wider to accommodate the larger rear overhang.

Raise pedestrian access walks or install wheel stops to prevent parked cars from blocking the walk (upper). Better yet, add trees to define the walk from a distance. The walk should be a minimum 7 feet wide to allow for vehicle overhangs (top of next page).

into the lot's asphalt surface to lessen the visual impact. For infrequently used parking areas, softer, more parklike materials such as crushed stone, Bermuda or St. Augustine's grass, or grass crete can be used. Surfaces planted with live ground cover reduce runoff problems.

Parking access and egress should be at one location. Traditional parking lots with continuous rolled curbs and with access over the length of the lot are visually degrading and infringe unnecessarily on pedestrian comfort and safety. For lots up to ten cars, a ten-foot wide entrance drive is adequate. This is not wide enough for cars to enter and exit simultaneously, but that happens so infrequently and causes minimal driver inconvenience. For larger lots, a 16-foot-wide apron provides adequate room for cars entering and exiting simultaneously. Using a different sidewalk pavement finish at the crossing helps call pedestrians' attention to the car danger. The sidewalk should be kept level with a ramp for cars.

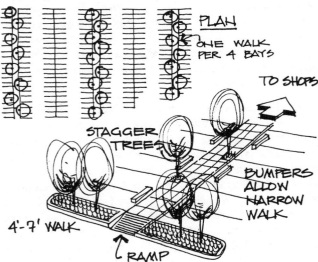

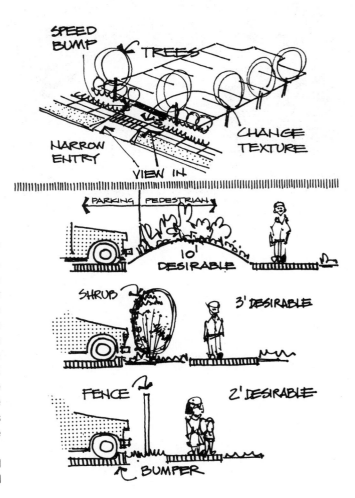

Buffer. Distance is the best method to separate parked cars from walkways. If a ten-foot-wide strip is available of can be argued for, it could be mounded with soil to form a four-foot-high berm and planted with shrubs to raise the total height to six feet. If ten feet isn't available, the size of the buffer space should be negotiated. A minimum strip would be three-feet-wide with large plants and tire bumpers to eliminate through driving. Large trees, at least 15-gallon size, are an absolute must for immediate visual relief. An 18-inch-wide planting space with a 5-foot tall fence and vines also works. Trees should be planted around the perimeter and between rows of parked cars. Minimum tree planting is two trees per three cars plus a shrub buffer. Trees should be at least 2½-inch caliber to provide immediate visual relief.

All planter spaces and pedestrian walks should be raised and have a curb. Crushed, colored gravel could be rolled

227

Perpendicular parking from roadways is commonplace in apartment complexes because of cost efficiency. However, it is dangerous for pedestrians who are forced to detour behind parked cars. For safety, it is preferable to route walks in front of the cars, using a diagonal connector walk. The sidewalk can then serve as a bumper stop for the parked cars and collect drives as they disembark. Walk width should be five feet to allow the 24-inch front auto-overhang.

Reduce the size and impact of large parking lots with organized crosswalks. This walk replaces 2 cars in each bay, but encourages foot crossing to the block of stores beyond. The system could be improved by raising the walk in the street to slow traffic and ease wheelchair and pram access (see above).

Standardizing "smaller parking lots". Most American parking lots are constructed too large, robbing space from planting, pedestrian use, new buildings or additional parking. Increased compact car use makes it possible to restripe parking lots according to two new parking lot standards and are as follows:

• *For standard American cars* (Chevys, Dodges, Fords and the like), all decreasing slightly in overall size and with shorter turning radii, smaller lots are in order. Nine-foot-wide stalls, with 20-foot deep bays and a 20-foot backout space are adequate. Single-loaded bays are 40 feet wide while double-loaded lots are 60 feet. The reduction of about one foot in stall width by five feet in bay width can add a sizeable space to the pedestrian realm. (See diagram.)

• *For compacts* (VW's, Volvos, Saabs, Hornets), an eight-foot stall width with 16-foot-deep bays and 18 feet of backout space works comfortably. Single-loaded lots are 34 feet deep, while double-loaded are 50 feet.

Maximize the potential of parking lots by integrating the lot with retail shops and increasing pedestrian use. Add wide walks, twist and turn the road to slow traffic and discourage driving between stores and to improve the visual impact of large lots.

Organize angle parking circulation to one-way to save space. This two-way access road could be narrowed if both parking bays were reached from one travel direction.

Parking for handicapped users should be provided near the main entrance to whatever facility the parking lot serves. There should be at least one space in every parking lot designated for handicapped users plus one additional space for each 50 cars. Parking spaces should be a minimum of 12 feet-6-inches wide and have a curb cut 36 inches wide leading from the parking space to a route accessible to the main entrance. Users should be able to reach that route directly without crossing streets or moving in the driveway. The route should have a sign with the international symbol of access and be designated as a handicapped parking space. With some planning the widened space adjacent to the handicapped parking can also be used by pedestrians as a walkway. Designating for handicapped use two spaces adjacent to the unloading area reduces the amount of space required since both can be used for two purposes.

Suburban downtowns. Suburban development has drastically changed the pattern of metropolitan land use and size of individual developments. Until the 1950's, most shopping was done in small towns with shops built on narrow parcels of land. Older suburban downtowns developed when the car was not extensively used, and when walking distance was the "design module". Parking was of incidental concern because it was available on the street or behind stores. Many people lived close enough to walk to shop and didn't need to drive. Others might drive close to their destination, walk between several shops and then drive home.

Later suburban development added more cars to the scene and increased the need for everyone to drive. An individual parking lot for each store became necessary for merchandising success, and the car became the "design module". As parking lots became larger, stores in older suburban downtowns without parking suffered, rents decreased, vacancy and turnover increased. In many instances these areas no longer serve pedestrians.

Suburban lifestyles continue to vascillate between these two extremes. On the one hand, people like the car's convenience and drive-to shopping. On the other hand, many visualize themselves as part of a small community and identify with a simpler, quiet, small town life. So, then, is the time right for adapting our deteriorated suburban small downtowns to the image and pedestrian character of yesterday?

Three actions are necessary to accomplish this: Organizing parking in small, landscaped lots or on the street; converting stores from auto-related to pedestrian-related; and changing the character and amenity of the core to better serve pedestrians.

Parking is needed, but shouldn't be the dominant visual element. Some parking can be on the street with the balance in small landscaped lots. People using the area should be able to park and walk to all stores and businesses. Employee parking should be on the outskirts of the shopping area to maximize close-in *customer* parking. Walks should lead from the parking to the main street and other stores. If rear parking is used, stores should open their back door to allow people to pass through. If all shopping is reachable on foot, driving between stores isn't necessary and fewer parking spaces are required.

Screen parking lots from sidewalks with a fence or structure such as this decorative trellis with bus stop, telephone, trash can and trees.

Drive-in businesses should be converted to walk-in businesses, such as cafes or restaurants with the former driveway space used for outdoor dining, or as a small garden sitting area.

Wheelchair and bicycle ramps should be installed at all intersections. Ramps must be wide enough for wheelchair use (a minimum of 36 inches), must not exceed 8 percent in grade and must be flush with the street and walk beyond. For more complete information, see page 47.

Ground level windows that allow pedestrians to view merchandise or inside the building may be the most important streetscape improvement possible. Most large office buildings are constructed with blank walls that eliminated pedestrian interest and activity along the street. Blank walls replaced former shops and pedestrian activity disappeared. There is nothing more discouraging than a blank wall for walkers, as it extends the apparent walk length considerably. Windows can be used for shopping display, or to let people see what is happening inside the building, or just to see other people and receive the benefit of visual relief from the walk.

Merchants may find it financially feasible to introduce pedestrian weather protection to encourage shopping during cold, wet days. Cold weather plus exaggerated wind conditions causes walkers to travel more directly in winter than spring or summer and reduce shopping. Likewise, noontime activity decreases in the winter, as the number of people willing to walk in winter is less.

It is important to encourage new business with a pedestrian character to locate in the shopping area. The planner should work with major property owners to help convert their land to accommodate pedestrian services. Once a trend is established, others may follow and the entire shopping area may have a face lift. Another approach is to seek businesses that can serve both pedestrians and motorists. These include restaurants, real-estate and specialty shops that will attract people in spite of where they are located. Shop owners should be encouraged to seek pedestrian-oriented tenants with each new vacancy.

Improving the physical condition of the shopping area could take place over a period of time and needn't be more complex initially than cleaning, painting and patching. Over time trees could be added, perhaps a small park constructed, safe-crosses added at the intersections, and sidewalks widened. Side streets could be closed off and converted to a park or pedestrian walk. New building should be constructed *directly* out on the street's edge, with setbacks space kept minimal but reserved for pedestrians as covered walkway space. Facades should be continuous to encourage window shopping and assure a pleasant walk. Driveway entries should be moved from main street to side streets.

RETHINKING THE SUPER BLOCK

Though the "idealized" suburban land use model makes sense in the abstract, it does not work in reality. The model includes a hierarchy of roads with heavily traveled through roads connecting to smaller access roads which connect to short local roads that, for all extents and purposes, go nowhere. Adjacent to all roads is a sufficient setback to minimize the nuisances of moving cars—the front lawn, parking area, etc.—and then buildings, be they residential, commercial, shopping, etc. Finally, there is an "open space system" that "ideally" would serve pedestrian circulation. Pedestrians would be safe, separate from the auto, and surrounded by green. There are two problems with this model;

1. The internal open space, safe from the annoyance of automobile conflicts, seldom extends or connects beyond the property line of the project. People using it can't walk beyond their property before they run into the fence or parking lot of another development. There is *no* through access. Additionally, the internal green spaces are often private, and the owners don't want to share their privacy. Through-moving pedestrians would compromise the life style of abutting residents.
2. The "real suburban community" functions from the roads. Access for every need—living, shopping, work, play, friends, etc.—is via the street. If you do not have access to and rights to use the streets, you cannot reach your daily needs.

The possible solutions range from; converting the *streets* to satisfy the pedestrian needs by constructing walks and places that eliminate the dangers and apparent dangers of automobiles to restructuring the internal arrangement to insure safe, continuous passage.

Of these two choices, this author favors restructuring the street system to increase pedestrian and bicycle access. Connecting places with the internal open space system, wherever practical, creates shortcuts and alternative routes that decrease travel distance and the boring nature of walking.

INDEX